# MATHEMATICS
## Structure and Method

## Course 2

**MARY P. DOLCIANI**
**EDWIN F. BECKENBACH**
**RICHARD G. BROWN**
**ROBERT B. KANE**
**WILLIAM WOOTON**

**HOUGHTON MIFFLIN COMPANY · BOSTON**

*Atlanta    Dallas    Geneva, Ill.    Lawrenceville, N.J.    Palo Alto    Toronto*

## Authors

MARY P. DOLCIANI  Professor of Mathematics, Hunter College, City University of New York.

EDWIN F. BECKENBACH  Professor of Mathematics, Emeritus, University of California, Los Angeles.

RICHARD G. BROWN  Mathematics Teacher, Phillips Exeter Academy, Exeter, New Hampshire.

ROBERT B. KANE  Director of Teacher Education and Head of the Department of Education, Purdue University.

WILLIAM WOOTON  former Professor of Mathematics, Los Angeles Pierce College.


## Editorial Advisers

ANDREW M. GLEASON  Hollis Professor of Mathematics and Natural Philosophy, Harvard University.

ALBERT E. MEDER, Jr.  Dean and Vice Provost and Professor of Mathematics, Emeritus, Rutgers, The State University of New Jersey.


## Consultants

CAROLYN AHO  Teacher Specialist, Mathematics, San Francisco Unified School District, San Francisco, California.

RUTH GREEN  Mathematics Teacher, Isaac Litton Junior High School, Nashville, Tennessee.

TIMOTHY HOWELL  Mathematics Coordinator, Hanover High School, Hanover, New Hampshire.

BETTY TAKESUYE  Mathematics Teacher, Chaparral High School, Scottsdale, Arizona.

# Contents

# 11

# 12

# SYMBOLS

| | | page | | | page |
|---|---|---|---|---|---|
| $10^1, 10^4$ | powers of 10 | 27 | ㄴ | right angle | 180 |
| $\{0, 1, 2, 3, \ldots\}$ | set of whole numbers | 31 | $\parallel$ | is parallel to | 185 |
| | | | $\triangle ABC$ | triangle $ABC$ | 190 |
| $>$ | is greater than | 34 | $\cong$ | is congruent to | 201 |
| $<$ | is less than | 34 | $\sim$ | is similar to | 206 |
| $=$ | is equal to | 37 | $\neq$ | is not equal to | 222 |
| $^-3$ | negative 3 | 66 | $\geq$ | is greater than or equal to | 222 |
| $|n|$ | absolute value of $n$ | 80 | | | |
| $6.\overline{47}$ | repeating decimal | 133 | $\leq$ | is less than or equal to | 222 |
| $\%$ | percent | 153 | | | |
| $\overline{AB}$ | segment $AB$ | 173 | $\varnothing$ | empty set | 227 |
| $AB$ | length of $\overline{AB}$ | 174 | $(6,8)$ | ordered pair of numbers | 336 |
| $\approx$ | is approximately equal to | 174 | $\sqrt{n}$ | positive square root of $n$ | 363 |
| $\pi$ | pi | 177 | | | |
| $\angle A$ | angle $A$ | 180 | $\sin A$ | sin of $\angle A$ | 379 |
| $30°$ | 30 degrees | 180 | $\cos A$ | cosine of $\angle A$ | 380 |
| $\perp$ | is perpendicular to | 180 | $\tan A$ | tangent of $\angle A$ | 380 |

# METRIC MEASURES

| PREFIXES | kilo- 1000 | hecto- 100 | deka- 10 | deci- 0.1 | centi- 0.01 | milli- 0.001 |
|---|---|---|---|---|---|---|

**LENGTH**
1 millimeter (mm) = 0.001 **meter** (m)       1 m = 1000 mm
1 centimeter (cm) = 0.01 m       1 m = 100 cm
1 kilometer (km) = 1000 m       1 cm = 10 mm

**MASS**
1 milligram (mg) = 0.001 **gram** (g)       1 g = 1000 mg
1 kilogram (kg) = 1000 g

**CAPACITY**
1 milliliter (mL) = 0.001 **liter** (L)       1 L = 1000 mL
1 L = 1000 cm³

**TIME**
1 minute (min) = 60 seconds (s)
1 hour (h) = 60 min
1 day (d) = 24 h
1 week = 7 d
1 year = 365 d
1 leap year = 366 d

**TEMPERATURE**
Degrees Celsius (°C)

0°C = freezing point of water
37°C = normal body temperature
100°C = boiling point of water

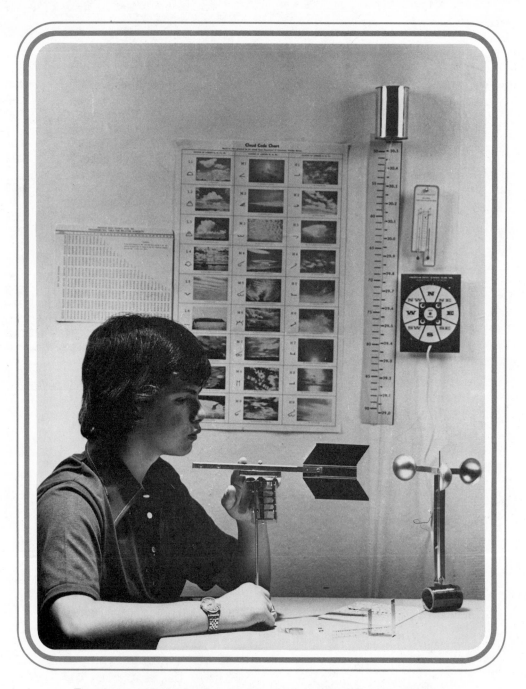

The photographs facing the chapter opening pages illustrate different aspects of students' lives. For the earlier chapters, they focus on school and home activities. For the later chapters, they broaden out to show community-related activities and, finally, careers in which some knowledge of mathematics is helpful.

# 1 Statistics and Graphs

## 1-1 Reading Tables and Charts

**Objective** To read and use information displayed in charts and tables.

In everyday life we see numerical facts called *data*, or *statistics*, presented in charts and tables. To make use of these data, we must be able to read such tables accurately.

For example, the table at the right uses a compact arrangement to show the distances between some European cities. As the red lines indicate, we find the distance between Budapest and London by going down the column labeled "Budapest" and finding where it meets with the row labeled "London." The distance is 1752 km. In the same way we find that the distance between London and Amsterdam is 530 km.

Distance in kilometers

| Amsterdam | Budapest | Helsinki | Istanbul | London | Vienna |
|---|---|---|---|---|---|
| 1425 | | | | | |
| 1803 | 2352 | | | | |
| 2807 | 1387 | 3739 | | | |
| 530 | 1752 | 2337 | 3141 | | |
| 1175 | 250 | 2102 | 1637 | 1502 | |

Some tables, like the one below, provide a variety of information. Notice that the distances of the trips around the world are given in kilometers. In the "Time" column, the "d," "h," and "m," indicate the units used are days, hours, and minutes. Study the table and tell which was the fastest trip and when it was made. Which trip covered the greatest distance? In what year was it made?

Fast Trips Around the World

| Craft | Person | Distance (km) | Time d | h | m | Year |
|-------|--------|---------------|--------|---|---|------|
| train, burro, jinriksha, ship | Nellie Bly | — | 72 | 6 | 11 | 1889 |
| Graf Zeppelin | — | 34,900 | 20 | 4 | 0 | 1929 |
| — | Wiley Post | 25,100 | 4 | 19 | 36 | 1933 |
| Zeppelin Hindenburg | H. R. Ekins | 41,300 | 18 | 11 | 15 | 1936 |
| — | Howard Hughes | 23,900 | 3 | 19 | 8 | 1938 |
| Pan Am Clipper | Clara Adams | — | 16 | 19 | 4 | 1939 |
| Reynolds Bombshell | Wm. P. Odom | 32,200 | 3 | 6 | 55 | 1947 |
| — | Pamela Martin | — | 3 | 18 | 59 | 1953 |
| 3 B-52's | — | 39,100 | 1 | 21 | 19 | 1957 |
| — | Sue Snyder | 34,100 | 2 | 14 | 59 | 1960 |
| Light plane | Robert and Joan Wallick | 37,200 | 5 | 6 | 17 | 1966 |

# Class Exercises

Using the table at the right, find the distances between these cities.

1. Honolulu and Montreal

2. Melbourne and Nairobi

3. Peking and Mexico City

4. Mexico City and Honolulu

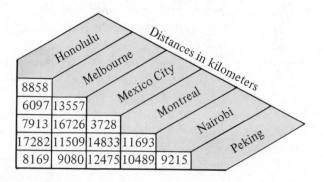

Distances in kilometers

| Honolulu | Melbourne | Mexico City | Montreal | Nairobi | Peking |
|----------|-----------|-------------|----------|---------|--------|
| 8858 | | | | | |
| 6097 | 13557 | | | | |
| 7913 | 16726 | 3728 | | | |
| 17282 | 11509 | 14833 | 11693 | | |
| 8169 | 9080 | 12475 | 10489 | 9215 | |

**5.** Melbourne and Peking

**6.** Nairobi and Montreal

**7.** Honolulu and Melbourne

**8.** Peking and Nairobi

**9.** Which cities in the table are closest to each other?

**10.** Which cities are farthest from each other?

Which is the shorter trip?

**11.** Melbourne to Montreal or to Mexico City?

**12.** Honolulu to Nairobi or to Peking?

**13.** Montreal to Mexico City or to Peking?

**14.** Nairobi to Honolulu or to Montreal?

## Exercises

Using the same table as for the Class Exercises, find the total distance for each trip.

A **1.** Honolulu to Melbourne to Peking

**2.** Melbourne to Mexico City to Peking

**3.** Nairobi to Peking to Honolulu

**4.** Nairobi to Montreal to Mexico City

**5.** Peking to Honolulu to Mexico City

**6.** Montreal to Peking to Melbourne

How much farther is it from

**7.** Honolulu to Melbourne than to Peking?

**8.** Mexico City to Nairobi than to Montreal?

**9.** Peking to Montreal than to Honolulu?

**10.** Melbourne to Montreal than to Honolulu?

How far would you travel if you made a round trip between the given cities?

**11.** Nairobi and Peking

**12.** Montreal and Mexico City

**13.** Melbourne and Nairobi

**14.** Honolulu and Melbourne

How far would a jet plane travel on the trip described?

**15.** 5 round trips between Montreal and Honolulu

**16.** 3 round trips between Nairobi and Peking

**17.** 6 round trips between Melbourne and Mexico City

**18.** 7 round trips between Peking and Honolulu

A satellite used by radio hams will pass over the Denver area at the times shown in the chart at the right. How many minutes will elapse between these orbits?

**B** **19.** 1540 and 1541

**20.** 1565 and 1566

**21.** 1615 and 1616

**22.** How many orbits will the satellite make between 12:11 P.M. on March 18 and 10:10 A.M. on March 20?

**23.** How much time will elapse between Orbits 1541 and 1565?

**24.** About how much time will the satellite take to make each orbit between Orbits 1541 and 1565? How does this compare with your answers to Exercises 19–21?

Satellite Data

| Date | Time | Orbit Number |
|------|------|--------------|
| 3/18 | 10:16 A.M. | 1540 |
|      | 12:11 P.M. | 1541 |
| 3/20 | 10:10 A.M. | 1565 |
|      | 12:05 P.M. | 1566 |
| 3/24 | 9:57 A.M. | 1615 |
|      | 11:52 A.M. | 1616 |

# Application

## Getting Your Money's Worth

Which is the better buy? A 400 g can of tomatoes for 60¢ or a 600 g can for 80¢? From the table below we see that if we buy the 400 g can, we are paying at a rate of $1.50 per kilogram. For the 600 g can the rate is $1.33 per kilogram. If the quality is the same and we can use the larger amount, the 600 g can is the better buy.

| No. of grams in containers | Price of container in dollars | | | | |
|---|---|---|---|---|---|
| | .20 | .40 | .60 | .80 | 1.00 |
| | Cost of food per kilogram in dollars | | | | |
| 200 | 1.00 | 2.00 | 3.00 | 4.00 | 5.00 |
| 400 | .50 | 1.00 | 1.50 | 2.00 | 2.50 |
| 600 | .33 | .67 | 1.00 | 1.33 | 1.67 |
| 800 | .25 | .50 | .75 | 1.00 | 1.25 |
| 1000 | .20 | .40 | .60 | .80 | 1.00 |

**Consumer Activity** Check a local supermarket to see how it displays unit prices. How would you use unit prices to get your money's worth?

# 1-2 Bar Graphs

Objective To read and make bar graphs.

We often use a **bar graph** to give a visual display of numerical data after they have been arranged in a table. The table and bar graph below show the number of kilojoules, kJ, of energy used up by one minute of different kinds of physical activity.

Energy Used

| Activity | kJ/min | Activity | kJ/min |
|----------|--------|----------|--------|
| Walking | 20 | Swimming | 44 |
| Bicycling | 32 | Running | 76 |

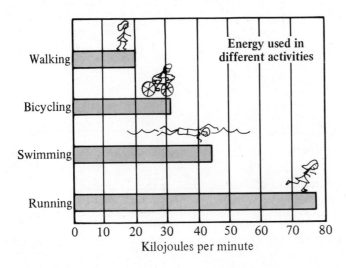

To make this graph, bars for the different activities were marked off along the vertical axis. Starting with zero, intervals of ten were marked off along the horizontal axis to represent the number of kilojoules per minute. Bars of the appropriate length were drawn for each activity. Finally, the bar graph was given its title, "Energy used in different activities."

Just by looking at the lengths of the bars, estimate about how many times more kilojoules are used in one minute of swimming than in one minute of walking, in one minute of running than in one minute of walking. We usually use bar graphs to make rough comparisons like these rather than for obtaining exact information.

The bar graph below uses different shades of color to indicate the years which the bars represent. Notice that each unit on the vertical axis represents 1000 metric tons, so that "500" on the vertical axis indicates 500,000 metric tons. A smaller unit could have been chosen to show a more exact picture.

Recyclable Materials

| Year | Metric Tons (1000) | | |
|------|------|----------|-------|
|      | Iron | Aluminum | Glass |
| 1975 | 260 | 50 | 250 |
| 1980 (est.) | 540 | 100 | 340 |
| 1985 (est.) | 1560 | 250 | 540 |

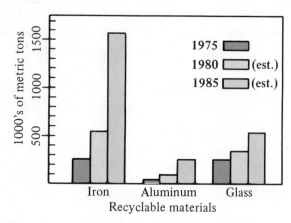

## Class Exercises

From the graph at the right, tell about how much water is used for each activity.

**1.** A 5-minute shower.

**2.** Watering the lawn for 15 minutes.

**3.** A bath.

**4.** A dishwasher load.

**5.** How much more water is used taking a bath than a 5-minute shower?

**6.** How much water is used watering the lawn for one hour?

**7.** The Smiths washed 18 loads of dishes one week. How much water did they use?

**8.** How much water would 12 members of the track team use if they each took a 5-minute shower?

**9.** The Browns watered their lawn for 30 minutes on each of 3 days. How much water did they use?

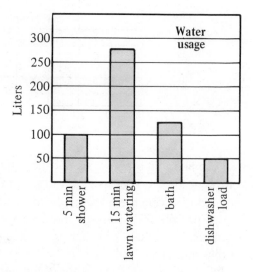

## Exercises

From the graph at the right, tell how far an automobile travels before stopping after the brakes are applied at the given speed.

A    **1.** 40 km/h    **2.** 56 km/h    **3.** 72 km/h

     **4.** 88 km/h    **5.** 94 km/h

B    **6.** What is the difference in stopping distances at 40 km/h and 72 km/h?

     **7.** What is the difference in stopping distances at 40 km/h and 94 km/h?

     **8.** A car traveling 72 km/h is 40 m from an intersection when the driver puts on the brakes. Will the car stop before it reaches the intersection?

**Automobile stopping distances**

Meters

Speeds when brakes are applied (km/h)

Draw a bar graph to illustrate the data in the table.

C    **9.**    Average Heights of Growth

| Flower | Centimeters |
|---|---|
| Dahlia | 56 |
| Hollyhock | 180 |
| Larkspur | 90 |
| Marigold | 30 |
| Petunia | 25 |
| Snapdragon | 40 |

**10.**    Leading Cacao-Bean-Growing Countries

| Country | Kilograms of Cacao Beans |
|---|---|
| Ghana | 353,000,000 |
| Brazil | 245,500,000 |
| Nigeria | 218,000,000 |
| Ivory Coast | 205,600,000 |
| Cameroon | 110,000,000 |

**11.**    Endangered Wildlife

| Mammal or Bird | No. in Captivity | Mammal or Bird | No. in Captivity |
|---|---|---|---|
| Golden lion marmoset | 83 | Reeve's muntjac | 161 |
| Bushdog | 19 | Eld's deer | 69 |
| Maned wolf | 75 | Pere David's deer | 777 |
| Onager | 142 | Florida sandhill crane | 109 |
| Scimitar-horned oryx | 298 | Rothschild's mynah | 565 |

# 1-3 Line Graphs

**Objective** To read and make line graphs.

The *broken-line graph* below shows the average monthly temperatures in degrees Celsius at Ottawa, Canada, from April through November. Broken-line graphs such as this are especially useful when we want to show how something changes over a period of time.

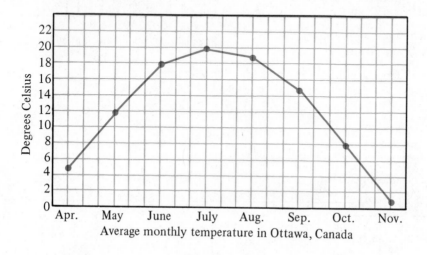

Average monthly temperature in Ottawa, Canada

Here are some things we can notice in this graph:

1. The lowest average temperature, 1°C, is recorded in November, and the highest, 20°C, in July.
2. The average temperature rises from April to July, and then falls from July to November.
3. The greatest increase in temperature from one month to the next occurs between April and May. This is an increase of 7°. Also, the line connecting the points for April and May has the steepest upward slant.
4. The least increase in temperature from one month to the next occurs between June and July. This increase is 2°. Also, the line between June and July has the least upward slant.
5. The temperature decreases the same number of degrees, 7°, from September to October as from October to November. Also, the line between September and October has the same downward slant as the line between October and November.

An almanac predicted the amount of rainfall for each month in a farm area as shown by the black figures in the table below. The actual rainfall is shown in red.

Centimeters of Rain

|  | Jan | Feb | Mar | Apr | May | Jun | Jul | Aug | Sept | Oct | Nov | Dec |
|---|---|---|---|---|---|---|---|---|---|---|---|---|
| Predicted | 2 | 3 | 3 | 6 | 10 | 9 | 9 | 8 | 4 | 1 | 1 | 0 |
| Actual | 3 | 5 | 6 | 7 | 8 | 6 | 4 | 2 | 1 | 0 | 0 | 1 |

A clearer way to display these data is by using a double-line graph as shown below.

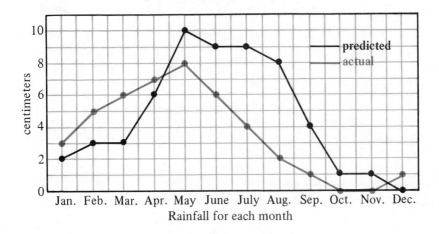

Rainfall for each month

Notice that in answering the questions in the example below, it is usually easier to use the graph than the table.

*Example*  **a. In what months did the actual rainfall and the predicted rainfall agree most closely?**

**b. By how many centimeters did they differ?**

**c. In those months, which was higher—the actual rainfall or the predicted rainfall?**

*Solution*  **a. In January, April, October, November, and December**

**b. 1 cm**

**c. The actual rainfall was higher in January, April, and December. The predicted rainfall was higher in October and November.**

Another kind of line graph is shown below. It uses vertical line segments to display the ranges of temperature during one day in August in several cities.

| City | Temperature range in °C on August 5 |
|------|-------------------------------------|
| Anchorage | 11–18 |
| Atlanta | 21–31 |
| Boston | 19–33 |
| Chicago | 22–29 |
| Denver | 14–29 |
| Honolulu | 23–31 |
| Las Vegas | 24–42 |
| Miami | 27–32 |
| Phoenix | 29–43 |
| San Francisco | 13–18 |

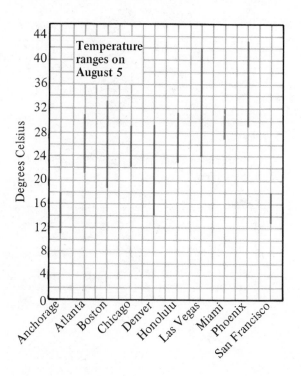

From the graph we can see at a glance which city had the highest temperature, the lowest temperature, or the greatest range in temperature.

## Class Exercises

From the graph at the right, read the population of the world, approximately, for the given year.

**1.** 1      **2.** 500      **3.** 1000

**4.** 1500      **5.** 2000

About how long did it take for the population to double from

**6.** 250 million to 500 million?

**7.** 500 million to 1 billion?

**8.** 1 billion to 2 billion?

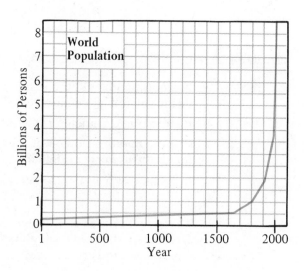

## Exercises

Using the graph at the right, what is the altitude, approximately, of a satellite which takes the given number of minutes to orbit Earth?

**A**

1. 100    2. 120

3. 140    4. 160

5. A communications satellite is in orbit 2000 km above Earth. About how long does it take to make one orbit?

6. A weather satellite is in orbit 1500 km above Earth. How long does it take to make one orbit?

7. A satellite was put into orbit at 3000 km at 9 A.M. When will it complete its first orbit?

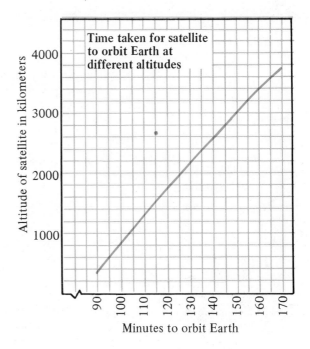

Draw a broken-line graph picturing the given data.

8.                     Number of Newspaper Customers

| Month | Jan | Feb | Mar | Apr | May | Jun |
|---|---|---|---|---|---|---|
| Customers | 42 | 45 | 38 | 45 | 50 | 53 |

**B**  9.              Population Growth of Cactus City

| Year | 1900 | 1910 | 1920 | 1930 | 1940 | 1950 | 1960 | 1970 | 1980 |
|---|---|---|---|---|---|---|---|---|---|
| Population | 4000 | 5500 | 6000 | 7000 | 6800 | 8000 | 11,000 | 13,500 | 14,500 |

Draw a vertical line-segment graph to show the given data.

10.                Temperature Ranges in Upland City

| Month | Jan | Feb | Mar | Apr | May | Jun |
|---|---|---|---|---|---|---|
| Range in °C | 2–8 | 4–9 | 7–11 | 8–14 | 12–20 | 14–22 |

# Application

## Wind Speed

When meteorologists talk about a "storm," they refer to weather conditions in which the wind is blowing in a range of 89–102 kilometers per hour. The graph below gives the names meteorologists use for winds of different speeds.

| Beaufort | Name | Speed range |
|---|---|---|
| 12 | Hurricane | greater than 117 |
| 11 | Violent storm | 103-117 |
| 10 | Storm | 89-102 |
| 9 | Strong gale | 75-88 |
| 8 | Gale | 62-74 |
| 7 | Near gale | 50-61 |
| 6 | Strong breeze | 39-49 |
| 5 | Fresh breeze | 29-38 |
| 4 | Moderate breeze | 20-28 |
| 3 | Gentle breeze | 12-19 |
| 2 | Light breeze | 6-11 |
| 1 | Light air | 1-5 |
| 0 | Calm | less than 1 |

Beaufort Scale

kilometers per hour
Wind Speed

The Beaufort Scale, shown to the left of the graph, assigns the numbers 0–12 to various ranges of wind speeds. This scale was invented in 1805 by Sir Thomas Beaufort. He assigned the numbers according to the effect of various winds on sailing ships. For example, he described a wind with a force of 12 as "that which no canvas can stand."

### Research Activities

1. Find out how wind speed is measured. What visible signs can be used to estimate wind speed?
2. Find out how artificial satellites are used to predict weather.
3. Find out how to make some simple instruments and set up your own weather station.

**Career Activity** Find out what kind of training a meteorologist needs.

## Self-Test

Words to remember:

data [p. 1]     statistics [p. 1]     bar graph [p. 5]     broken-line graph [p. 8]

Use the table at the right for Exercises 1–4.

**Layers of Earth**

[1-1]

| Layer | Depth below surface (km) |
|---|---|
| Crust | 0–30 |
| Mantle | 30–3000 |
| Outer Core | 3000–5000 |
| Inner Core | 5000–6000 |

1. What is the outermost layer called?

2. What is the deepest layer called?

3. How deep is the outer core?

4. Which layer is beneath the crust?

Use the bar graph at the right for Exercises 5–8.

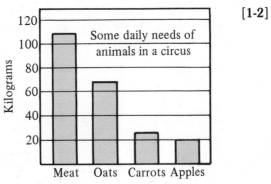

[1-2]

5. How much meat do the animals eat?

6. How much oats do they eat?

7. How much carrots and apples do they eat altogether?

8. How much more meat do they eat than apples?

Use the graph at the right for Exercises 9–12.

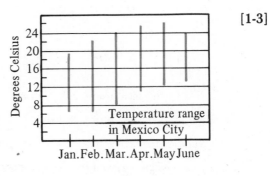

[1-3]

9. What is the range of temperature in February?

10. Which months have the greatest range?

11. Which has the least range?

12. Which has the hottest temperature?

Self-Test answers and Extra Practice are at the back of the book.

# 1-4 **Making a Histogram**

**Objective** To display data by means of a histogram.

A **histogram** is a type of bar graph that displays numerical data which have been organized into equal intervals. To organize the data, we first list them in increasing order as we did with the test scores at the right. Then we mark the data off into equal intervals. We used intervals of 41–50, 51–60, and so on, for the test scores. Next we count the number of scores that occur in each interval and make a table like the one at the left below. We call this a *frequency distribution*. The table shows, for example, that there was one score in the interval of 41–50, three scores in the interval of 51–60, and so on. Finally, we draw the histogram. The height of each bar shows the number of test scores which occurred in its interval. Notice that there are no spaces between the bars of a histogram.

| Test Scores | Intervals |
|---|---|
| 47] | 41–50 |
| 51] | |
| 53] | 51–60 |
| 57] | |
| 62] | |
| 65] | 61–70 |
| 70] | |
| 71] | |
| 72 | |
| 74 | |
| 74 | |
| 74 | 71–80 |
| 74 | |
| 80 | |
| 80] | |
| 81] | |
| 83 | |
| 83 | |
| 83 | 81–90 |
| 86 | |
| 88 | |
| 90] | |
| 93] | |
| 93 | |
| 96 | 91–100 |
| 99 | |
| 99] | |

Frequency distribution
of test scores

| Interval | Frequency |
|---|---|
| 41–50 | 1 |
| 51–60 | 3 |
| 61–70 | 3 |
| 71–80 | 8 |
| 81–90 | 7 |
| 91–100 | 5 |

Test Scores

## Class Exercises

Exercises 1–5 refer to the histogram at the right.

1. How many students had a test score in the interval 61–70?

2. In which interval were the fewest test scores made?

3. Which interval had the greatest number of test scores?

4. How many more students scored in the 91–100 interval than in the 61–70 interval?

5. How many students had a score of 70 or less?

Mathematics test scores

## Exercises

Exercises 1–3 refer to the data given at the right.

A  **1.** Arrange the data in order from least to greatest.

**2.** Organize the data into intervals of 51–60, 61–70, and so on, and make a frequency distribution table.

B  **3.** Make a histogram for the data.

Numbers of meteors spotted
in one hour by members
of the Astronomy Club

| | | | | |
|---|---|---|---|---|
| 74 | 65 | 88 | 89 | 82 |
| 53 | 73 | 94 | 102 | 91 |
| 96 | 56 | 77 | 90 | 61 |
| 107 | 94 | 106 | 87 | 65 |
| 106 | 80 | 94 | 99 | 82 |

Draw histograms for the following sets of data.

C  **4.** Data recorded by a marine biologist for an experiment.

Lengths of lobsters in centimeters

| | | | | | | | | | | | | |
|---|---|---|---|---|---|---|---|---|---|---|---|---|
| 6 | 8 | 20 | 15 | 33 | 24 | 12 | 10 | 5 | 32 | 19 | 21 | 17 |
| 9 | 31 | 19 | 11 | 25 | 8 | 18 | 18 | 13 | 12 | 32 | 19 | 15 |

(Hint: Use intervals of 0–6, 7–12, and so on.)

**5.** Data recorded in a survey taken at Shopper's Mall.

Distances in kilometers from
shoppers' homes to the mall

| | | | | | | | | | | | | |
|---|---|---|---|---|---|---|---|---|---|---|---|---|
| 18 | 2 | 5 | 12 | 7 | 2 | 13 | 16 | 4 | 4 | 15 | 3 | 10 |
| 9 | 4 | 2 | 3 | 13 | 19 | 1 | 20 | 11 | 5 | 4 | 6 | 3 |

(Hint: Use intervals of 0–5, 6–10 and so on.)

**6.** Data recorded in a frog-jumping contest. Select a reasonable interval.

Distances in centimeters jumped by frogs

| | | | | | | | | | |
|---|---|---|---|---|---|---|---|---|---|
| 333 | 235 | 350 | 358 | 338 | 281 | 345 | 221 | 279 | 344 |
| 247 | 357 | 305 | 280 | 211 | 300 | 213 | 202 | 298 | 276 |

# *EXTRA!* Another Broken-Line Graph

Sometimes we use a histogram as the basis for drawing a broken-line graph. This kind of broken-line graph is called a *frequency polygon.* Here is an example of how to draw a frequency polygon.

In an experiment, some students were asked to estimate the number of beans in a glass jar. They made a frequency distribution table of their estimates and drew a histogram as shown below.

| Estimates of number of beans | Frequency |
|---|---|
| 251–300 | 7 |
| 301–350 | 10 |
| 351–400 | 16 |
| 401–450 | 12 |

How many beans?

Estimates of number of beans

They also drew the red broken-line graph which connects the midpoints of the tops of the bars of the histogram. This graph is the frequency polygon. Notice that the frequency polygon is also connected to the horizontal axis half an interval to the left and to the right of the histogram.

**Research Activity** Collect some statistics about some activity that interests you, for example, football, or energy conservation. Make a frequency distribution table and draw a histogram and a frequency polygon to display on a bulletin board.

# 1-5 Using Numbers to Describe Data

**Objective** To calculate the range, mean, median, and mode.

Suppose we want to compare the number of cartons of yogurt sold daily during one month at two different stores as recorded in these tables.

Bestfood's

| S | M | T | W | T | F | S |
|---|---|---|---|---|---|---|
|   | 46 | 53 | 58 | 47 | 64 |   |
|   | 72 | 64 | 55 | 73 | 63 |   |
|   | 48 | 39 | 45 | 50 | 79 |   |
|   |   | 52 | 51 | 60 | 64 |   |

Eatrite's

| S | M | T | W | T | F | S |
|---|---|---|---|---|---|---|
|   | 31 | 55 | 34 | 56 | 55 | 48 |
|   | 42 | 50 | 34 | 34 | 45 | 62 |
|   | 62 | 72 | 46 | 60 | 64 | 61 |
|   |   | 34 | 40 | 43 | 50 |   |

First we list each set of numbers in increasing order. The **range** of a set of numbers is the difference between the greatest and least numbers.

$$\text{Range for Bestfood's} = 79 - 39 = 40$$
$$\text{Range for Eatrite's} \ \ = 72 - 31 = 41$$

The **mean,** or **average,** is the sum of the numbers divided by the number found by counting them.

$$\text{Mean for Bestfood's} = \frac{1083}{19} = 57$$

$$\text{Mean for Eatrite's} \ \ = \frac{1078}{22} = 49$$

The **median** is the middle number in the set if their count is odd. If their count is even, the median is the mean of the two middle numbers.

$$\text{Median for Bestfood's} = 55$$
$$\text{Median for Eatrite's} \ \ = \frac{48 + 50}{2} = 49$$

The **mode** is the number which occurs most frequently.

$$\text{Mode for Bestfood's} = 64$$
$$\text{Mode for Eatrite's} \ \ = 34$$

| Bestfood's (19 days) | Eatrite's (22 days) |
|---|---|
| 39 | 31 |
| 45 | 34 |
| 46 | 34 |
| 47 | 34 |
| 48 | 34 |
| 50 | 40 |
| 51 | 42 |
| 52 | 43 |
| 53 | 45 |
| 55 | 46 |
| 58 | 48 |
| 60 | 50 |
| 63 | 50 |
| 64 | 55 |
| 64 | 55 |
| 64 | 56 |
| 72 | 60 |
| 73 | 61 |
| 79 | 62 |
| 1083 | 62 |
|  | 64 |
|  | 72 |
|  | 1078 |

Note that while the range was almost the same for both stores, there were considerable differences in the other statistics:

1. The means show that Bestfood's sold 8 more cartons of yogurt per day on the average than Eatrite's.
2. The medians show that on half the days Bestfood's was open, it sold more than 55 cartons of yogurt per day. On half the days Eatrite's was open, it sold only 49 or more cartons of yogurt per day.
3. The modes show that the day's sales of yogurt most frequently made by Bestfood's was 64, and by Eatrite's was 34.

## Class Exercises

Exercises 1–7 refer to the data at the right.

1. Arrange the data in order from least to greatest.

2. What is the range?

3. What is the sum of the data?

4. How many items are there in the set of data?

5. What is the mean?

6. What is the median?

7. What is the mode?

Number of peas in
16 different pods

| 6 | 5 | 2 | 9 |
|---|---|---|---|
| 12 | 6 | 5 | 6 |
| 11 | 9 | 6 | 4 |
| 7 | 8 | 10 | 6 |

## Exercises

For the data at the right, find the

**B** 1. range

2. mean

3. median

4. mode

Centimeters of rain each
month at Muddy Valley

| J | F | M | A | M | J |
|---|---|---|---|---|---|
| 25 | 36 | 52 | 48 | 76 | 85 |
| J | A | S | O | N | D |
| 90 | 90 | 81 | 77 | 52 | 43 |

For the data at the right, find the

5. range

6. mean

7. median

8. mode

Numbers of puppies
in 13 litters

| 3 | 5 | 4 | 4 | 6 | 8 | 5 |
|---|---|---|---|---|---|---|
| 3 | 4 | 6 | 7 | 8 | 2 | |

Words to remember:

histogram [p. 14]     frequency distribution [p. 14]     range [p. 17]
mean [p. 17]          median [p. 17]                      mode [p. 17]

For Exercises 1–4, use the data given at the right.

**Students' heights in cm**

| | | | | |
|---|---|---|---|---|
| 143 | 157 | 161 | 155 | 146 |
| 153 | 148 | 144 | 147 | 155 |
| 152 | 169 | 164 | 142 | 146 |
| 156 | 159 | 168 | 150 | 163 |

[1-4]

1. Organize the data into intervals of 140–144, 145–149, and so on. Make a frequency distribution table.

2. Make a histogram.

3. Which interval has the greatest number of students?

4. How many students are at least 160 cm tall?

For the data at the right, find the

5. range     6. mean

7. median    8. mode

**Quiz scores**

| | | | |
|---|---|---|---|
| Sep. | 9 | Feb. | 8 |
| Oct. | 10 | Mar. | 9 |
| Nov. | 10 | Apr. | 10 |
| Dec. | 9 | May | 10 |
| Jan. | 7 | Jun. | 8 |

[1-5]

Self-Test answers and Extra Practice are at the back of the book.

# A Biologist

Rachel Carson (1907–1964) became interested in the environment when, as a young woman, she spent long hours observing nature. Upon completing college and graduate school she worked as an aquatic biologist. In 1941 she wrote her first book, *Under the Sea Wind,* after which she became editor-in-chief of the Fish and Wildlife Service. Her succeeding book, *The Sea Around Us,* was translated into thirty languages. Being an observant person, Carson became increasingly troubled by the consequences of technology on nature. Her last book, *Silent Spring,* published in 1962, produced a world-wide awareness of the dangers of chemical sprays. Statistics played an important role in her work.

# Chapter Review

Write the letter that labels the correct answer.

Use the table below for Exercises 1–4.

### Price Chart for Wearwell Tire Company

| Automobile | Four-Ply | Belted | Radial |
|---|---|---|---|
| subcompact | $20.00 | $23.00 | $36.00 |
| compact | $22.50 | $27.00 | $45.00 |
| mid-size | $25.50 | $31.50 | $45.00 |

1. A four-ply tire for a mid-size car costs __?__        **[1-1]**
     **A.** $22.50      **B.** $31.50      **C.** $20.00      **D.** $25.50

2. A radial tire for a subcompact car costs __?__
     **A.** $36.00      **B.** $23.00      **C.** $45.00      **D.** $31.50

3. Four belted tires for a mid-size car cost __?__
     **A.** $102.00      **B.** $126.00      **C.** $144.00      **D.** $180.00

4. Five belted tires for a compact car cost __?__
     **A.** $135      **B.** $108      **C.** $157.50      **D.** $162

Exercises 5–8 refer to the bar graph at the right.

Electricity used by different appliances

5. The number of watts used by a radio is closest to __?__    **[1-2]**
     **A.** 55 W      **B.** 75 W
     **C.** 85 W      **D.** 65 W

6. A __?__ uses about 15 W.
     **A.** stereo      **B.** clock
     **C.** shaver      **D.** sharpener

7. A __?__ uses the least electricity.
     **A.** radio      **B.** shaver      **C.** clock      **D.** stereo

8. A __?__ uses the most electricity.
     **A.** clock      **B.** stereo      **C.** sharpener      **D.** radio

Exercises 9–12 refer to the line graph at the right.

**Cost to run a standard-sized car**

9. The cost per kilometer of running a standard-sized car in its 4th year is closest to ___?___
   **A.** 9¢
   **B.** 10¢
   **C.** 11¢
   **D.** 12¢

[1-3]

10. It is least expensive to drive a car in its ___?___ year.
    **A.** 3rd
    **B.** 2nd
    **C.** 1st
    **D.** 4th

11. The cost of driving a car 20 km in its 1st year is ___?___.
    **A.** 20¢
    **B.** 2¢
    **C.** $2.00
    **D.** $200.00

12. The cost of driving a car 30 km in its 4th year is ___?___.
    **A.** $6.00
    **B.** $9.00
    **C.** 60¢
    **D.** $3.30

Exercises 13–14 refer to the histogram at the right.

**Wool production of Merino sheep**

[1-4]

13. The number of sheep producing between 9 kg and 11 kg of wool is ___?___
    **A.** 12
    **B.** 8
    **C.** 11
    **D.** 9

14. The interval with the greatest number of sheep is ___?___
    **A.** 7 kg–9 kg
    **B.** 9 kg–11 kg
    **C.** 11 kg–13 kg
    **D.** over 13 kg

In Exercises 15–16, refer to the chart for Exercises 1–4.

15. The median price is ___?___.
    **A.** $27.00
    **B.** $29.75
    **C.** $30.25
    **D.** $31.50

[1-5]

16. The mode is ___?___.
    **A.** $36.00
    **B.** $27.00
    **C.** $30.00
    **D.** $45.00

# Displaying Information

Many kinds of information are displayed by graphs. The type of graph used depends on the nature of the information being shown. Sometimes special visual effects are used as attention-getters.

The graph at the right uses a 3-dimensional effect to display some weather information. Notice that the numbers on the vertical scale at the left serve two purposes:

1. They refer to centimeters when reading the precipitation graph.
2. They refer to degrees Celsius when reading the temperature graph.

What was the lowest average monthly temperature? In what month did it occur? In what month was there the greatest average amount of precipitation? How many centimeters was it?

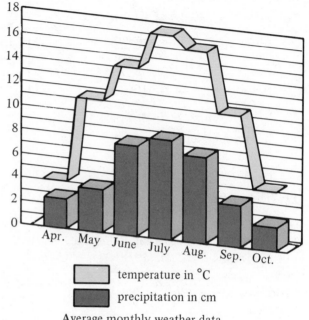

temperature in °C

precipitation in cm

Average monthly weather data for Edmonton, Alberta, Canada

The graph below uses visual symbols to indicate when total eclipses of the sun and moon will occur. This kind of graph is called a *pictograph.*

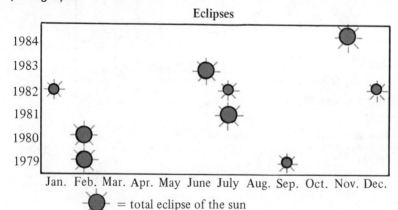

= total eclipse of the sun

= total eclipse of the moon

In what year does both a total eclipse of the sun and of the moon occur? Is there a total eclipse of the sun in all the years shown?

Another form of pictograph is shown below. It indicates the noise levels of various everyday situations. A *decibel* is a unit for measuring the level of sound. Wavy lines are used instead of bars because they suggest sound waves.

NOISE LEVELS

| | | |
|---|---|---|
| Quiet office | 〰〰 | 40 decibels |
| Average home | 〰〰〰 | 50 |
| Vacuum cleaner | 〰〰〰〰 | 70 |
| Heavy truck | 〰〰〰〰〰 | 90 |
| Motorcycle | 〰〰〰〰〰〰 | 100 |
| Amplified rock music | 〰〰〰〰〰〰〰 | 115 |
| Jet plane (at ramp) | 〰〰〰〰〰〰〰〰 | 117 |

**Research Activity** Find out about noise pollution and the effect of loud noises on one's hearing.

We can use graphs to help us plan how to spend our money.

Suppose you have $18 to spend. You like records, but you also enjoy mystery books. Records cost $6 and books cost $3 apiece. How many of each can you afford?

You can spend exactly $18 if you buy any of the following combinations:

| records | mysteries |
|---------|-----------|
| 0 | 6 |
| 1 | 4 |
| 2 | 2 |
| 3 | 0 |

The combinations can also be shown by dots on a graph. The line connecting these dots is called your budget line. You can afford any combination which is represented by dots on or below the budget line.

1. How much would 1 record and 4 mystery books cost?
2. How much would 1 record and 3 mystery books cost?
3. If you wanted to save $5 of your $18, how much would you have left to spend on mystery books and records? What combinations of books and records could you buy?

# Chapter Test

Exercises 1 and 2 refer to the table below.

1. What was the least amount of peaches picked from a tree?

2. Which row produced the most peaches?

| Kilograms of peaches picked from 15 peach trees | | | | | |
|---|---|---|---|---|---|
| Row 1 | 120 | 140 | 95 | 125 | 190 |
| Row 2 | 105 | 160 | 135 | 150 | 175 |
| Row 3 | 145 | 200 | 175 | 180 | 155 |

[1-1]

Exercises 3 and 4 refer to the bar graph at the right.

3. What is the swimming speed of a dolphin?

4. How far can a pike swim in 3 hours?

[1-2]

Exercises 5 and 6 refer to the line graph at the right which shows automobile registrations in Canada.

5. About how many automobiles were registered in 1950?

6. In what year were there about 3 million automobiles registered?

[1-3]

Exercises 7–10 refer to the table for Exercises 1 and 2.

7. Organize the data into intervals of 91–120, 121–150, 151–180, and 181–210. Draw a histogram.

omit

[1-4]

8. How many trees produced 150 kg of peaches or less?

9. What is the mean of the data?

[1-5]

10. What is the median of the data?

24

# Skill Review

Perform the indicated operation.

1. 31
   +50

2. 72
   +19

3. 44
   +63

4. 86
   + 7

5. 65
   +89

6. 27
   + 4

7. 53
   +43

8. 90
   +78

9. 18
   +65

10. 49
    +72

11. 705
    +261

12. 634
    +948

13. 975
    + 73

14. 318
    +842

15. 432
    +995

16. 79
    54
    +40

17. 31
    82
    +36

18. 64
    10
    +97

19. 862
    473
    +315

20. 506
    994
    +282

21. 48
    −36

22. 70
    −15

23. 39
    − 2

24. 75
    −45

25. 63
    −28

26. 36
    −17

27. 82
    −50

28. 51
    −29

29. 72
    − 4

30. 99
    −91

31. 748
    −273

32. 745
    −639

33. 640
    −268

34. 119
    −107

35. 682
    −488

36. 9817
    −4321

37. 6257
    −5603

38. 8651
    − 764

39. 8340
    −8219

40. 4094
    −1380

41. 24
    × 3

42. 81
    × 7

43. 53
    × 5

44. 94
    × 2

45. 60
    × 8

46. 71
    ×49

47. 23
    ×60

48. 54
    ×76

49. 63
    ×13

50. 92
    ×58

51. 197
    × 6

52. 405
    × 3

53. 870
    × 32

54. 458
    × 84

55. 946
    × 91

56. 6)‾72‾

57. 4)‾96‾

58. 9)‾369‾

59. 3)‾195‾

60. 5)‾540‾

61. 2)‾758‾

62. 7)‾413‾

63. 8)‾624‾

64. 4)‾260‾

65. 3)‾282‾

66. 67)‾536‾

67. 29)‾783‾

68. 56)‾728‾

69. 13)‾416‾

70. 48)‾336‾

25

# 2 The Decimal System

## 2-1 Powers of Ten

**Objective** To identify powers of ten and write their products.

The decimal numeral for the amount of money mentioned in the newspaper headline at the right is 1,000,000. We can show 1,000,000 as a product of *factors* of 10. A **factor** is any of two or more numbers which are multiplied to form a product.

$$1,000,000 = \underbrace{10 \times 10 \times 10 \times 10 \times 10 \times 10}_{\text{6 factors of 10}}$$

We say that 1,000,000 is a *power* of 10. A **power** is a product of *equal* factors. Since 1,000,000 is the product of 6 factors of 10, we say 1,000,000 is the **6th power of 10.** A simpler way to show this is

$$1,000,000 = 10^6$$

with exponent 6 and base 10.

The *exponent* 6 shows the number of times the base 10 is used as a factor. The numeral $10^6$ is read "the 6th power of 10," or "10 to the 6th (power)." Notice that there are 6 zeros in the numeral 1,000,000.

NEW SPORTS CENTER COSTS $1 MILLION

factors
$$4 \times 5 = 20$$
product

**27**

The product of two powers of 10 can be found rapidly. For example

$$10^2 \times 10^3 = (10 \times 10) \times (10 \times 10 \times 10) = 10^{2+3} = 10^5$$

Note that the exponent in the product equals the sum of those in the factors, that is, $2 + 3 = 5$.

---

**Example 1** | **Express $10^4 \times 10^5$ as a single power of 10.**

*Solution* | $10^4 \times 10^5 = 10^{4+5} = 10^9$

---

The number system we use is based on powers of ten and is called a decimal system. (The word *decimal* comes from *decem*, the Latin word for *ten*.) For example, we can show the number 3972 in expanded form as

$$3972 = (3 \times 1000) + (9 \times 100) + (7 \times 10) + 2,$$

or, using exponents, as

$$3972 = (3 \times 10^3) + (9 \times 10^2) + (7 \times 10^1) + 2.$$

Parentheses are used above to group operations which should be done first.

---

**Example 2** | **Write in expanded form, using exponents.**
 | **a. 13,599**
 | **b. 8035**

*Solution* | **a.** $13,599 = (1 \times 10,000) + (3 \times 1000) + (5 \times 100) + (9 \times 10) + 9$
 | $= (1 \times 10^4) + (3 \times 10^3) + (5 \times 10^2) + (9 \times 10^1) + 9$
 | **b.** $8035 = (8 \times 1000) + (0 \times 100) + (3 \times 10) + 5$
 | $= (8 \times 10^3) + (0 \times 10^2) + (3 \times 10^1) + 5$
 | $= (8 \times 10^3) + (3 \times 10^1) + 5$

---

**Example 3** | **Write the decimal numeral for the expanded form.**
 | **a.** $(2 \times 10^2) + (4 \times 10^1) + 3$
 | **b.** $(3 \times 10^3) + (0 \times 10^2) + (5 \times 10^1) + 8$

*Solution* | **a. 243**
 | **b. 3058**

## Class Exercises

Read each numeral as a power of 10.

**1.** 100          **2.** 100,000          **3.** 1000          **4.** 10,000,000          **5.** 10,000

Tell how many zeros there are in the decimal numeral for the power of 10.

**6.** $10^3$          **7.** $10^6$          **8.** $10^1$          **9.** $10^4$          **10.** $10^8$

Complete the table below.

| | Number | Decimal Numeral | Number of Zeros | Numeral with an Exponent |
|---|---|---|---|---|
| **11.** | million | 1,000,000 | 6 | ? |
| **12.** | thousand | 1,000 | ? | $10^3$ |
| **13.** | hundred | 100 | ? | ? |
| **14.** | hundred million | 100,000,000 | ? | ? |
| **15.** | ten thousand | 10,000 | ? | ? |
| **16.** | hundred thousand | 100,000 | ? | ? |

## Exercises

Express as a single power of 10.

**A**   **1.** $10^1 \times 10^2$       **2.** $10^4 \times 10^3$       **3.** $10^2 \times 10^2$       **4.** $10^5 \times 10^1$       **5.** $10^6 \times 10^3$

Write in expanded form using exponents.

**6.** 243          **7.** 5812          **8.** 62,334          **9.** 8049          **10.** 30,057

Write the decimal numeral for the expanded form.

**11.** $(7 \times 1000) + (4 \times 100) + (7 \times 10) + 5$

**12.** $(9 \times 10,000) + (0 \times 1000) + (6 \times 100) + (4 \times 10) + 2$

**13.** $(6 \times 100,000) + (3 \times 10,000) + (1 \times 1000) + (0 \times 100) + (6 \times 10) + 0$

**14.** $(5 \times 10,000) + (0 \times 1000) + (0 \times 100) + (0 \times 10) + 2$

**15.** $(2 \times 10^3) + (5 \times 10^2) + (7 \times 10^1) + 3$

**16.** $(9 \times 10^4) + (0 \times 10^3) + (3 \times 10^2) + (4 \times 10^1) + 4$

**17.** $(8 \times 10^6) + (4 \times 10^5) + (0 \times 10^4) + (7 \times 10^3) + (4 \times 10^2) + (5 \times 10^1) + 9$

**18.** $(1 \times 10^5) + (9 \times 10^4) + (1 \times 10^3) + (7 \times 10^2) + (1 \times 10^1) + 0$

Using some or all of the digits 8, 2, 7, 5, 4, write the number described. Each digit can be used just once in the number.

19. The largest 2-digit number

20. The smallest 2-digit number

21. The largest 3-digit number

22. The smallest 3-digit number

23. The largest 3-digit number whose second digit is 8

24. The smallest 3-digit number whose second digit is 8

25. The largest 4-digit number

26. The next-to-the-largest 4-digit number

27. The smallest 4-digit number

28. The name for the 100th power of 10, or $10^{100}$, is one *googol*. How many zeros are there in the decimal numeral for one googol?

# EXTRA!

## Powers of Bases Other than 10

We can use exponents to express powers of any number, not just 10. For example,

$2^1 = 2$                        $5^1 = 5$
$2^2 = 2 \times 2 = 4$           $5^2 = 5 \times 5 = 25$
$2^3 = 2 \times 2 \times 2 = 8$  $5^3 = 5 \times 5 \times 5 = 125$
$2^4 = 2 \times 2 \times 2 \times 2 = 16$   $5^4 = 5 \times 5 \times 5 \times 5 = 625$

**Calculator Activity** Use a calculator for the following exercises if you wish. Operations in parentheses are to be done first.

1. **a.** $16^2 - 13^2$        **b.** $(16 + 13) \times (16 - 13)$
2. **a.** $45^2 - 23^2$        **b.** $(45 + 23) \times (45 - 23)$
3. **a.** $73^2 - 69^2$        **b.** $(73 + 69) \times (73 - 69)$
4. **a.** $124^2 - 42^2$       **b.** $(124 + 42) \times (124 - 42)$

Do you see a pattern?

# 2-2 Decimals

**Objective** To read and write decimals.

The decimal numbers we used in the preceding section are called whole numbers. We can show the set of whole numbers like this:

$$\{0, 1, 2, \ldots\}$$

We read this "the set whose members are 0, 1, 2, and so on." The three dots show that there is no end to the list of whole numbers.

You are already familiar with another set of numbers, called fractions. For example, numbers like $\frac{1}{2}$, $\frac{4}{7}$, and so on, are fractions. A fraction whose denominator is a power of ten can be written in decimal form.

| Fraction | Decimal |
|----------|---------|
| $\frac{3}{10}$ | 0.3 |
| $\frac{5}{10}$ or $\frac{1}{2}$ | 0.5 |

decimal point

The table below shows some fractions and decimals used to name the quotient when one is divided by successive powers of ten.

1 unit

$\frac{1}{10}$ unit

$\frac{1}{100}$ unit

| Fraction | Decimal | In Words |
|----------|---------|----------|
| $\frac{1}{10}$ | 0.1 | one tenth |
| $\frac{1}{10^2}$ or $\frac{1}{100}$ | 0.01 | one hundredth |
| $\frac{1}{10^3}$ or $\frac{1}{1000}$ | 0.001 | one thousandth |
| $\frac{1}{10^4}$ or $\frac{1}{10,000}$ | 0.0001 | one ten-thousandth |
| . . . . . . . . | . . . . . | . . . . . . . . . . . |

Notice that as we read down the table, each succeeding decimal is equal to 0.1 of the decimal above it. That is,

$$0.01 = 0.1 \times 0.1, \quad 0.001 = 0.1 \times 0.01, \quad \text{and so on.}$$

Look at the multiplications with fractions and decimals on page 32.

$$\frac{1}{100} = \frac{1}{10} \times \frac{1}{10} \qquad \text{or} \qquad 0.01 \quad = 0.1 \times 0.1$$

$$\frac{1}{1000} = \frac{1}{10} \times \frac{1}{100} \qquad \text{or} \qquad 0.001 \; = 0.1 \times 0.01$$

$$\frac{1}{10,000} = \frac{1}{10} \times \frac{1}{1000} \qquad \text{or} \qquad 0.0001 = 0.1 \times 0.001$$

The chart below shows the place values for some decimals.

**Place-value Chart**

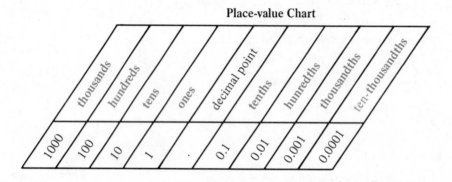

As we move to the right, place values decrease, because each new place is only one tenth of the preceding place value. The whole numbers are to the left of the decimal point and the decimals for fractions between 0 and 1 are to its right.

In the decimal 0.387,
the place value of the digit 3 is one tenth, or 0.1,
the number which 3 represents is 3 × 0.1, or 0.3.

In expanded form,
0.387 = 0.3 + 0.08 + 0.007
= (3 × 0.1) + (8 × 0.01) + (7 × 0.001)

Here are some examples of how to read decimals. Notice that, we read the decimal point as "and."

| Decimal | In words |
|---------|----------|
| 0.5 | five tenths, or one half |
| 6.32 | six and thirty-two hundredths |
| 0.387 | three hundred eighty-seven thousandths |
| 548.9 | five hundred forty-eight and nine tenths |

## Class Exercises

Name the place value of the underlined digit.

**1.** 6945      **2.** 83.45      **3.** 692.01      **4.** 12.336      **5.** 40.6253

Read each number.

**6.** 5732      **7.** 24.6      **8.** 6.13      **9.** 1052.482

**10.** 34.5067      **11.** 0.0015      **12.** 8.0008      **13.** 0.70605

## Exercises

Write each number in expanded form.

**A**

**1.** 65.4      **2.** 6.54      **3.** 0.654      **4.** 0.0654

**5.** 29.86      **6.** 10.305      **7.** 0.0472      **8.** 9.00623

Write the decimal numeral for the expanded form.

**9.** $(4 \times 0.1) + (7 \times 0.01) + (9 \times 0.001)$

**10.** $(6 \times 10) + 5 + (6 \times 0.1) + (8 \times 0.01)$

**11.** $(5 \times 100) + (7 \times 10) + 2 + (0 \times 0.1) + (8 \times 0.01)$

**12.** $(3 \times 1000) + (0 \times 100) \times (4 \times 10) + 0 + (7 \times 0.1) + (0 \times 0.01) + (7 \times 0.001)$

**13.** $(1 \times 10) + 3 + (0 \times 0.1) + (0 \times 0.01) + (5 \times 0.001) + (2 \times 0.0001)$

**14.** $(9 \times 0.1) + (3 \times 0.01) + (0 \times 0.001) + (4 \times 0.0001) + (5 \times 0.00001)$

**15.** $(6 \times 100) + 4 + (3 \times 0.1) + (7 \times 0.001)$

**16.** $(2 \times 10) + (3 \times 0.01) + (4 \times 0.0001)$

Write in words.

**17.** 26.5      **18.** 2.48      **19.** 0.312      **20.** 7.076

**21.** 0.0011      **22.** 92.072      **23.** 401.0906      **24.** 300.0036

Write the decimal.

**25.** fourteen and seven tenths      **26.** thirty-three and seven hundredths

**27.** five hundred and fifteen thousandths      **28.** seven and sixty-four ten-thousandths

**29.** two hundred fifty and three hundred forty-six thousandths

**30.** one thousand and twenty-nine ten-thousandths

## 2-3 The Number Line

**Objective** To graph numbers on the number line and compare them by the use of inequality symbols.

The *graphs* of the whole numbers 0 through 6 are shown on the number line below. The **graph** of a number is the point paired with

the number on a number line. The number paired with a point is called the **coordinate** of the point. Looking at the number line above we can see that:

1. The graph of 0 is called the *origin*.
2. The graphs of consecutive whole numbers are equally spaced.
3. The graph of 3 is point *A*.
4. The coordinate of point *B* is 6.
5. Coordinates increase as we move to the right.

Since *B* lies to the right of *A*,

coordinate of *B*                   coordinate of *A*

6 is greater than 3.

In symbols we write           $6 > 3$

We can also say

3 is less than 6

In symbols we write           $3 < 6$

We call the symbols $<$ and $>$ **inequality symbols.** To avoid confusing these symbols, think of them as arrowheads whose small ends point toward the smaller numbers.

We can indicate that 4 is between 3 and 6 by combining two inequalities $3 < 4$ and $4 < 6$ and writing

$$3 < 4 < 6$$

*Example 1* | Write the sentence using an inequality symbol or symbols.
a. 2 is less than 5
b. 18 is greater than 7
c. 30 is between 20 and 40

*Solution* | a. $2 < 5$
b. $18 > 7$
c. $20 < 30 < 40$

The number line below is marked off in tenths. On it are shown the graphs of some decimals.

| Number | Graph |
|--------|--------|
| 0.3 | point *C* |
| 0.7 | point *D* |
| 1.1 | point *E* |
| 1.4 | point *F* |

In the same way we can draw number lines marked off in hundredths, thousandths, and so on, and on them show the graphs of decimals to the hundredths' and thousandths' places.

*Example 2* | Write the sentence using an inequality symbol or symbols.
a. 0.2 is less than 0.8
b. 1.3 is greater than 0.6
c. 0.9 is between 0.5 and 1.4
d. 3.06 is between 3.02 and 3.15
e. 12.637 is between 12.630 and 12.640

*Solution* | a. $0.2 < 0.8$
b. $1.3 > 0.6$
c. $0.5 < 0.9 < 1.4$
d. $3.02 < 3.06 < 3.15$
e. $12.630 < 12.637 < 12.640$

## Class Exercises

Use the number line below for Exercises 1–6.

**1.** The graph of 0.5 is point ___?___ .

**2.** The graph of 1.1 is point ___?___ .

**3.** The coordinate of point $B$ is ___?___ .

**4.** The coordinate of point $E$ is ___?___ .

**5.** Point $A$ is called the ___?___ .

**6.** Since $D$ lies to the right of $B$, 1.1 ___?___ 0.2.
$(<, >)$

Read each sentence.

**7.** $2 < 8$      **8.** $0.8 > 0.2$      **9.** $3.2 > 0.3$      **10.** $5 < 7.7$

**11.** $16 > 5 > 0$     **12.** $0.3 < 0.5 < 1.6$     **13.** $10.6 < 11 < 11.6$     **14.** $1.2 > 1.02 > 1.002$

## Exercises

For each exercise, draw a number line and graph the given numbers.

**A**  **1.** $0, 2, 5, 6, 8$

**2.** $0, 0.2, 0.5, 0.6, 0.8$

**3.** $0.3, 0.7, 1, 1.2, 1.4$

**4.** $0.4, 0.6, 0.8, 1, 1.2$

**5.** $1.4, 0.9, 0.5, 1.2, 1.3$

**6.** $1.4, 0, 0.7, 1.6, 0.8$

Write the sentence using an inequality symbol.

**7.** 9 is less than 15.

**8.** 14 is less than 24.

**9.** 21 is greater than 19.

**10.** 7 is between 4 and 10.

**11.** 0.8 is greater than 0.5.

**12.** 4.7 is less than 4.72.

**13.** 6.3 is between 6.1 and 6.5.

**14.** 0.5 is between 1.7 and 0.4.

**15.** 1.53 is greater than 1.43.

**16.** 9.01 is between 9.001 and 9.1.

Replace each ___?___ with $>$ or $<$ to make a true sentence.

**17.** $21$ ___?___ $16$

**18.** $13$ ___?___ $15$

**19.** $4$ ___?___ $9$ ___?___ $11$

**20.** $0.5$ ___?___ $0.7$

**21.** $3.8$ ___?___ $2.8$

**22.** $5.72$ ___?___ $1.67$

**23.** $0.08$ ___?___ $0.26$

**24.** $12.04$ ___?___ $12.97$

**25.** $0.26$ ___?___ $0.46$ ___?___ $0.66$

**26.** $0.44$ ___?___ $0.4$

**27.** $1.765$ ___?___ $1.76$

**28.** $8.303$ ___?___ $8.33$

**29.** $4.7$ ___?___ $4.76$

**30.** $6.045$ ___?___ $6.12$

**31.** $1.13$ ___?___ $1.093$

# 2-4 Equations and Variables

**Objective** To use variables to represent numbers.

In Section 2-3, you learned the meaning of the inequality symbols $<$ and $>$. You are probably much more familiar with the **equality symbol,** $=$, which stands for "is equal to." When we write the *equation*

$$5 + 6 = 11$$

we mean that the *numerical expressions* $5 + 6$ and $11$ name the same number. $5 + 6 = 11$ is a *true* equation. Not all equations are true; for example, $5 + 6 = 13$ is a *false* equation.

Another kind of symbol we use is called a *variable*. A **variable** is a letter which is used to stand for any member of a given set of numbers. The given set of numbers is called the **replacement set.** Each number in the set is called a **value of the variable.** The letter $x$ is used as a variable in Example 1, below.

*Example 1* | **What is the sum, $x + 8$, if**
           | **a. $x = 2$?**        **b. $x = 9$?**

*Solution* | **a. $2 + 8 = 10$**      **b. $9 + 8 = 17$**

In Example 1,
     2 and 9 are the values of $x$.
     $\{2, 9\}$ is the replacement set for $x$.
Replacing a variable in an expression with one of its values and then doing the indicated arithmetic is called **finding the value of the expression,** or **evaluating the expression.**

*Example 2* | **Evaluate $5 \times n$ if the replacement set for $n$ is $\{3, 7, 11\}$.**

*Solution* | $5 \times n = ?$
     | $5 \times 3 = 15$
     | $5 \times 7 = 35$
     | $5 \times 11 = 55$

When variables are used in products, the multiplication symbol, $\times$, is often omitted. Thus we write $5n$ in place of $5 \times n$, and $ab$ in place of $a \times b$.

## Class Exercises

1. What is the difference, $20 - x$, if: **a.** $x = 11$?   **b.** $x = 3$?

2. What is the sum, $y + 5$, if: **a.** $y = 9$?   **b.** $y = 67$?

3. What is the product, $8n$, if: **a.** $n = 12$?   **b.** $n = 40$?

4. What is the quotient, $42 \div n$, if: **a.** $n = 2$?   **b.** $n = 7$?

Replace the variable with the given value and state whether the resulting equation is true or false.

*Example*   | $9 - x = 2;\ x = 3$
*Solution*  | $9 - 3 = 2$, or $6 = 2$. **False**

| | |
|---|---|
| 5. $x + 7 = 12; x = 5$ | 6. $24 - y = 20; y = 3$ |

7. $10x = 320; x = 35$

8. $93 - n = 6; n = 33$     9. $7y = 56; y = 8$     10. $m + 6 = 72; m = 62$

## Exercises

Complete the table.

| | | Expression | Value of $x$ | Value of the Expression |
|---|---|---|---|---|
| A | 1. | $x + 13$ | 5 | ? |
| | 2. | $x + 13$ | 25 | ? |
| | 3. | $24 - x$ | 11 | ? |
| | 4. | $24 - x$ | 22 | ? |
| | 5. | $15x$ | 21 | ? |
| | 6. | $15x$ | 72 | ? |
| | 7. | $25 + x$ | 67 | ? |
| | 8. | $x - 132$ | 416 | ? |
| | 9. | $58x$ | 39 | ? |
| | 10. | $217 \div x$ | 7 | ? |

Evaluate the given expression for the given replacement set.

11. $x + 9; \{3, 5, 16\}$

12. $21 + x; \{4, 17, 19\}$

13. $16n; \{2, 16, 18\}$

14. $45n; \{8, 20, 31\}$

**15.** $37 - y$; $\{11, 15, 24\}$    **16.** $y - 16$; $\{74, 191, 26\}$    **17.** $63x$; $\{27, 11, 20\}$

**18.** $n + 184$; $\{52, 133, 326\}$    **19.** $120 \div x$; $\{4, 10, 60\}$    **20.** $144 \div y$; $\{3, 36, 9\}$

**B**  **21.** $2x + 1$; $\{3, 7, 10\}$    **22.** $39 - 4x$; $\{1, 5, 9\}$    **23.** $5x - 4$; $\{4, 7, 9\}$

**24.** $3(x + 4)$; $\{6, 10, 15\}$    **25.** $6(x - 3)$; $\{7, 11, 21\}$    **26.** $21(x + 32)$; $\{2, 47, 83\}$

## Self-Test

Symbols and words to remember:

$>$ [p. 34]                      $<$ [p. 34]                      $=$ [p. 37]
factor [p. 27]              power [p. 27]              exponent [p. 27]
inequalities [p. 34]      equation [p. 37]          expression [p. 37]
variable [p. 37]           replacement set [p. 37]

**1.** Write 10,000 as a power of 10.                                              [2-1]

**2.** Express $10^3 \times 10^5$ as a single power of 10.

**3.** Write 40,807 in expanded form, using exponents.

**4.** Write the decimal numeral for the following:

$$(8 \times 1000) + (6 \times 100) + (9 \times 10) + 1.$$

**5.** Name the place value of the underlined digit in 38.0$\underline{5}$5.          [2-2]

**6.** Write 7.246 in expanded form.

**7.** Write the decimal for the following:

$$(4 \times 100) + (0 \times 10) + 3 + (6 \times 0.1) + (2 \times 0.01).$$

**8.** Write the decimal for sixty-five and nine thousandths.

**9.** Draw a number line. Graph 0.1, 0.7, 0.9, 1, 1.2.                      [2-3]

Replace each __?__ with $<$ or $>$ to make a true sentence.

**10.** 8.3 __?__ 8.03    **11.** 0.91 __?__ 0.916    **12.** 5 __?__ 5.28 __?__ 5.3

Evaluate the given expression for the given replacement set.

**13.** $8 + n$; $\{0, 9, 23\}$          **14.** $x - 13$; $\{17, 53, 108\}$          [2-4]

**15.** $12y$; $\{3, 8, 40\}$          **16.** $t \div 24$; $\{96, 240, 408\}$

Self-Test answers and Extra Practice are at the back of the book.

# 2-5 Inverse Operations

**Objective** To show the relationship between addition and subtraction and between multiplication and division.

Finding the difference of two numbers, or subtraction, can be looked at as the process of finding a missing addend as shown below.

addend addend sum     addend (difference) sum addend

$$n + 3 = 7 \qquad\qquad n = 7 - 3$$
$$4 + 3 = 7 \qquad\qquad 4 = 7 - 3$$
$$n = 4 \qquad\qquad\qquad n = 4$$

We say that adding 3 and subtracting 3 are *inverse operations*. In the same way, for every addition equation we can write a related subtraction equation. Adding a number is the inverse of subtracting the same number.

| | |
|---|---|
| *Example 1* | Write a related subtraction equation and find the value of *n*.<br><br>**a.** $n + 5 = 12$        **b.** $n + 14 = 23$ |
| *Solution* | **a.** $\quad n = 12 - 5$    **b.** $\quad n = 23 - 14$<br>         $n = 7$                 $n = 9$ |

Multiplying by a number and dividing by the same number are inverse operations also. Finding the quotient of two numbers, or division, can be thought of as finding a missing factor.

(divisor) (quotient) (dividend)
factor    factor    product        quotient dividend divisor

$$4 \times y = 8 \qquad\qquad y = 8 \div 4$$

| | |
|---|---|
| *Example 2* | Write a related division equation and find the value of *y*.<br><br>**a.** $5 \times y = 15$        **b.** $7 \times y = 56$ |
| *Solution* | **a.** $\quad y = 15 \div 5$    **b.** $\quad y = 56 \div 7$<br>         $y = 3$                 $y = 8$ |

## Class Exercises

**1.** If $n + 4 = 12$, then $n = 12 - \underline{\phantom{?}}$, and $n = \underline{\phantom{?}}$.

**2.** If $y + 5 = 16$, then $y = \underline{\phantom{?}} - \underline{\phantom{?}}$, and $y = \underline{\phantom{?}}$.

**3.** If $8 \times y = 32$, then $y = 32 \div \underline{\phantom{?}}$, and $y = \underline{\phantom{?}}$.

**4.** If $6 \times m = 42$, then $m = \underline{\phantom{?}} \div \underline{\phantom{?}}$, and $m = \underline{\phantom{?}}$.

State a related subtraction or division equation and find the value of $n$.

**5.** $n + 6 = 14$     **6.** $n + 20 = 25$     **7.** $n + 2 = 12$     **8.** $n + 30 = 40$

**9.** $2 \times n = 16$     **10.** $7 \times n = 21$     **11.** $3 \times n = 33$     **12.** $5 \times n = 40$

## Exercises

Write a related subtraction equation and find the value of $x$.

A

**1.** $x + 83 = 102$     **2.** $x + 47 = 96$     **3.** $x + 116 = 242$     **4.** $x + 38 = 276$

**5.** $x + 133 = 200$     **6.** $x + 88 = 217$     **7.** $x + 135 = 235$     **8.** $x + 716 = 900$

**9.** $x + 299 = 316$     **10.** $x + 308 = 803$     **11.** $x + 671 = 719$     **12.** $x + 136 = 631$

Write a related division equation and find the value of $y$.

**13.** $12 \times y = 156$     **14.** $31 \times y = 961$     **15.** $25 \times y = 600$     **16.** $18 \times y = 360$

**17.** $44 \times y = 132$     **18.** $19 \times y = 323$     **19.** $18 \times y = 1818$     **20.** $17 \times y = 289$

**21.** $71 \times y = 781$     **22.** $34 \times y = 1462$     **23.** $16 \times y = 2000$     **24.** $101 \times y = 7272$

# Application

**Calculator Activity** Take your calculator and

|  | Example |
|---|---|
| **1.** Press any 3 digits. | 723 |
| **2.** Repeat the digits. | 723,723 |
| **3.** Divide by 7. | ? |
| **4.** Divide by 11. | ? |
| **5.** Divide by 13. | ? |

What is your answer? Now multiply your answer by 1001. Explain your result.

# 2-6 Properties of Addition and Multiplication

**Objective** To use the properties of addition and multiplication.

Addition and multiplication follow certain basic properties as shown below.

## properties

**Commutative Property**
Changing the order of the addends in a sum, or the factors in a product, does not change the sum or product.

$$7 + 3 = 3 + 7 \qquad 9 \times 5 = 5 \times 9$$

In general, for any numbers $a$ and $b$,

$$a + b = b + a \qquad a \times b = b \times a$$

**Associative Property**
Changing the grouping of addends in a sum, or of factors in a product, does not change the sum or product.

$$(4 + 2) + 5 = 11 \qquad (2 \times 3) \times 5 = 30$$
$$4 + (2 + 5) = 11 \qquad 2 \times (3 \times 5) = 30$$

In general, for any numbers $a$, $b$, and $c$,

$$(a + b) + c = a + (b + c) \qquad (a \times b) \times c = a \times (b \times c)$$

**The Property of Zero in Addition**
The sum of zero and any given number is the given number.

$$9 + 0 = 9$$

In general, for any number $a$, $a + 0 = a$

**The Property of Zero in Multiplication**
The product of zero and any given number is zero.

$$6 \times 0 = 0$$

In general, for any given number $a$, $a \times 0 = 0$

## properties

*The Property of One in Multiplication*
The product of one and any given number $a$ is the given number.

$$2 \times 1 = 2$$

In general, for any number $a$, $a \times 1 = a$

*The Distributive Property of Multiplication over Addition*
The following computation illustrates this property.

$$3 \times (2 + 1) = 3 \times 3 \quad (3 \times 2) + (3 \times 1) = 6 + 3$$
$$= 9 \qquad\qquad\qquad = 9$$

Therefore,
$$3 \times (2 + 1) = (3 \times 2) + (3 \times 1)$$

In general, for any numbers $a$, $b$, and $c$,

$$a \times (b + c) = (a \times b) + (a \times c)$$

In the numerical examples of the properties shown above we have used only whole numbers, for the sake of simplicity. However, these properties hold true for all the numbers you will study in this text.

| *Example* | Replace each variable to make a true equation. |
|---|---|
| | **a.** $6 + 5 = 5 + n$ |
| | **b.** $4 \times 2 = 2 \times n = x$ |
| *Solution* | **a.** $6 + 5 = 5 + n$ |
| | $6 + 5 = 5 + 6$, so $n = 6$ |
| | **b.** $4 \times 2 = 2 \times n = x$ |
| | $4 \times 2 = 2 \times 4 = 8$, so $n = 4$ and $x = 8$ |

## Class Exercises

Name the property of addition or multiplication illustrated.

**1.** $18 \times 0 = 0$     **2.** $4 \times 8 = 8 \times 4$     **3.** $(6 + 2) + 8 = 6 + (2 + 8)$

**4.** $7 + 0 = 7$     **5.** $23 \times 1 = 23$     **6.** $9 \times (6 + 2) = (9 \times 6) + (9 \times 2)$

## Exercises

Use the commutative and associative properties to simplify each expression.

| *Example* | $16 + 25 + 4$ |
|---|---|
| *Solution* | $16 + 25 + 4 = 16 + 4 + 25$ |
| | $= 20 + 25 = 45$ |

**A**

**1.** $8 + 27 + 12$      **2.** $17 + 44 + 3$      **3.** $15 + 87 + 5$

**4.** $62 + 95 + 8$      **5.** $5 + 13 + 15 + 7$      **6.** $6 + 12 + 24 + 8$

**7.** $2 \times 12 \times 5$      **8.** $15 \times 7 \times 4$      **9.** $5 \times 52 \times 2$

**10.** $4 \times 32 \times 5 \times 25$      **11.** $75 \times 12 \times 4 \times 5$      **12.** $6 \times 45 \times 15 \times 2$

Use the distributive property to simplify each expression.

| *Example* | **a.** $(4 \times 6) + (4 \times 14)$ |
|---|---|
| | **b.** $6 \times 58$ |
| *Solution* | **a.** $(4 \times 6) + (4 \times 14) = 4(6 + 14)$ |
| | $= 4(20) = 80$ |
| | **b.** $6 \times 58 = 6(50 + 8)$ |
| | $= (6 \times 50) + (6 \times 8)$ |
| | $= 300 + 48 = 348$ |

**13.** $(3 \times 7) + (3 \times 13)$      **14.** $(5 \times 21) + (5 \times 9)$

**15.** $(18 \times 6) + (18 \times 24)$      **16.** $(22 \times 18) + (22 \times 2)$

**17.** $8 \times 43$      **18.** $6 \times 89$      **19.** $4 \times 57$      **20.** $12 \times 35$

Use any of the properties to simplify each expression.

**B**

**21.** $44 + 19 + 2 + 16 + 81 + 58$

**22.** $(18 + 46) + (12 + 4) + (8 \times 17) + (23 \times 8)$

**23.** $(12 \times 7) + (56 \div 8) + (13 \times 12)$

**24.** $5(81 \div 3) + 5(63 \div 1) - 450$

**25.** $116 + 7(48 + 15) + (15 + 22)7 + 34$

**26.** $(78 \times 1) + (99 \times 78) - (101 + 0 + 99)$

**27.** $(3 \times 10^2) + (22 \times 10^2) + (4 \times 10^3)$    **28.** $43(2^3 + 2) + (10 \times 27)$

# 2-7 Adding and Subtracting Decimals

**Objective** To use the addition and subtraction processes
with decimals.

The procedures used to add or subtract whole numbers in decimal
notation extend almost without change to other decimal numbers.

**Example 1** | Compute **72.8 + 6.349 + 0.76**

*Solution*

| Step 1 | Step 2 | Step 3 |
|---|---|---|
| Write the given numerals in a column with the decimal points in line. | (Not usually shown) Add as if the numerals named whole numbers. | Write the sum. |

| Step 1 | Step 2 | Step 3 |
|---|---|---|
| 72.8 | 72,800 | 72.8 |
| 6.349 | 6,349 | 6.349 |
| + 0.76 | + 760 | + 0.76 |
|  | 79,909 | 79.909 |

WHY
IT
WORKS

$$72,800 \times 0.001 = 72.8$$
$$6,349 \times 0.001 = 6.349$$
$$760 \times 0.001 = 0.76$$
$$79,909 \times 0.001 = 79.909$$

In the same way, we can justify the subtraction process.

**Example 2** | Compute **1495.76 − 321.492**

*Solution*

| Step 1 | Step 2 | Step 3 |
|---|---|---|
| Write the given numerals in a column with the decimal points in a line. | (Not usually shown) Subtract as if the numerals named whole numbers. | Write the difference. |

| Step 1 | Step 2 | Step 3 |
|---|---|---|
| 1495.76 | 1,495,760 | 1495.760 |
| − 321.492 | − 321,492 | − 321.492 |
|  | 1,174,268 | 1174.268 |

## Class Exercises

Compute the sum or difference.

**1.**   34.3
    +23.5

**2.**   72.04
    +16.7

**3.**   5.18
    +5.605

**4.**   12.7
    + 6.298

**5.**   20.347
    +30.62

**6.**   5.2
    +17.706

**7.**   9.73
    −5.11

**8.**   24.868
    −14.254

**9.**   9.043
    +7.03

**10.**   12.827
    − 2.6

**11.**   8.47
    −3.454

**12.**   18.6
    −13.255

## Exercises

Compute the sum.

**A**

**1.**   71.5
    +16.3

**2.**   46.53
    +21.46

**3.**   6.297
    +8.434

**4.**   5.06
    +6.952

**5.**   27.954
    +16.21

**6.**   18.6364
    +13.4372

**7.**   34.72
    +18.6049

**8.**   126.328
    + 9.4078

**9.**   7.805
    0.46
    +15.936

**10.**   25.6
    9.372
    +105.17

**11.**   1.6256
    6.006
    2.9
    +1.49

**12.**   24.603
    18.4
    9.36
    + 0.216

**13.** 6.38 + 5.246

**14.** 21.329 + 16.4

**15.** 1.37 + 5.5 + 2.66

**16.** 18.205 + 11.7251 + 3.6

**17.** 2.4 + 7.608 + 3.1 + 7.27

**18.** 37.5 + 2.0056 + 3.21 + 7.8

Compute the difference.

**19.**   66.8
    −26.2

**20.**   18.48
    − 9.37

**21.**   3.406
    −1.872

**22.**   18.3
    −15.72

**23.**   21.607
    − 9.85

**24.**   143.2
    − 79.604

**25.**   27.205
    −19.6384

**26.**   19.65
    − 9.3728

Compute the difference.

**27.** 46.96 − 3.98

**28.** 53.405 − 27.3

**29.** 106.8 − 36.47

**30.** 18 − 6.52

**31.** 716.32 − 521.9046

**32.** 137.05 − 8.6

## Problems

Solve.

A **1.** Carla bought a pair of hiking boots on sale for $29.79. Later the same day, she saw the same boots in another store for $36.95. How much did she save by buying the boots on sale?

**2.** Harry set a goal of hiking 24 km each month. In May, he took hikes of 4.25 km, 6.8 km, 5.65 km, and 7.125 km. Did he reach his goal?

# An Inventor

Did you ever wonder who invented the citizen's-band radio, or the telephone, or the walkie-talkie? Did you ever wish that you could invent a faster and better method of communication?

During his lifetime, Granville T. Woods (1856–1910) designed and acquired patents for fifty inventions ranging from an egg incubator to a steam-boiler furnace. His ability to use mathematics contributed greatly to his success.

After studying mechanical engineering at college, Woods became an engineer aboard a steamer. Later, as a steam-locomotive engineer, he patented his most ingenious invention, the Synchronous Multiplex Railway Telegraph. The purpose of his telegraph was both to prevent railway accidents by keeping each train aware of the location of nearby trains, and to enable moving trains to communicate with stations. Woods marketed his many inventions through his own company.

**Research Activity** Many persons have contributed to the invention and development of today's computers. Find out who some of them are and what their contributions have been.

**Career Activity** What career do you think you would like to follow when you finish school? Find out what important inventions are used in this field of activity.

# 2-8 Multiplying Decimals

**Objective** To use the multiplication process with decimals.

We can use the same procedure to multiply mixed numbers as we used for whole numbers. The only difference is that we need a plan for placing the decimal point in the product.

**Example 1** | Compute 2.3 × 6.85

*Solution* | **Align the right-hand digits of the factors and multiply as if they were whole numbers.**

**The number of places to the right of the decimal point in the product is the sum of the places to the right of the decimal point in the factors.**

$$
\begin{array}{r}
6.8\,5 \longleftarrow \text{2 places} \\
\times\quad 2.3 \longleftarrow \text{1 place} \\
\hline
2\,0\,5\,5 \\
13\,7\,0\phantom{0} \\
\hline
15.7\,5\,5 \longleftarrow \text{3 places}
\end{array}
$$

**WHY IT WORKS**

$$
\begin{aligned}
2.3 \times 6.85 &= (23 \times 0.1)\,(685 \times 0.01) \\
&= (23 \times 685)\,(0.1 \times 0.01) \\
&= (15{,}755)\,(0.001) \\
&= 15.755
\end{aligned}
$$

**Example 2** | Compute 24.7 × 362.008

*Solution*

$$
\begin{array}{r}
36\,2.00\,8 \longleftarrow \text{3 places} \\
24.7 \longleftarrow \text{1 place} \\
\hline
253\,4\,05\,6 \\
1448\,0\,32\phantom{0} \\
7240\,1\,6\phantom{00} \\
\hline
8941.5\,97\,6 \longleftarrow \text{4 places}
\end{array}
$$

It can be very helpful to check your answers by rounding and estimating. A rule for rounding decimal numbers can be stated as follows:

| | 24.7 | 362.008 |
|---|---|---|
| **1.** Find the place to which you wish to round, and mark it with a caret ( ). Look at the digit to the right. | | |
| **2.** If the digit to the right is 5 or greater, add 1 to the marked digit. If the digit to the right is less than 5, leave the marked digit unchanged. | 2 | 6 |
| **3.** Replace each digit to the right of the marked place with "0". | 20.0 | 360.000 |

Estimate the product in Example 2: 24.7 × 362.008

$$20 \times 360 = 7200$$

Since 7200 is in rough agreement with 8941.5976, you know that the decimal point in the product is in the correct place.

## Class Exercises

State the product.

**1.** 7 × 0.3  **2.** 15 × 0.2  **3.** 4 × 5.1  **4.** 50 × 0.4

**5.** 0.5 × 0.5  **6.** 0.3 × 0.9  **7.** 0.27 × 0.2  **8.** 0.4 × 0.011

The correct digits are given for the product. State the product with the decimal point correctly inserted. Then check your answer by estimating.

**9.** 3.7 × 2.68; 9916  **10.** 0.5 × 8.65; 4325  **11.** 7.25 × 4.09; 296525

**12.** 2.4 × 3.702; 88848  **13.** 6.201 × 5.72; 3546972  **14.** 0.96 × 52.303; 5021088

## Exercises

Compute the product. Check your answer by estimating.

**A**

**1.**  5.9
× 7

**2.**  23.8
× 42

**3.**  7.2
×7.7

**4.**  5.66
× 9.2

**5.**  24.4
×0.61

**6.**  3.807
× 6.8

**7.**  13.405
× 21.3

**8.**  643.21
× 1.626

**9.** 8.34 × 0.16  **10.** 37.44 × 5.9  **11.** 0.462 × 0.93

**12.** 0.012 × 5.37  **13.** 0.0025 × 0.602  **14.** 0.0007 × 0.923

Simplify.

**B**   **15.** $(24.6 - 9.9) \times (43.7 - 18.5)$       **16.** $(3.01 + 14.6) \times (2.7 + 4.08)$

**17.** $0.058 \times (0.82 + 3.7 + 14.03)$      **18.** $6.2 \times 4.3 \times 0.08$

## Problems

Solve.

**A**   **1.** An oil tank holds 1050 L. If a liter of oil costs 13¢, how much does it cost to fill the tank?

**B**   **2.** Janice bought 6 rolls of film at $1.29 each. Four rolls cost $2.89 each for development. For the last 2 rolls, she changed companies and was charged only $2.27 each. How much did she spend in all for her photographs?

# Application
## Estimating Electricity Costs

In trying to keep your electric bills and usage at a minimum, it is useful to know approximately what each appliance costs to run. The table gives a partial list of average costs in one community. For example, a stereo costs 0.5¢ per hour to run, or $100 \times \$0.005 = \$0.50$ for 100 hours.

| Appliance | Typical wattage | Cost per hour |
|---|---|---|
| Air Conditioner | 1500 | 7.9¢ |
| Attic Fan | 375 | 2¢ |
| Hi-Fi/Stereo | 100 | 0.5¢ |
| Radio | 75 | 0.4¢ |
| TV (B + W) | 55 | 0.3¢ |
| TV (Color) | 200 | 1.1¢ |

1. Which costs less to run, a black and white TV or a color TV? How much would it cost to run each for 150 hours?
2. Which costs less, listening to a radio for 50 hours or playing a stereo for 30 hours?
3. How much less does it cost to run an attic fan for 240 hours than an air conditioner for 240 hours?

**Consumer Activity** Find out the average costs for electricity in your community.

## 2-9 Dividing Decimals

**Objective** To use the division process with decimals.

The chart below reviews the way division relates to multiplication.

| factor | | | | | | | quotient |
|---|---|---|---|---|---|---|---|
| | factor | | | | divisor | | |
| | | product | | dividend | | | |
| 8 | × | 0.07 | = | 0.56 | 0.56 ÷ 0.07 | = | 8 |
| 8 | × | 0.7 | = | 5.6 | 5.6 ÷ 0.7 | = | 8 |
| 8 | × | 7 | = | 56 | 56 ÷ 7 | = | 8 |
| 8 | × | 70 | = | 560 | 560 ÷ 70 | = | 8 |

In the column at the right above, the quotient in each case is 8, but the dividend and divisor change. We can see that multiplying the dividend and divisor by the same power of ten does not change the quotient. This fact means that we can always change the divisor into a counting number.

#### rule

1. **Multiply the dividend and divisor by the least power of 10 needed to produce a counting number as divisor.**
2. **In the quotient, place the decimal point directly above the decimal point in the new dividend.**
3. **Divide as with whole numbers.**

*Example 1*  Compute 20.35 ÷ 3.7

*Solution*  Estimate the quotient: 20.35 ÷ 3.7

$$20 \div 4 = 5$$

Multiply dividend and divisor by 10 so that the divisor will be a counting number, then divide. The arrows show you the new position of the decimal point. Notice where the decimal point is placed in the quotient.

$$
\begin{array}{r}
5.5 \\
3.7\,)\overline{20.3\,5} \\
18\,5 \\
\hline
1\,8\,5 \\
1\,8\,5 \\
\hline
0 \\
\end{array}
$$

remainder

In the next example the division process does not lead to a remainder of zero. In a case like this, the quotient may be approximated to a nearest place value.

*Example 2* | Compute 7.812 ÷ 0.43 to the nearest hundredth.

*Solution* | **Estimate the quotient: 7.812 ÷ 0.43**

$$8 \div 0.4 = 8 \times 10 \div 0.4 \times 10$$
$$= 80 \div 4 = 20$$

Compute to the thousandths' place and round to hundredths.

```
        18.167              Check:      18.1 67
0.43 )7.81 200                        ×     0.43
      4 3                                 54 5 01
      3 51                                7 26 6 8
      3 44                                7.81 1 81
        7 2                              +0.00 0 19
        4 3                               7.81 2 00
        2 90
        2 58
          320
          301
           19
```

To the nearest hundredth, 7.812 ÷ 0.43 = 18.17.

Notice that the number of decimal places to the right of the decimal point in the remainder, 0.00019, is the same as the number of decimal places in the product of the divisor and quotient, 0.43 × 18.167.

Notice also that the original estimate of the quotient, 20, is in rough agreement with the computed quotient. The check by multiplication, however, is a better guarantee of accuracy.

## Class Exercises

State the least power of ten which makes the divisor a counting number.

1. $0.8\overline{)168}$

2. $1.5\overline{)45}$

3. $9.25\overline{)18}$

4. $0.46\overline{)2.3}$

5. $0.012\overline{)6.06}$

6. $3.7\overline{)1.48}$

7. $8.01\overline{)16.2}$

8. $1.246\overline{)9.76}$

The correct digits are given for the quotient. Place the decimal point and state the quotient.

**9.**
$$\frac{27}{4.3)\overline{1.161}}$$

**10.**
$$\frac{5\ 89}{6.2)\overline{365.18}}$$

**11.**
$$\frac{41}{0.37)\overline{1.517}}$$

**12.**
$$\frac{2\ 08}{3.52)\overline{732.16}}$$

**13.**
$$\frac{157}{0.68)\overline{10.676}}$$

**14.**
$$\frac{36}{0.358)\overline{1.2888}}$$

## Exercises

**a.** Divide. If the division is not exact, round to the nearest hundredth.
**b.** Check.

A

**1.** $16.24 \div 5.6$  **2.** $18.09 \div 6.7$  **3.** $2.55 \div 0.34$  **4.** $3.57 \div 0.42$

**5.** $61.476 \div 14.1$  **6.** $90.072 \div 32.4$  **7.** $1.06172 \div 5.08$  **8.** $0.50142 \div 7.32$

**9.** $0.28)\overline{8.7553}$  **10.** $0.46)\overline{0.0361}$  **11.** $2.3)\overline{96.14}$  **12.** $1.9)\overline{88.92}$

**13.** $0.068)\overline{3.5156}$  **14.** $0.049)\overline{1.4357}$  **15.** $1.78)\overline{90.068}$  **16.** $20.9)\overline{361.57}$

**17.** $1.14912 \div 0.0057$  **18.** $6.4272 \div 0.0103$  **19.** $7.33 \div 0.8$

**20.** $37.7 \div 0.6$  **21.** $6.834 \div 0.39$  **22.** $6.08 \div 0.92$

**23.** $0.3321 \div 0.004$  **24.** $0.3692 \div 0.058$  **25.** $87.391 \div 0.161$

**26.** $10.078 \div 5.04$  **27.** $570 \div 74.7$  **28.** $26.923 \div 1.001$

## Problems

Solve.

A

**1.** A photographer makes $295 for a 35-hour week. What is the hourly rate to the nearest cent?

**2.** A chemist has 558 mL of a solution and needs to prepare samples of it, each containing 23.25 mL. How many samples can be prepared?

B

**3.** For a graduation party, the Donaldsons budgeted $25 for cold cuts. If the cold cuts cost $6.19 a kilogram, how many kilograms can they buy? How much money will they have left over?

**4.** Mario bought three packages of weather-stripping tape. Each package contained 9 m of tape. How many windows can be weather-stripped if each window needs 4.85 m? Will there be enough tape left to weather-strip a window needing 2.55 m of tape?

# Application
## The Metric System

Just like our number system, the metric system of measurement is based on powers of ten. For example, the meter, a unit of length, can be multiplied by 10, 100, 1000, and so on to form longer units of length.

$$10 \text{ meters} = 1 \text{ dekameter}$$
$$100 \text{ meters} = 1 \text{ hectometer}$$
$$1000 \text{ meters} = 1 \text{ kilometer}$$

Shorter units of length can be formed by multiplying the meter by 0.1, 0.01, 0.001, and so on.

$$0.1 \text{ meter} = 1 \text{ decimeter}$$
$$0.01 \text{ meter} = 1 \text{ centimeter}$$
$$0.001 \text{ meter} = 1 \text{ millimeter}$$

The table at the right lists some of the prefixes used in the metric system and their symbols. Using the symbol m for meter, we can write, for example,

$$1000 \text{ m} = 1 \text{ km}$$
$$0.01 \text{ m} = 1 \text{ cm}$$

and so on.

**Metric Prefixes**

| Multiply by | Prefix | Symbol |
|---|---|---|
| 10 | deka | da |
| 100 | hecto | h |
| 1000 | kilo | k |
| 0.1 | deci | d |
| 0.01 | centi | c |
| 0.001 | milli | m |

Here are some other examples of relationships in the metric system.

| | |
|---|---|
| 2000 m = 2.000 km | 0.01 m = 1 cm |
| 2500 m = 2.500 km | 0.02 m = 2 cm |
| 2530 m = 2.530 km | 0.72 m = 72 cm |
| 2538 m = 2.538 km | 3.72 m = 372 cm |

Complete the following.

1. 3000 m = ___?___ km
2. 3764 m = ___?___ km
3. 764 m = ___?___ km
4. ___?___ m = 0.064 km
5. 1 m = ___?___ cm
6. 2.5 m = ___?___ cm
7. 50 cm = ___?___ m
8. 300 cm = ___?___ m
9. 1 m = ___?___ mm
10. 1 cm = ___?___ mm
11. 375 mm = ___?___ m
12. 375 mm = ___?___ cm

# 2-10 Solving Problems

**Objective** To solve simple word problems including the use of one or more arithmetic operations.

Word problems tell you how certain numbers are related and then ask a question about them. Using a plan, such as the following, is a good way to gain skill in solving problems.

| Plan for Solving Problems |
|---|
| **1.** Read the problem carefully. Make sure you understand all the words used. |
| **2.** Use questions like these in planning the solution:<br>• What is asked for?<br>• What facts are given?<br>• Are enough facts given? If not, what else is needed?<br>• Are unnecessary facts given? If so, what are they?<br>• Will a sketch or diagram help? |
| **3.** Which operation or operations can be used to solve the problem? |
| **4.** Perform the operations carefully. |
| **5.** Check your result with the facts given in the problem. Is your result reasonable? |

*Example 1*

During a blizzard, 64.5 cm of snow fell on Prairie City. Two weeks later another storm dropped 35.6 cm of snow. How much more snow fell in the first storm than in the second?

*Solution*

• The problem asks for the difference in the depths of the snowfalls.
• Given facts: 64.5 cm of snow in first storm
           35.6 cm of snow in second storm
To find how much more snow fell in the first storm, we subtract: $64.5 - 35.6 = 28.9$.
28.9 cm more snow fell in the first storm than in the second.

*Example 2*    After 15 selling days, the cost of a calculator was reduced $2.99 to a sale price of $8.59. What was the original cost of the calculator?

*Solution*    · The problem asks for the original cost of the calculator.

· Given facts: $2.99, amount of reduction

$8.59, sale price after reduction

15 selling days, fact not needed

To find the original cost, we add:

$2.99 + $8.59 = $11.58

The original cost of the calculator was $11.58.

## Problems

Solve.

**A**
1. A bird-feeder holds 0.5 kg of mixed bird seed. Sal filled it 3 times in one week. How much bird seed did the birds eat that week?

2. During a flood, a river reached a high-water mark of 4.6 m. This was 1.4 m lower than the record high. What was the record high?

3. A microwave oven uses 1.5 kW · h of electricity in 15 minutes. How much electricity does it use in 5 minutes?

4. A baked potato has 31 mg of vitamin C. How many milligrams of vitamin C do 8 potatoes have?

**B**
5. Sue wrote five checks in May: $255, $14.63, $75, $47.59, and $82.90. She made one deposit of $624. What was her balance at the end of May if her balance at the beginning of May was $681.70?

6. A certain long distance telephone call costs $1.95 for the first 3 minutes and $.32 for each additional minute. How much does a 17-minute call cost?

7. A photograph is enlarged so that its new dimensions are 4 times its original dimensions. If the new dimensions are 19.2 cm by 25.6 cm, what were the original dimensions?

8. Martin bought 0.8 kg of bananas at $.55 a kilogram, 1.5 kg of tomatoes at $1.54 a kilogram, and 18 oranges at 6 oranges for $.59. How much did Martin pay?

## Self-Test

Words to remember:
inverse operations [p. 40]          commutative property [p. 42]
associative property [p. 42]        distributive property [p. 43]

Write a related equation. Find the value of $n$.

**1.** $14 + n = 21$  **2.** $n + 8 = 32$  **3.** $6n = 48$  **4.** $8 \times n = 24$  **[2-5]**

Replace each variable to make a true equation.

**5.** $(7 + 2) + 5 = 7 + (x + 5)$          **6.** $24 \times n = 0$          **[2-6]**

**7.** $3 \times (1 + 9) = (3 \times 1) + (t \times 9)$      **8.** $6 \times 8 = y \times 6$

Add or subtract.

**9.** $42.566 + 7.08$          **10.** $3.9 + 6.141 + 8$          **[2-7]**

**11.** $71.354 - 62.86$          **12.** $25.3 - 25.297$

Multiply.

**13.** $5.1 \times 3.04$          **14.** $0.72 \times 0.85$          **[2-8]**

**15.** $4.96 \times 0.003$          **16.** $6.017 \times 2.2$

Divide. If the division is not exact, round to the nearest hundredth.

**17.** $120.13 \div 29.3$          **18.** $4.758 \div 0.096$          **[2-9]**

**19.** $3.0804 \div 0.37$          **20.** $1.8927 \div 7.01$

Solve.

**21.** A swimming pool is 24 m long. Sam swam its length 3 times.  **[2-10]**
How far did he swim?

**22.** Rita commutes to work 1.7 km by subway and 3.8 km by bus.
How far is that in all?

**23.** The Rays planned a 2-day canoe trip of 26.8 km. They traveled
19.9 km the first day. How far did they have left to travel?

**24.** Jack bought a paperback book for $2.75. He gave the clerk a
$5 bill. How much did he receive in change?

Self-Test answers and Extra Practice are at the back of the book.

# Chapter Review

Write the letter that labels the correct answer.

1. 100,000,000 may be written as __?__ .       [2-1]
   A. $10^6$      B. $10^9$      C. 10      D. $10^8$

2. The expanded form for 519 is __?__ .
   A. $(5 \times 1000) + (1 \times 100) + (9 \times 10)$
   B. $(5 \times 10^2) + (1 \times 10^1) + 9$
   C. $(5 \times 10^3) + (1 \times 10^2) + 9$
   D. $(5 \times 10) + 19$

3. In 384.9617, the 6 is in the __?__ place.       [2-2]
   A. hundreds'    B. thousandths'    C. tenths'    D. hundredths'

4. The decimal for $8 + (2 \times 0.1) + (0 \times 0.01) + (7 \times 0.001)$ is __?__ .
   A. 8.27      B. 8207      C. 8.027      D. 8.207

In Exercises 5 and 6, use the number line shown.

5. The graph of 1.3 is __?__ .       [2-3]
   A. the origin    B. point $K$      C. point $M$    D. point $N$

6. The coordinate of point $L$ is __?__ .
   A. 9      B. 0.9      C. 1      D. 1.1

What is the value of the expression when $x = 14$?

7. $x + 9$       [2-4]
   A. 23      B. 5      C. 125      D. 104

8. $112 \div x$
   A. 7      B. 18      C. 8      D. 17

Find the value of $n$.

9. $8 + n = 16$       [2-5]
   A. 24      B. 8      C. 2      D. 9

**10.** $5n = 35$
    **A.** 7             **B.** 6            **C.** 30            **D.** 40

**11.** $(53 + 89) + 27 = \underline{\ \ ?\ \ } + (89 + 27)$      **[2-6]**
    **A.** 0             **B.** 27         **C.** 89         **D.** 53

**12.** $23(14 + 6) = (\underline{\ \ ?\ \ } \times 14) + (\underline{\ \ ?\ \ } \times 6)$
    **A.** 20         **B.** 23         **C.** 14         **D.** 6

**13.** $0.692 + 5.5 = \underline{\ \ ?\ \ }$                     **[2-7]**
    **A.** 1.242      **B.** 6.192      **C.** 5.192      **D.** 4.808

**14.** $47.516 - 46.903 = \underline{\ \ ?\ \ }$
    **A.** 1.613      **B.** 1.387      **C.** 1.413      **D.** 0.613

**15.** An estimate for $94.771 \times 0.62$ is $\underline{\ \ ?\ \ }$.     **[2-8]**
    **A.** 50          **B.** 5.6         **C.** 5.875      **D.** 0.58

**16.** $4.99 \times 3 = \underline{\ \ ?\ \ }$
    **A.** 1.497      **B.** 14.97      **C.** 149.7      **D.** 1497

**17.** An estimate for $5.428 \div 0.92$ is $\underline{\ \ ?\ \ }$.     **[2-9]**
    **A.** 0.05      **B.** 0.5        **C.** 5          **D.** 50

**18.** To the nearest hundredth, $1.4538 \div 0.017 = \underline{\ \ ?\ \ }$.
    **A.** 85         **B.** 85.5      **C.** 85.51      **D.** 85.52

Solve.

**19.** Anna jogged 9.5 km each day for 5 days. How far did she jog    **[2-10]**
    in all?
    **A.** 4.75 km    **B.** 74.5 km    **C.** 47.5 km    **D.** 475 km

**20.** A car can go 600 km on 1 tank of gas. How many kilometers
    can it go on 2.5 tanks of gas?
    **A.** 1200 km    **B.** 1850 km    **C.** 1500 km    **D.** 240 km

# The Binary System

The number system that we use is, of course, the decimal system. The place value of each digit in a number is a power of ten. In the *binary system,* place values are based on powers of two. The only digits used in the binary system are zero and one.

Place Value Chart

| ... | $2^6$ | $2^5$ | $2^4$ | $2^3$ | $2^2$ | $2^1$ | 1 |
|---|---|---|---|---|---|---|---|
| ... | 64 | 32 | 16 | 8 | 4 | 2 | 1 |

*Example 1*　Write $1011_{two}$ as a decimal number.

*Solution*
$$1011_{two} = (1 \times 2^3) + (0 \times 2^2) + (1 \times 2^1) + 1$$
$$= 8 + 0 + 2 + 1$$
$$= 11$$

*Example 2*　Write 27 as a binary number.

*Solution*

Find the greatest power of 2 that is less than or equal to 27: $16 < 27 < 32$.

$27 = 2^4 + 11$
$27 = 16 + 11$

Find the greatest power of 2 that is less than or equal to 11: $8 < 11 < 16$.

$27 = 2^4 + 2^3 + 3$
$27 = 16 + 8 + 3$

Repeat this process.

$27 = 2^4 + 2^3 + 2^1 + 1$
$27 = 16 + 8 + 2 + 1$

Write the binary number:
$$(1 \times 2^4) + (1 \times 2^3) + (0 \times 2^2) + (1 \times 2^1) + 1$$
$$= 11011_{two}$$

The binary system is important in the operation of digital computers. The digits in a number are represented by switches that are either in the on or off positions. Zero is represented by a switch that is off and one is represented by a switch that is on.

## Exercises

Write the binary number as a decimal number.

**1.** $101_{two}$      **2.** $110_{two}$      **3.** $1011_{two}$      **4.** $10000_{two}$      **5.** $10111_{two}$

**6.** $11110_{two}$      **7.** $101100_{two}$      **8.** $111001_{two}$      **9.** $111111_{two}$      **10.** $1011100_{two}$

Write the decimal number as a binary number.

**11.** 7      **12.** 8      **13.** 10      **14.** 19      **15.** 20      **16.** 25

**17.** 31      **18.** 64      **19.** 52      **20.** 46      **21.** 87      **22.** 100

**23.** Complete the binary addition table at the right.

| + | 0 | 1 |
|---|---|---|
| 0 | ? | ? |
| 1 | ? | ? |

Add. Check your work by writing the addition in base ten.

**24.** $\begin{array}{r} 1001_{two} \\ +1100_{two} \end{array}$      **25.** $\begin{array}{r} 1111_{two} \\ +10010_{two} \end{array}$      **26.** $\begin{array}{r} 100100_{two} \\ +110110_{two} \end{array}$      **27.** $\begin{array}{r} 1011010_{two} \\ +\ 101000_{two} \end{array}$

**28.** Complete the binary multiplication table at the right.

| × | 0 | 1 |
|---|---|---|
| 0 | ? | ? |
| 1 | ? | ? |

Multiply. Check your answer by writing the multiplication in base ten.

**29.** $\begin{array}{r} 11_{two} \\ \times 10_{two} \end{array}$      **30.** $\begin{array}{r} 1101_{two} \\ \times\ 100_{two} \end{array}$      **31.** $\begin{array}{r} 10001_{two} \\ \times 11010_{two} \end{array}$      **32.** $\begin{array}{r} 10101_{two} \\ \times\ 1101_{two} \end{array}$

**Research Activity** Look up digital computers in an encyclopedia. Find out more about the role played by the binary system in digital computers.

# Chapter Test

1. Write 1708 in expanded form, using exponents. [2-1]

2. Write the decimal numeral for the following:
   $(2 \times 10,000) + (9 \times 1000) + (0 \times 100) + (0 \times 10) + 5$.

3. Write 0.5164 in expanded form. [2-2]

4. Write 20.32 in words.

5. Draw a number line. Graph 0, 0.3, 0.6, 1.1. [2-3]

6. 12.163 $\underset{<,>}{\underline{\quad ? \quad}}$ 12.5

Evaluate the expression for the given replacement set

7. $n + 15$; $\{8, 16, 22\}$    8. $900 \div n$; $\{5, 30, 225\}$ [2-4]

Write a related equation. Find the value of $n$.

9. $n + 24 = 72$    10. $5n = 50$ [2-5]

Replace each variable to make a true equation.

11. $37 \times n = 37$    12. $9 + 14 = 14 + x$ [2-6]

Add or subtract.

13. $21.28 + 9.5034$    14. $67.7 - 43.19$ [2-7]

Multiply.

15. $5.06 \times 18.3$    16. $0.042 \times 0.795$ [2-8]

Divide. If the division is not exact, round the quotient to the nearest hundredth.

17. $0.31548 \div 2.96$    18. $1737.68 \div 74.9$ [2-9]

Solve.

19. A bee travels about 0.4 km in 1 minute. About how far does a bee travel in 5 minutes? [2-10]

20. A hiker climbed from a base camp at 1560 m above sea level to a hut 3680 m above sea level. How far did she climb?

## Skill Review

Add.

**1.**    7.3
    +1.2

**2.**    4.08
    +5.96

**3.**    38.571
    + 9.466

**4.**    6.29
    +75.03

**5.**    0.45
    +5.138

**6.**    0.007
    +3.6

**7.**    290.01
    + 77.4

**8.**    0.8602
    +0.093

**9.** 6307.59 + 478.223

**10.** 3.721 + 145.08

**11.** 0.0064 + 0.092

**12.** 501.47 + 29.0033

Subtract.

**13.**    12.4
    − 9.8

**14.**    55.903
    −54.081

**15.**    5.27
    −2.76

**16.**    0.0606
    −0.0039

**17.**    7.05
    −2

**18.**    38.014
    −36.9

**19.**    50.2
    −47.158

**20.**    0.6
    − 0.1105

**21.** 1.007 − 0.03

**22.** 219.38 − 54.64

**23.** 8790.72 − 606.1435

**24.** 5.943 − 5.8886

Multiply.

**25.**    8.4
    ×3.9

**26.**    57.1
    ×0.06

**27.**    2.053
    × 4.08

**28.**    0.904
    × 0.25

**29.**    0.095
    ×0.017

**30.**    0.0082
    × 6.09

**31.**    7.33
    ×0.01

**32.**    40.06
    ×0.0052

**33.** 8.921 × 508

**34.** 0.2852 × 0.0437

**35.** 19.74 × 3.601

**36.** 0.952 × 0.0836

Divide. If the division is not exact, round to the nearest hundredth.

**37.** $28\overline{)267.4}$    **38.** $45\overline{)1.62}$    **39.** $6.5\overline{)20.79}$    **40.** $0.37\overline{)0.2294}$

**41.** $0.9\overline{)40}$    **42.** $0.03\overline{)1.95}$    **43.** $8.04\overline{)7.36}$    **44.** $0.016\overline{)5.12}$

**45.** 1.4505 ÷ 3.92

**46.** 32.53718 ÷ 0.598

**47.** 7.903 ÷ 61.3

**48.** 2.4 ÷ 0.0458

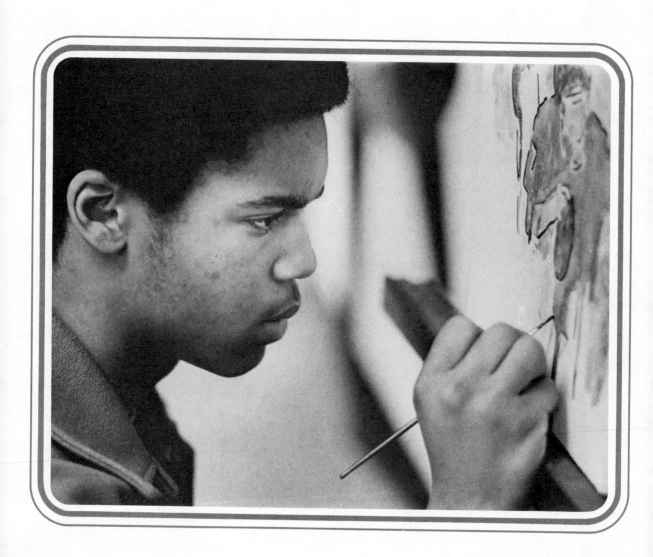

64

# 3

# Positive and Negative Numbers

## 3-1 The Extended Number Line

**Objective** To construct an extended number line and to graph numbers on it.

When engineers want to describe the state of a rocket launching at any particular moment, they use the time at which the rocket is to be fired as their reference point, and they denote it by zero. Then they use *negative numbers* to refer to time before that point and *positive numbers* to refer to time after it.

We use positive and negative numbers to measure many *opposite* quantities, such as profit and loss, distance up and down, or points won or lost in a game. The weather thermometer at the right illustrates one such use. It pictures the idea of an extended number line in which a two-way scale extends above and below a **zero reference point.**

°Celsius

50
40
30
20
10
0
—10
—20
—30
—40

**65**

In Section 2-3 we graphed numbers to the right of the origin, or 0, on a horizontal number line. By extending the number line to the left of the origin we can graph both positive and negative numbers as shown in the figure below.

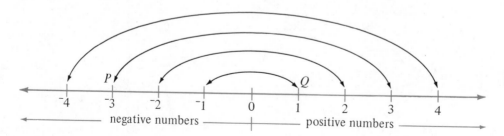

Coordinates of points to the right of 0 are positive. Those to the left are negative. The coordinate of *P* is ⁻3, which we read as "negative three." The coordinate of *Q* is 1, which we read as "positive one," or simply "one." The symbol "+1" is sometimes used for positive one, for emphasis.

*Example 1* | Show the graphs of ⁻2, ⁻5, 0, and 3 on a number line.

*Solution*

Notice that each point on the number line has an opposite point, located the same distance from the origin but on the opposite side of it. The coordinates of such a pair of points are said to be **opposites** of one another. For example, 1 and ⁻1, 2 and ⁻2, 3 and ⁻3, 4 and ⁻4 are pairs of opposite numbers. The opposite of 0 is simply 0.

In Section 2-2 we learned that the set of whole numbers is

$$\{0, 1, 2, 3, \ldots\}.$$

The set whose members are the whole numbers and their opposites,

$$\{\ldots, -3, -2, -1, 0, 1, 2, 3, \ldots\},$$

is called the set of **integers.**

An *unraised* minus sign before a number is frequently used to show subtraction as, for example, in $7 - 4 = 3$. Sometimes, however, an unraised minus sign is used to mean "the opposite of." For example,

$-2$ means the opposite of positive 2

$-(^-4)$ means the opposite of negative 4

From the figure on page 66, you can see that

$$-2 = {}^-2 \quad \text{and} \quad -(^-4) = 4.$$

*Example 2* | State the opposite of the given number.

a. $^-6$     b. 18     c. 0

*Solution* | a. 6     b. $^-18$     c. 0

Earlier, we used variables to stand for positive numbers and zero. We can also use variables to stand for negative numbers. Thus,

$p = 4$    is read    $p$ is equal to positive 4

$q = {}^-3$    is read    $q$ is equal to negative 3

We can also use an unraised minus sign with a variable. For example,

$-m = 2$    is read    the opposite of $m$ is equal to positive 2

$-x = {}^-5$    is read    the opposite of $x$ is equal to negative 5

*Example 3* | a. If $m = 3$, then $-m = $ __?__

b. If $n = {}^-7$, then $-n = $ __?__

c. If $-p = 5$, then $p = $ __?__

d. If $-q = {}^-2$, then $q = $ __?__

*Solution* | a. $^-3$

b. 7

c. $^-5$

d. 2

## Class Exercises

**1.** If east is called the positive direction, what is the negative direction?

**2.** If down is the negative direction, then what is up?

State the number implied by the given phrase.

**3.** 5 meters below sea level

**4.** 2 minutes after the start of the game

**5.** 20 degrees below zero

**6.** 3 seconds before blast-off

State the opposite of the given number.

**7.** 4                     **8.** ⁻3                     **9.** ⁻7                     **10.** 5

**11.** ⁻27                  **12.** 0                     **13.** 167                  **14.** ⁻583

Supply the missing word or phrase as you read the given sentence aloud.

**15.** The opposite of 8 is ___?___ .                **16.** The opposite of ⁻9 is ___?___ .

**17.** The opposite of 0 is ___?___ .                **18.** The symbol $-(^-6)$ denotes the ___?___ of ⁻6.

**19.** If $m = 11$, then $-m =$ ___?___ .            **20.** If $n = ^-2$, then $-n =$ ___?___ .

**21.** If $-p = ^-5$, then $p =$ ___?___ .           **22.** If $-q = 0$, then $q =$ ___?___ .

State the letter above the graph of the *opposite* of the given number.

*Example* | **a.** ⁻8        **b.** 1

*Solution* | **a.** The opposite of ⁻8 is 8. The letter is *K*.
           | **b.** The opposite of 1 is ⁻1. The letter is *D*.

**23.** ⁻4                   **24.** ⁻3                   **25.** 6                    **26.** 5

**27.** 8                    **28.** 1                    **29.** ⁻6                   **30.** 0

## Exercises

Write as a positive or negative number.

**A**  **1.** A loss of 4 kg

**2.** A gain of 8 grade points

**3.** A profit of $46

**4.** A debt of $25

Copy the number line and write the coordinates of the points shown.

**5.**

**6.**

Show the graph of each of the given numbers on a number line.

**7.** 0  **8.** 1  **9.** $^-4$  **10.** $^-1$  **11.** 4  **12.** $^-3$

**13.** $^-8$  **14.** 7  **15.** 6  **16.** $^-6$  **17.** 5  **18.** 3

Write the opposite of the given number.

**19.** 6  **20.** 2  **21.** $^-1$  **22.** 13  **23.** $^-19$  **24.** $^-37$

**25.** 118  **26.** $^-56$  **27.** 1776  **28.** $^-2001$  **29.** $^-26{,}475$  **30.** 999,999

Show the graph of the opposite of the given number on a number line.

**31.** 4  **32.** $^-3$  **33.** 0  **34.** $^-12$  **35.** 11  **36.** $^-7$

Write the missing word.

**B**  **37.** If the opposite of a certain number is a negative number, then the number itself is a __?__ number.

**38.** If the opposite of a certain number is a positive number, then the number itself is a __?__ number.

Write the missing number.

**C**  **39.** If $-n = 6$, then $n = $ __?__ .

**40.** If $-n = 7$, then $n = $ __?__ .

**41.** If $-(-n) = ^-0.75$, then $n = $ __?__ .

**42.** If $-(-n) = 1.6$, then $n = $ __?__ .

**43.** If $-(-n) = -n$, then $n = $ __?__ .

**44.** If $n = 5$, then $-(n + 2) = $ __?__ .

**45.** If $-n = ^-7$, then $-(n - 3) = $ __?__ .

**46.** If $n = ^-8$, then $-(-n + 1) = $ __?__ .

# 3-2 Arrows on the Number Line

**Objective** To picture numbers on the number line by graphs and by directed line segments, or arrows.

The decimals like 1.5, 2.97, and 8, that you studied in Chapter 2, are called *positive decimals*. Their opposites, like ⁻1.5, ⁻2.97, and ⁻8 are *negative decimals*. The positive decimals, negative decimals, and zero, all belong to the set of decimal numbers. Notice that the integers are included in this set.

**Example 1** | **Graph these decimals on the number line: ⁻2.5, ⁻2, ⁻0.75, 0, 0.75, 2.**

*Solution*

We can also use directed line segments, or arrows, to picture numbers on a number line. For example, in the figure below, the arrow directed to the right represents 2, and the arrow directed to the left represents ⁻2.5.

Any arrow directed to the left (the negative direction) represents a negative number, while any arrow directed to the right (the positive direction) represents a positive number. The *length* of the arrow is always a *positive number or zero*, even when the direction of the arrow is negative.

An arrow representing a number may have its starting point at any point on the number line, as long as it has the length and direction indicated by that number. Each of the arrows shown in color in the figure below has length 2; but since each extends to the left, each represents ⁻2.

*Example 2*

**a.** On a number line, picture an arrow that starts at 4 and ends at ⁻3.

**b.** By inspection, find the number represented by the arrow.

*Solution*

**a.**

**b.** The arrow is 7 units long and is directed to the left. It represents ⁻7.

## Class Exercises

State the letter written above the graph of the given number.

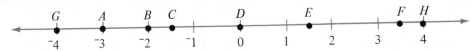

**1.** 3.5    **2.** ⁻1.5    **3.** ⁻3    **4.** 0    **5.** 1.5    **6.** ⁻2    **7.** −(⁻4)    **8.** ⁻4

State the starting point of the directed arrow.

**9.**

**10.**

**11.**

**12.**

State the endpoint of the arrow in the given exercise.

**13.** Exercise 9    **14.** Exercise 10    **15.** Exercise 11    **16.** Exercise 12

State the length of the arrow and the number represented by the arrow in the given exercise.

**17.** Exercise 9    **18.** Exercise 10    **19.** Exercise 11    **20.** Exercise 12

Tell how you would complete the table.

| | Coordinate of Starting Point | Coordinate of Endpoint | Length of Arrow | Number Represented |
|---|---|---|---|---|
| **21.** | 2 | 5 | ? | ? |
| **22.** | 2 | −4 | ? | ? |
| **23.** | −1 | ? | ? | −4 |
| **24.** | −4 | ? | ? | 3 |
| **25.** | −3 | ? | ? | 5 |
| **26.** | 4 | ? | ? | −6 |

## Exercises

Graph the numbers on a number line.

A
1. 2, −1.5, 0, −10, 5.4, −1.2          2. −4, 6.2, 7.3, 0, −3.5, −2.5

3. −1.1, −12.4, −2, −3.0, 0.7          4. −3.9, −9, 1, 2.8, 1.4, −0.5

Draw an arrow starting at the origin to represent the given number.

5. 2          6. 5          7. −3          8. −4          9. −3.5          10. 4.5

Draw an arrow starting at the graph of −3 to represent the given number.

11. 4          12. 3          13. −2          14. −1          15. 2.5          16. −1.5

Draw an arrow with endpoint at the graph of 2 to represent the given number.

17. 3          18. 4          19. −2.5          20. −1.25          21. −3          22. 1.75

Copy and complete.

| | Coordinate of Starting Point | Coordinate of Endpoint | Length of Arrow | Number Represented |
|---|---|---|---|---|
| **23.** | 2 | ? | ? | 3 |
| **24.** | −4 | ? | ? | 3 |
| **25.** | −2 | −5 | ? | ? |
| **26.** | 3 | −2 | ? | ? |

Copy and complete.

| | | | |
|---|---|---|---|
| **B** **27.** | −6.25 | ? | ? | 3.75 |
| **28.** | 4.58 | ? | ? | −2.61 |
| **29.** | −3.125 | ? | ? | −6.75 |
| **30.** | ? | 7.25 | ? | −2.85 |
| **C** **31.** | ? | −0.75 | ? | −0.35 |
| **32.** | ? | 2.53 | ? | −1.46 |

# *EXTRA!* Order on the Number Line

We can use the number line to help us put decimals in order. For example, if we wish to arrange 2.6, −1.2, 0, −1.4, and 3.2 in increasing order from least to greatest, we can first graph them on a number line.

Then we list them as they appear from left to right:

$$-1.4, \ -1.2, \ 0, \ 2.6, \ 3.2$$

They are now listed in order from least to greatest.
   On the number line above, notice that, for example,
   −3 < −2 (−3 is less than −2)
while
   3 > 2 (3 is greater than 2).

Graph the numbers on a number line and then list them in order from least to greatest.

**1.** 3, 4, −1, 0, −5    **2.** −2, 2, 6, −5, 3    **3.** 0, −3, −4, −1, 2

**4.** 2.5, 2, −1.5, 3    **5.** −4, −2.5, 0, 3.5    **6.** 1, −0.5, −1, 0.5

Replace each __?__ with < or >.

**7.** 5 __?__ 1    **8.** −5 __?__ −1    **9.** 5 __?__ −1    **10.** −5 __?__ 1

**11.** 2 __?__ −4    **12.** −3 __?__ 0    **13.** 6 __?__ −6    **14.** −7 __?__ 3

# 3-3 The Sum of Two Numbers of the Same Sign

**Objective** To find the sum of two numbers when both are positive or both are negative, and to picture the addition on a number line.

We can picture the addition of two numbers on a number line by three arrows: an arrow for each addend and an arrow for the sum. The first arrow starts at the origin. The second arrow starts where the first arrow ends. The arrow for the sum *starts* where the *first* arrow starts and *ends* where the *second* arrow ends.

The arrows in the diagram below show an addition in which both addends are positive: $2 + 3 = 5$.

Since the addends and their sum are positive, all three of the arrows are directed to the right. This suggests the following rule:

## rule

**The sum of two positive numbers is a positive number.**

If one of the addends is 0, then the arrow for the sum is identical with that for the other addend. For example, $4 + 0 = 4$, and also $0 + 0 = 0$.

**Example 1** | Find the sum of 1.8 and 3.6.

*Solution* | The length of the arrow for the sum is $1.8 + 3.6$, or 5.4. Since both addends are positive, the sum is positive. Hence, $1.8 + 3.6 = 5.4$.

The diagram below shows an addition in which both addends are negative: $^-3 + {}^-1 = {}^-4$.

Since the addends and their sum are negative, all three of the arrows are directed to the left.

## rule

**The sum of two negative numbers is a negative number.**

***Example 2*** | Find the sum of $^-2.5$ and $^-3.5$.

*Solution* | The length of the arrow for the sum is $2.5 + 3.5$, or **6. Since each of the addends is negative, the sum is negative. Therefore, $^-2.5 + {}^-3.5 = {}^-6$.**

## Class Exercises

Look at the diagram at the right.

1. The first addend is __?__ .

2. The second addend is __?__ .

3. The sum is __?__ .

4. Name the starting point and the endpoint of the arrow for the first addend; for the second addend; for the sum.

5–8. Repeat Exercises 1–4 for the diagram at the right.

State the first addend, the second addend, and the sum. Then read the equation as a number sentence.

9.

10.

11.

12.

13. In arrow addition of positive numbers, the arrows are __?__ (never, sometimes, always) directed to the right.

14. In arrow addition of negative numbers, the arrows are always directed to the __?__ .

15. If two addends are positive, their sum is __?__ (never, sometimes, always) positive.

16. If two addends are negative, their sum is always __?__ .

State the sum.

17. ⁻2.8 + ⁻3.1　　18. ⁻10 + ⁻2.4　　19. ⁻2 + 0　　20. 0 + ⁻3.7

21. 0.4 + 0.2　　22. 0.6 + 1.4　　23. ⁻0.3 + ⁻0.6　　24. ⁻2.7 + ⁻0.2

# Exercises

Draw a number line and find the sums of the given numbers by arrow addition.

A

1. 4 + 5　　2. 2 + 3　　3. ⁻4 + ⁻5　　4. ⁻2 + ⁻3

5. ⁻16 + ⁻14　　6. ⁻20 + ⁻35　　7. ⁻2.5 + ⁻4.5　　8. ⁻3.75 + ⁻4.25

Write the sum.

9. 3.8 + 8.3　　10. 4.9 + 7.6　　11. ⁻1.7 + ⁻1.7　　12. ⁻2.5 + ⁻2.6

13. ⁻78 + ⁻69　　14. ⁻64 + ⁻87　　15. ⁻148 + ⁻256　　16. ⁻409 + ⁻208

17. ⁻0.8 + ⁻0.5　　18. ⁻2.4 + ⁻2.2　　19. ⁻2.4 + ⁻4.6　　20. ⁻5.2 + ⁻2.8

Supply the missing addend.

**B**  **21.** $^-7 + \underline{\ ?\ } = {^-}15$    **22.** $^-9 + \underline{\ ?\ } = {^-}23$    **23.** $^-47 + \underline{\ ?\ } = {^-}93$

**24.** $\underline{\ ?\ } + {^-}6 = {^-}13$    **25.** $\underline{\ ?\ } + {^-}24 = {^-}41$    **26.** $\underline{\ ?\ } + {^-}128 = {^-}257$

## Problems

Solve.

**A**  **1.** Some research scientists drilled 92 m below the surface of the Ross Ice Shelf in Antarctica when their drill broke. After fixing it, they drilled 206 m deeper. How far below the surface had they then drilled?

**2.** A parachutist jumped from an airplane flying at an altitude of 1100 m, dropped 200 m in the first 25 seconds, and then dropped 350 m in the next 35 seconds. How many meters did the parachutist drop in 60 seconds?

# Application

## Ups and Downs

The Rocky Ledge Inn has 15 floors. It is located on a steep hill overlooking the ocean and must be entered at the sixth floor from the top. To number the floors, the management uses the positive and negative integers from 5 to −9, with the entrance floor or lobby assigned the number 0. The floors above the lobby are assigned positive integers, and those below the lobby are assigned negative integers.

**1.** If an elevator rises two floors from the lobby and then rises two more floors, it is then located at the floor assigned the integer ___?___ .

**2.** This floor is ___?___ (above/below) the lobby.

**3.** If the elevator drops two floors from the lobby and then drops an additional four floors, it is located at the floor assigned the integer ___?___ .

**4.** This floor is ___?___ (above/below) the lobby.

# 3-4 The Sum of Two Numbers of Opposite Sign

**Objective** To find the sum of two numbers when one is positive and the other is negative, and to picture the addition on a number line.

When the addend with the longer arrow is positive, the sum is positive.

$$3 + {}^-2 = 1$$

When the addend with the longer arrow is negative, the sum is negative.

$$1 + {}^-5 = {}^-4$$

When the addends have arrows of equal length, the sum is 0.

$$3 + {}^-3 = 0$$

Notice that, in each case, the length of the arrow for the sum is the *difference* of the lengths of the two arrows for the addends. The sum has the same sign as that of the addend with the longer arrow.

*Example* | Find the sum.

a. ⁻6 and 4    b. 2.6 and ⁻1.2

*Solution* | a. The length of the arrow for the sum is the difference 6 − 4, or 2. Since the addend with the longer arrow is ⁻6, the sum is negative. Thus, ⁻6 + 4 = ⁻2.

b. The arrows have lengths of 2.6 and 1.2. The difference is 2.6 − 1.2, or 1.4. Since the addend with the longer arrow is 2.6, the sum is positive. Hence, 2.6 + ⁻1.2 = 1.4.

With practice, you should become able to abbreviate this process and simply write, for example,

$$8 + {}^-5 = 3, \quad 2.6 + {}^-5.8 = {}^-3.2, \quad {}^-7 + 7 = 0$$

## Class Exercises

**1.** Positive numbers are represented by arrows directed to the __?__.

**2.** Negative numbers are represented by arrows directed to the __?__.

**3.** The length of the arrow for the sum of two numbers of opposite sign is the __?__ of the lengths of the arrows for the addends.

**4.** The sum of two numbers of opposite sign has the same sign as the addend with the __?__ arrow.

State the first addend, the second addend, and the sum. Then read the equation as a number sentence.

**5.** $5.5 + {}^-3.2 = 2.3$

**6.** $2 + {}^-3 = {}^-1$

**7.** ${}^-5 + 3 = {}^-2$

**8.** ${}^-2.5 + 4.5 = 2$

## Exercises

Draw a number line and find the sum by arrow addition.

**A**
**1.** $5 + {}^-2$
**2.** $4 + {}^-3$
**3.** $2 + {}^-3$
**4.** $3 + {}^-5$

**5.** ${}^-2 + 4$
**6.** ${}^-6 + 4$
**7.** ${}^-3 + 3$
**8.** $4 + {}^-4$

Write the sum.

**9.** $8.2 + {}^-3.2$
**10.** $7.4 + {}^-2.3$
**11.** ${}^-8.7 + 5.2$
**12.** ${}^-2.4 + 1.3$

**13.** $28 + {}^-25$
**14.** $17 + {}^-23$
**15.** $42 + {}^-54$
**16.** ${}^-248 + 236$

**17.** ${}^-8.3 + 5.6$
**18.** $8.2 + {}^-2.4$
**19.** $1.7 + {}^-2.3$
**20.** ${}^-4.5 + 2.2$

Supply the missing addend.

**B**  **21.** $^-5 + \underline{\phantom{?}?\phantom{?}} = ^-3$       **22.** $^-2 + \underline{\phantom{?}?\phantom{?}} = 4$       **23.** $3 + \underline{\phantom{?}?\phantom{?}} = ^-4$

**24.** $7 + \underline{\phantom{?}?\phantom{?}} = 4$       **25.** $4.3 + \underline{\phantom{?}?\phantom{?}} = ^-1.6$       **26.** $^-3.25 + \underline{\phantom{?}?\phantom{?}} = 1.75$

## Problems

Solve.

**A**  **1.** After take-off, an airliner rose steadily to an elevation of 11,000 m, then descended 4000 m to avoid a storm, and next rose 3000 m. What was its elevation at that time?

**2.** Because of a grain shortage, the price of a loaf of bread increased by 2 cents. When grain again became plentiful, the price decreased by 4 cents, but later it again rose by 5 cents because of inflation. If the original price was 46 cents per loaf, what was the final price?

# EXTRA! Absolute Value

On page 70 we stated that the length of a directed line segment is always a positive number or zero, even when the direction of the arrow is negative. This number is called the **absolute value** of the number represented by the arrow.

A directed line segment representing 3 has a length 3, so the absolute value of 3 is 3.

A directed line segment representing $^-5$ has a length 5, so the absolute value of $^-5$ is 5.

The symbol we use to indicate "the absolute value of the number $n$" is $|n|$. Thus we can write

$$n = 9, \quad \text{and} \quad |9| = 9$$
$$n = ^-1.2, \quad \text{and} \quad |^-1.2| = 1.2$$
$$n = 0, \quad \text{and} \quad |0| = 0$$

We use absolute value to find the sum of two numbers. For example, find $^-5 + 2$.

$|^-5| = 5$   and   $|2| = 2$
The absolute value of the sum, $|^-5 + 2|$, is $5 - 2$, or 3.
Since $|^-5| > |2|$, the sign of the sum is negative.
So, $^-5 + 2 = ^-3$.

Use absolute value, as shown on page 80, to find the sum.

**1.** 8 + ⁻7        **2.** ⁻8 + 7        **3.** 5 + ⁻5

**4.** 32 + ⁻40       **5.** ⁻32 + 40      **6.** 58 + ⁻106

## Self-Test

Words to remember:
positive number [p. 66]        negative number [p. 66]
opposite numbers [p. 66]       integers [p. 66]
directed line segment [p. 70]     arrow [p. 70]

Show the graph of the opposite of the number on a number line.

**1.** 21                **2.** 701                **[3-1]**

Write the missing number.

**3.** If $n = {}^-6$, then $-n = \underline{\ ?\ }$    **4.** If $-n = ({}^-1.2)$, then $n = \underline{\ ?\ }$

Graph the numbers on a number line.

**5.** ⁻3.5 and 0.7         **6.** 3.5 and ⁻0.7       **[3-2]**

**7.** Draw an arrow starting at the graph of ⁻5 to represent the number 7.

**8.** Draw an arrow with endpoint at the graph of ⁻3 to represent the number 4.

Complete.

**9.** $^-3.6 + {}^-1.8 = \underline{\ ?\ }$      **10.** $1.6 + 5.9 = \underline{\ ?\ }$      **[3-3]**

**11.** $\underline{\ ?\ } + {}^-4.2 = {}^-4.8$       **12.** $17.76 + \underline{\ ?\ } = 19.75$

**13.** $^-6 + 3 = \underline{\ ?\ }$           **14.** $5.1 + {}^-1.3 = \underline{\ ?\ }$      **[3-4]**

**15.** $4 + \underline{\ ?\ } = 0$            **16.** $^-10.25 + 6.54 = \underline{\ ?\ }$

Self-Test answers and Extra Practice are at the back of the book.

# 3-5 The Difference of Two Numbers

**Objective** To find the difference of two numbers by finding a missing addend.

We learned in Section 2-5 that for every subtraction equation we can write a related addition equation. Thus, finding the difference of two numbers can be looked at as the process of finding a missing addend.

The arrow diagram below pictures a sum, 3, and one of its addends, $^-2$. The dashed arrow for the missing addend, labeled $d$, represents the difference of 3 and $^-2$, namely 5.

To indicate that 5 is the difference of 3 and $^-2$, we write

$$3 - {}^-2 = 5.$$

From the arrow diagram, you can also see another difference, namely,

$$3 - 5 = {}^-2.$$

Each of these subtraction facts corresponds to the addition fact that

$$^-2 + 5 = 3.$$

Thus, we have the following property:

---

## property

For any numbers $a$, $b$, and $c$, if

$$a + b = c,$$

then it is also true that

$$c - a = b, \text{ and } c - b = a.$$

*Example* | Write two differences corresponding to the sum
$$4 + {}^-6 = {}^-2$$
$$(a + b = c)$$

*Solution* | $$^-2 - 4 = {}^-6 \quad \text{and} \quad {}^-2 - {}^-6 = 4$$
$$(c - a = b) \qquad\qquad (c - b = a)$$

## Class Exercises

For the given arrow diagram, state the value of the missing addend.

**1.**

**2.**

In the given exercise, express *d* as a difference.

  **3.** Exercise 1

                    **4.** Exercise 2

Find the value of the given expression.

  **5.** $12 - 6$       **6.** $^-12 - {}^-6$       **7.** $12 - {}^-6$       **8.** $^-12 - 6$

  **9.** $6 - 12$       **10.** $^-6 - {}^-12$       **11.** $6 - {}^-12$       **12.** $^-6 - 12$

State two differences corresponding to the given sum.

  **13.** $25 + {}^-15 = 10$     **14.** $3 + {}^-12 = {}^-9$     **15.** $^-4 + 5 = 1$     **16.** $^-7 + 3 = {}^-4$

  **17.** $5 + 10 = 15$     **18.** $4 + 6 = 10$     **19.** $^-4 + {}^-7 = {}^-11$     **20.** $^-2 + {}^-3 = {}^-5$

  **21.** Use examples to explain why the difference of two whole numbers is not always a whole number.

  **22.** Use examples to explain why the difference of two integers must always be an integer.

## Exercises

Picture the given difference on a number line.

**A**   **1.** $6 - 8$         **2.** $4 - 7$         **3.** $^-6 - {}^-4$         **4.** $^-4 - {}^-6$

    **5.** $3 - {}^-2$         **6.** $^-4 - 2$         **7.** $^-5 - 0$         **8.** $0 - {}^-5$

Find the given difference.

**9.** $20 - 14$      **10.** $12 - 1$      **11.** $^-52 - ^-15$      **12.** $^-75 - 20$

**13.** $12 - 20$      **14.** $^-32 - ^-21$      **15.** $^-1 - ^-34$      **16.** $68 - 52$

**B**   **17.** $^-8 - ^-16$      **18.** $35 - 43$      **19.** $^-8 - ^-42$      **20.** $23 - ^-133$

**21.** $^-15 - ^-7$      **22.** $3 - ^-17$      **23.** $60 - ^-100$      **24.** $^-88 - 90$

Write two differences corresponding to the given sum.

**25.** $22 + ^-6 = 16$      **26.** $9 + 6 = 15$      **27.** $^-13 + 29 = 16$

**28.** $^-20 + ^-12 = ^-32$      **29.** $^-36 + 15 = ^-21$      **30.** $^-76 + 23 = ^-53$

## Problems

Solve.

**A**   **1.** Two stages of a rocket burn for a total of 114.5 seconds. If the first stage burns for 86.8 seconds, how long does the second stage burn?

     **2.** On Judy's paper route during June, her papers cost her $72.50 and she collected $68.75. What was her profit or loss for the month?

## *EXTRA!* Calculating Quickly

Show your friends you can add faster than a calculator.

**A.** Choose a 6-digit number and write it down.

**B.** Ask a friend to choose a number.

**C.** You choose, making sums of 9 with the digits of your friend's number.

**D.** Ask your friend to choose another number.

**E.** You choose again, making sums of 9.

**F.** While your friend uses a calculator to find the sum, you quickly write it down. It is your original number minus 2, plus 2 million. (2 is the number of choices your friend made.)

Example

| | |
|---|---|
| 730,598 | **(A)** |
| 343,716 | **(B)** |
| 656,283 | **(C)** |
| 174,662 | **(D)** |
| 825,337 | **(E)** |
| 2,730,596 | **(F)** |

$8 - 2$

$2 \times 1,000,000$

# 3-6 Subtraction as Adding the Opposite

**Objective** To find the difference of two numbers by adding the opposite of the second to the first.

At the left below is an arrow diagram for the difference $6 - 2$. Compare this with the figure at the right showing the sum of 6 and *the opposite* of 2.

You can see that the arrow for the difference $6 - 2$ has the same length and direction as the arrow for the sum $6 + (-2)$. That is:

$$6 - 2 = 6 + (-2)$$

subtract    add the opposite

(Remember that the unraised minus sign is used to denote *subtraction* as well as the *opposite*.)

In general, we can say:

To subtract a number, add its opposite.

---

## property

**For any numbers $a$ and $b$,**

$$a - b = a + (-b).$$

---

We learned how to add any two numbers (positive, negative, or zero) in Sections 3-3 and 3-4. The simplest way to find the *difference* of any two numbers is to rewrite it as a sum and then add. The example which follows on the next page illustrates this method of finding differences.

| *Example* | Find the difference by first expressing it as a sum. |
|---|---|

**a.** $^-5 - {}^-8$          **b.** $^-5 - 6$

**c.** $^-4.7 - 2.8$          **d.** $7 - {}^-8$

*Solution*

**a.** $^-5 - {}^-8 = {}^-5 + (-{}^-8) = {}^-5 + 8 = 3$

**b.** $^-5 - 6 = {}^-5 + (-6) = {}^-5 + {}^-6 = {}^-11$

**c.** $^-4.7 - 2.8 = {}^-4.7 + (-2.8) = {}^-4.7 + {}^-2.8 = {}^-7.5$

**d.** $7 - {}^-8 = 7 + (-{}^-8) = 7 + 8 = 15$

## Class Exercises

Express the given difference as a sum.

**1.** $7 - 4$  **2.** $8 - 2$  **3.** $^-10 - 5$  **4.** $^-3 - {}^-8$

**5.** $1.8 - 4.7$  **6.** $^-2.3 - {}^-1.7$  **7.** $0.6 - {}^-1.3$  **8.** $^-4.5 - 2.4$

Express the given sum as a difference.

**9.** $4.9 + {}^-2.8$  **10.** $^-3.2 + {}^-1.5$  **11.** $0.8 + 0.2$  **12.** $^-3 + 2$

**13.** Subtracting 6 is the same as adding __?__ .

**14.** Subtracting $^-2$ is the same as adding __?__ .

Find the difference in the given exercise

**15.** Exercise 1  **16.** Exercise 2  **17.** Exercise 3  **18.** Exercise 4

## Exercises

Write the given difference as a sum.

A

**1.** $7.5 - {}^-1.3$  **2.** $^-2.1 - {}^-5.1$  **3.** $1.3 - 3.4$  **4.** $^-21.1 - 4.2$

**5.** $33.3 - 46.5$  **6.** $18.9 - {}^-25.6$  **7.** $3.56 - {}^-8.73$  **8.** $40.03 - 19.97$

Find the given difference.

**9.** $23 - 18$  **10.** $12 - 18$  **11.** $^-3 - 17$  **12.** $10 - {}^-12$

**13.** $7.4 - {}^-2.5$  **14.** $3.5 - {}^-4.5$  **15.** $^-1.8 - 2.7$  **16.** $^-0.02 - 0.31$

**17.** $13.15 - 2.27$  **18.** $17.3 - 2.4$  **19.** $^-3.5 - 9.5$  **20.** $^-4.7 - {}^-5.8$

**21.** $66.30 - {}^-32.12$  **22.** $50.05 - 65.11$  **23.** $97.44 - {}^-2.01$  **24.** $0.75 - 26.15$

## Problems

Solve.

A  1. At the beginning of October, Jean Johnson had a balance of $538.27 in her checking account. During the month, she made a deposit of $203.80 and wrote checks for $112.42, $89.17, $209.06, and $250.00. What was the balance in her account at the end of the month?

2. During a week, the stock of United Environmental Control Corporation had the following daily changes in price: Monday, up $3; Tuesday, up $4; Wednesday, down $5; Thursday, up $1; Friday, down $9. What was the change in price of the stock for the week?

# A Nutritionist

Do you know what kinds of vitamins and minerals your body needs? Do you know what kinds of foods contain these vitamins and minerals?

As a nutritionist, Hsien Wu (1893–1959) often dealt with the above questions. His research on food composition and the effects of eating habits on health made him the foremost nutrition scientist in China. Perhaps Wu's most notable discovery was his development of a system of analyzing blood for research and testing. His methods enabled scientists to measure the content of blood with only 10 mL samples. Hsien Wu wrote over 150 research papers which brought him international recognition and an honorary membership on the Standing Advisory Committee on Nutrition of the Food and Agriculture Organization of the United Nations, among other memberships.

**Career Activity** Besides doing research, some nutritionists coordinate nutrition programs as part of public health programs. Find out if there is a nutrition program at your school or in your neighborhood. How is the program organized?

# 3-7 The Product of Two Integers

**Objective** To find the product of two integers by applying the rules of sign for multiplication.

On page 67, we saw that, for instance, $-2 = {}^-2$, that is, the opposite of two is negative two.

Notice! From now on, we shall use an unraised minus sign in denoting:

a negative number:  $-2$ can stand for *negative 2*
the opposite of a number:  $-2$ can stand for *the opposite of 2*
subtraction:  $-2$, as in $4 - 2$, means *subtract 2*

In earlier work with whole numbers we have seen that if all the addends in a given sum are the *same* whole number, we can use multiplication to find the sum. For example, to add

$$3 + 3 + 3 + 3 + 3 = 15$$

we can, instead, multiply

$$5 \times 3 = 15$$

This is true also if all the addends are the same *integer*.

*Example 1* | **Find the product $2(-3)$ with the aid of an arrow diagram.**

*Solution* |

**Therefore, $2(-3) = -6$**

We cannot picture a product like

$$-2(3) \text{ or } -2(-3)$$

on a number line, because in each case the first factor indicates that a *negative* number of arrows of equal length must be drawn. Nevertheless, if we assume that the distributive property holds for all integers, then we can decide what such a product must be.

$$(4 + -2)(3) = (4)(3) + (-2)(3)$$
$$(2)(3) = 12 \quad + (-2)(3)$$
$$6 = 12 \quad + (-2)(3)$$

But
$$6 = 12 \quad + -6$$

so $(-2)(3)$ must be equal to $-6$.

---

## rule

**The product of a negative integer and a positive integer is a negative integer.**

---

In the same way

$$(4 + -2)(-3) = (4)(-3) + (-2)(-3)$$
$$2(-3) = -12 \quad + (-2)(-3)$$
$$-6 = -12 \quad + (-2)(-3)$$

But
$$-6 = -12 \quad + 6$$

so $(-2)(-3)$ must be equal to 6.

---

## rule

**The product of two negative integers is a positive integer.**

---

The following table summarizes the facts about products of integers.

| Two Factors | Product | Example |
|---|---|---|
| both positive | positive | $3(2) = 6$ |
| both negative | positive | $-3(-2) = 6$ |
| of opposite sign | negative | $-3(2) = -6$ |
| one or both 0 | 0 | $-3(0) = 0$ |

*Example 2* | Find the product.
**a.** 3(5)   **b.** −3(5)   **c.** −3(−5)   **d.** 0(−5)

*Solution* | **a.** 15   **b.** −15   **c.** 15   **d.** 0

## Class Exercises

Express the given sum as a product.

**1.** $5 + 5 + 5$

**2.** $0 + 0 + 0 + 0$

**3.** $(-6) + (-6)$

**4.** $(-1) + (-1) + (-1)$

**5.** $(-3.5) + (-3.5)$

**6.** $(-4.8) + (-4.8)$

**7.** $(-8.2) + (-8.2)$

**8.** $(-2) + (-2) + (-2)$

Express the given product as a sum.

**9.** $3(-4)$

**10.** $5(0)$

**11.** $6(-1)$

**12.** $4(-12)$

Find the product.

**13.** $5(10)$

**14.** $5(-10)$

**15.** $-5(10)$

**16.** $-5(-10)$

**17.** $-2(-3)$

**18.** $-1(-1)$

**19.** $1(-7)$

**20.** $-1(7)$

## Exercises

Draw an arrow diagram picturing the given product.

**A**

**1.** $3(-4) = -12$

**2.** $5(-3) = -15$

**3.** $4(-6) = -24$

**4.** $2(-5) = -10$

Find the product.

**5.** $8(-9)$

**6.** $7(-6)$

**7.** $6(-8)$

**8.** $10(-100)$

**9.** $-11(12)$

**10.** $-13(10)$

**11.** $-16(16)$

**12.** $-40(28)$

**13.** $-4(-3)$

**14.** $-3(-5)(-2)$

**15.** $-20(-30)$

**16.** $-25(-15)(4)$

**17.** $-42(-40)$

**18.** $-50(-50)$

**19.** $-100(24)$

**20.** $25(-25)$

**B**

**21.** $-27(42 + 28)$

**22.** $-15(37 + 13)$

**23.** $-20(40) + 60(-10)$

**24.** $-15(12) + 50(-20)$

**25.** $-42(17 - 10)$

**26.** $-52(28 - 14)$

**27.** $-33(8 - 15)$

**28.** $-75(13 - 34)$

**C**

**29.** $[-14 + 18 + (-27)][-22 + 14 + (-12)]$

**30.** $[-50 - 17 + 13][-43 + 14 + (-21)]$

# 3-8 The Product of Two Numbers

**Objective** To find the product of any two given numbers by applying the rules of sign for multiplication.

You can use the same rules of sign you used with integers to simplify expressions for products of any numbers.

**Example 1** | Multiply $-4.21(1.6)$

*Solution* | First, note that one factor is positive and one negative, so the product is negative. Then multiply $4.21(1.6)$.

$$\begin{array}{r} 4.2\,1 \\ 1.6 \\ \hline 2\,5\,2\,6 \\ 4\,2\,1 \\ \hline 6.7\,3\,6 \end{array}$$

Since the product is negative,
$-4.21(1.6) = -6.736$

**Example 2** | Multiply $-0.7(-0.6)$

*Solution* | Since both factors are negative, the product is positive. Working with positive numbers only, you have:
$$0.7(0.6) = 0.42$$
Since the given product is positive, you therefore have
$$-0.7(-0.6) = 0.42$$

**Example 3** | Multiply $5.25(-3)$

*Solution* | Note that the product is negative.
Multiply: $5.25(3) = 15.75$
Therefore, $5.25(-3) = -15.75$

## Class Exercises

Multiply.

**1.** $-3(2)$        **2.** $4(-10)$        **3.** $-2(1.5)$        **4.** $-3(1.2)$

**5.** $2(-14)$        **6.** $-10(6)$        **7.** $3(-12)$        **8.** $15(-2)$

**9.** $-1.2(-1.2)$        **10.** $-0.8(-0.2)$        **11.** $-0.4(-0.4)$        **12.** $-1.5(-0.5)$

**13.** $-0.5(-0.5)$        **14.** $-0.4(-0.3)$        **15.** $-1.5(0.5)$        **16.** $-2.5(4)$

## Exercises

**A**

1. $7.4(-1.3)$
2. $8.3(-2.6)$
3. $-5.6(7.1)$
4. $-4.8(1.2)$
5. $-3.4(-5.6)$
6. $-9.2(-7.3)$
7. $-10.1(-8.9)$
8. $-12.3(-4.3)$
9. $2.8(-5.7)$
10. $4.5(-2.3)$
11. $-5.3(2.7)$
12. $-6.5(3.3)$
13. $-5.6(-3.2)$
14. $-3.4(-8.9)$
15. $-1.5(-1.4)$
16. $-3.6(-5.2)$
17. $-4.15(1.15)$
18. $2.14(-7.30)$
19. $-2.25(-3.12)$
20. $6.28(2.16)$

**B**

21. $4(3)(-3)$
22. $-15(-2)(4)$
23. $1.2(-4.8)(-3.1)$
24. $-7.6(2.3)(-4.1)$
25. $-4.5(-1.3)(-0.23)$
26. $-6.8(4.1)(-1.1)$

**C**

27. $(4.02 - 6.7)(-2.1 + 1.2)$
28. $(52.8 - 107.3)(86.1 - 92.7)$
29. $(7.1 - 9.4)(4.2 - 8.5)$
30. $[-6.7 + (+4.53)][-5.1 + 2.12]$

## Problems

Solve.

**A**

1. Mary had an allowance of $10 for her lunch at school during the month. She spent 45¢ for lunch each of the 22 school days. How much money did she have left at the end of the month?

2. In Summit City 78 cm of snow fell on Sunday. It melted an average of 5.8 cm each day. How much snow remained six days later?

# EXTRA! Zero and Negative Exponents

On page 28 we noted that we can find the product of two powers of 10 by adding the exponents. For example,

$$10^2 \times 10^3 = 10^{2+3} = 10^5$$

Thus we have the following property:

**property**

**For all positive integers $a$ and $b$, $10^a \times 10^b = 10^{a+b}$**

Does the symbol $10^0$ stand for a number? If it does, and if the property on page 92 is to apply to this power, then we must have

$$10^1 \times 10^0 = 10^{1+0} = 10$$
$$10^2 \times 10^0 = 10^{2+0} = 10^2$$

and so on. That is,

$$10^a \times 10^0 = 10^a$$

Since multiplying a given power of 10 by $10^0$ produces the given power of 10, $10^0$ must be equal to 1. Thus we can write

$$10^0 = 1$$

If the property on page 92 is also to apply to *negative* exponents, we must have

$$10^1 \times 10^{-1} = 10^{1+(-1)} = 10^0 = 1$$
$$10^2 \times 10^{-2} = 10^{2+(-2)} = 10^0 = 1$$

and so on. Since we know that

$$10^1 \times \frac{1}{10} = 1 \qquad \text{and} \qquad 10^2 \times \frac{1}{10^2} = 1$$

we then must have

$$10^{-1} = \frac{1}{10} \qquad \text{and} \qquad 10^{-2} = \frac{1}{10^2}$$

Thus we can write

$$10^{-a} = \frac{1}{10^a}$$

Copy and complete the following table.

|  | Fraction | Decimal | $10^a$ |
|---|---|---|---|
| **1.** | $\frac{1}{10}$ | 0.1 | ? |
| **2.** | $\frac{1}{10^2}$ | ? | $10^{-2}$ |
| **3.** | ? | 0.001 | ? |
| **4.** | ? | ? | $10^{-4}$ |

# 3-9 The Quotient of Two Numbers

**Objective** To find quotients of numbers by applying the rules of sign for multiplication.

In Section 2-5 we learned that division can be thought of as the process of finding a missing factor. You can use this fact, together with the rules of sign for multiplication, in finding quotients.

**Example 1** | Find the quotient $q = 15 \div (-5)$.

**Solution** | If $q = 15 \div (-5)$, then $q \times (-5) = 15$. Since the product, 15, is positive and one of its factors, $-5$, is negative, you know that the other factor, $q$, must be negative. Thus, $q = -3$.

**Example 2** | Find the quotient $0 \div (-4)$.

**Solution** | If $q = 0 \div (-4)$, then $q \times (-4) = 0$. Since the product is 0, at least one of the factors must be 0, so $q = 0$. Hence $0 \div (-4) = 0$.

**Example 3** | If possible, find the quotient $(-4) \div 0$.

**Solution** | If $q = (-4) \div 0$, then $q \times 0 = -4$. But the product of 0 and any number is 0, so there is no such value $q$. We cannot divide by 0.

From examples such as the ones above, we have the following facts about quotients:

| Dividend and divisor | Quotient | Example |
|---|---|---|
| both positive | positive | $6 \div 3 = 2$ |
| both negative | positive | $-6 \div (-3) = 2$ |
| of opposite sign | negative | $-6 \div 3 = -2$ <br> $6 \div (-3) = -2$ |
| dividend 0 <br> divisor not 0 | 0 | $0 \div 3 = 0$ |

*Example 4* | Divide 126 by $-9$.

*Solution* | Apply the division process to the positive numbers 126 and 9. Since 126 is positive and $-9$ is negative, their quotient is negative. Therefore, $126 \div (-9) = -14$.

$$
\begin{array}{r}
14 \\
9\overline{)126} \\
9 \\
\hline
36 \\
36 \\
\hline
0
\end{array}
$$

*Example 5* | Divide $-6.58$ by $-1.4$.

*Solution* | Apply the division process to positive numbers. Since $-6.58$ and $-1.4$ are both negative, their quotient is positive. Therefore, $(-6.58) \div (-1.4) = 4.7$.

$$
\begin{array}{r}
4.7 \\
1.4\overline{)6.58} \\
56 \\
\hline
98 \\
98 \\
\hline
0
\end{array}
$$

*Example 6* | What is one third of $-21$?

*Solution* | Divide 21 by 3:
$$21 \div 3 = 7$$
Since $-21$ is negative and 3 is positive, their quotient is negative. Therefore, $-21 \div 3 = -7$, or one third of $-21$ is $-7$.

## Class Exercises

Find the quotient. If the expression is meaningless, so state.

**1.** $-8 \div 2$      **2.** $-9 \div 3$      **3.** $10 \div (-5)$      **4.** $12 \div (-4)$

**5.** $-4 \div (-2)$      **6.** $-25 \div 5$      **7.** $-25 \div (-5)$      **8.** $25 \div (-5)$

**9.** $0 \div (-6)$      **10.** $2 \div 0$      **11.** $0 \div 0$      **12.** $0 \div 4$

## Exercises

Find the quotient.

A
1. $-42 \div 7$
2. $-56 \div 8$
3. $-85 \div (-5)$
4. $-132 \div (-12)$

5. $-1.6 \div 2$
6. $-2.8 \div 4$
7. $6.3 \div (-7)$
8. $8.4 \div (-7)$

9. $0 \div 12$
10. $0 \div (-25)$
11. $3.23 \div (-1.9)$
12. $22.1 \div (-1.3)$

13. $-12.768 \div (-0.48)$
14. $-0.31705 \div (-8.5)$

15. $-24.984 \div 720$
16. $5.544 \div (-3.6)$

Simplify.

B
17. $[32.3 \times (-1.84)] \div 2.8$
18. $[4.36 \times (-1.84)] \div (-14.4)$

19. $(-134.86 \div 110) \div (-0.36)$
20. $(-10.1144 \div 470) \div (-0.04)$

C
21. $(-0.7)(4.2)(-3.8) \div (0.02)(-7.1)(2.3)$

22. $(5.6)(-2.1)(0.36) \div (-4.9)(0.008)(49.7)$

## Problems

Solve.

B
1. John had a week's allowance of $3.00 for school lunches. He spent the same amount on each school day and had 50¢ left over. How much did he spend each day?

2. A farmer had 360 kg of fertilizer. He spread 0.8 of it evenly on 3 fields of the same size. How much did he spread on each field?

# EXTRA! Comparing Calculators

Does your calculator round off quotients? To find out, divide 5 by 3. If your answer is 1.6666...7, then your calculator rounds. If your answer is 1.6666..., then your calculator "cuts off," or "truncates" any digits not shown on the display.

Two students used different calculators to do the following multiplication problem: $0.0000008 \times 0.2 \times 2$. One student got an answer of 0.0000004 and the other got an answer of 0.0000002. Can you explain the difference in answers?

# Self-Test

Find the given difference.

1. $7 - 15$

2. $-2 + {}^+6$ $_{+4}$            [3-5]

Write two differences corresponding to

3. $9 + 2 = 11$

4. $-37 + 29 = -8$

Write the given difference as a sum.

5. $1.2 - 3.6$

6. $8.72 - {}^-13.51$            [3-6]

Find the difference.

7. $6.5 - 1.8 = \underline{\ ?\ }$

8. $6.12 - {}^-8.47$

Find the product.

9. $2(-3.1)$

10. $-81(-5)$            [3-7]

11. $-16(-12 + 12)$

12. $(-14 - 3)(6 - 9)$

Find the product.

13. $0.6(-1.5)$

14. $(-3.7)(-5.1)$            [3-8]

15. $3.12(-7.04)$

16. $-9.55(-7.34)$

Simplify.

17. $-24 \div 6$

18. $13.68 \div (-1.8)$            [3-9]

19. $(-73.44 \div 5.1) \div (-3.2)$

20. $(0.6)(-4.2) \div (-6)(-0.7)$

Self-Test answers and Extra Practice are at the back of the book.

97

# Chapter Review

Write the letter that labels the correct answer.

**1.** If $t = 0$, then $-t$ is ___?___                                            [3-1]
    **A.** a positive number    **B.** a negative number
    **C.** zero    **D.** 0.1

**2.** The opposite of $^-12$ is ___?___
    **A.** 12    **B.** $^-12$    **C.** 0    **D.** $\frac{-1}{12}$

Use the diagram below for Exercises 3–4.

**3.** The coordinate of the starting point of the arrow is ___?___        [3-2]
    **A.** $^-4$    **B.** $^-2$    **C.** 2    **D.** $^-6$

**4.** The coordinate of the endpoint of the arrow is ___?___
    **A.** $^-4$    **B.** 2    **C.** 6    **D.** $^-6$

Use the diagram for Exercises 5–6.

**5.** The diagram shows the sum ___?___                                          [3-3]
    **A.** $1.5 + 2.5$    **B.** $^-1.5 + {}^-2.5$    **C.** $1.5 + {}^-2.5$    **D.** $^-1.5 + 2.5$

**6.** The sum of the addends is ___?___
    **A.** 4    **B.** $^-4$    **C.** $^-3$    **D.** $^-1$

**7.** $47 + {}^-19 =$ ___?___                                                       [3-4]
    **A.** 28    **B.** $^-28$    **C.** 66    **D.** $^-66$

**8.** $6.3 + {}^-2.9 =$ ___?___
    **A.** 9.2    **B.** $^-9.2$    **C.** 3.4    **D.** $^-3.4$

**9.** $^-8 - 30 = \underline{\phantom{?}?\phantom{?}}$  [3-5]

    **A.** 22      **B.** $^-22$      **C.** 38      **D.** $^-38$

**10.** $16 - {}^-22 = \underline{\phantom{?}?\phantom{?}}$

    **A.** 38      **B.** $^-38$      **C.** 6      **D.** $^-6$

The given difference expressed as a sum in Exercises 11–12 is $\underline{\phantom{?}?\phantom{?}}$

**11.** $^-5.1 - {}^-4.9 = \underline{\phantom{?}?\phantom{?}}$  [3-6]

    **A.** $^-5.1 + 4.9$      **B.** $^-5.1 + {}^-4.9$

    **C.** $5.1 + {}^-4.9$      **D.** $5.1 + 4.9$

**12.** $0.86 - {}^-0.11 = \underline{\phantom{?}?\phantom{?}}$

    **A.** $0.86 + 0.11$      **B.** $^-0.86 + {}^-0.11$

    **C.** $^-0.86 + 0.11$      **D.** $0.86 + {}^-0.11$

**13.** $8(-2) = \underline{\phantom{?}?\phantom{?}}$  [3-7]

    **A.** 4      **B.** $-4$      **C.** 16      **D.** $-16$

**14.** $-7(-35) = \underline{\phantom{?}?\phantom{?}}$

    **A.** 245      **B.** $-245$      **C.** 5      **D.** $-5$

**15.** $-2.9(-3) = \underline{\phantom{?}?\phantom{?}}$  [3-8]

    **A.** 87      **B.** $-87$      **C.** 8.7      **D.** $-8.7$

**16.** $0.01(-6.45) = \underline{\phantom{?}?\phantom{?}}$

    **A.** 0.645      **B.** $-0.645$      **C.** 0.0645      **D.** $-0.0645$

**17.** $6.298 \div -0.94 = \underline{\phantom{?}?\phantom{?}}$  [3-9]

    **A.** 0.67      **B.** $-0.67$      **C.** 6.7      **D.** $-6.7$

**18.** $-0.03787 \div -0.007 = \underline{\phantom{?}?\phantom{?}}$

    **A.** 5.41      **B.** $-5.41$      **C.** 54.1      **D.** $-54.1$

# Scientific Notation

Scientists often have to work with very large or extremely small quantities from their observations. For example, the diameter of a giant star is about 2,700,000,000 km, while that of a hydrogen atom is approximately $\frac{1}{100,000,000}$ cm.

Scientists have adopted a standard method for abbreviating numbers known as scientific notation. It makes use of positive exponents to show large numbers and negative exponents to show small numbers. Negative exponents were explained on page 93.

Notice that

$$4800 = 4.8 \times 1000 = 4.8 \times 10^3$$

$$0.000507 = 5.07 \times \frac{1}{10,000} = 5.07 \times 10^{-4}$$

$$835.62 = 8.3562 \times 100 = 8.3562 \times 10^2$$

## rule

**To express any positive number in scientific notation, you write it as the product of a power of ten and a number between 1 and 10.**

Here are some things to know about scientific notation:

| Decimal Number | Scientific Notation | Comments |
| --- | --- | --- |
| 2600 | $2.6 \times 10^3$ | Read, "Two point six times ten to the third" |
| 0.0000394 | $3.94 \times 10^{-5}$ | Read, "Three point nine four times ten to the minus fifth" |
| 7.46 | 7.46 | The second factor, $10^0 = 1$, can be omitted. |
| 1,000,000 | $10^6$, or $1 \times 10^6$ | The first factor, 1, can be omitted. |
| 3 or −3 | 3 or −3 | The notation for any integer from −9 to 9 remains unchanged. |

To express a positive number in scientific notation, we can follow these steps:

1. Shift the decimal point to *standard position,* that is, to just after the first nonzero digit.
2. Then multiply by $10^n$ if you shifted the decimal point $n$ places to the left, or by $10^{-n}$ if you shifted the decimal point $n$ places to the right.

| Number | Scientific notation |
|--------|---------------------|
| 3407.2 | $3.4072 \times 10^3$ |
| 0.0951 | $9.51 \times 10^{-2}$ |

Express in scientific notation.

**1.** 3,460,092        **2.** 2001        **3.** 0.00659

**4.** 99.44        **5.** 385        **6.** 0.1728

**7.** The diameter of a red blood cell is about $7.4 \times 10^{-4}$ cm, and the diameter of a white blood cell is about 0.0015 cm. Which blood cell is the larger and by about how many times?

**8.** The diameter of a hydrogen atom is approximately $\frac{1}{100,000,000}$ cm. Express this in scientific notation.

**9.** Light travels at a speed of about $3 \times 10^5$ km per second. Express this as a decimal numeral.

**10.** The sun has a mass of $1.99 \times 10^{33}$ g. Express this as a decimal numeral.

**11.** Earth has a mass of $5.98 \times 10^{27}$ g. Express this as a decimal numeral.

**12.** What is the difference between the mass of the sun and Earth's mass?

**13.** The sun has a radius of 69,600,000,000 cm. Express this in scientific notation.

**14.** Earth has a radius of 637,100,000 cm. Express this in scientific notation.

## Chapter Test

1. Show the graph of the following numbers on a number line: **[3-1]**
   $4, ^-3, 0, ^-1$.

2. Write the opposite of each number.
   **a.** 38     **b.** $^-12$     **c.** 0

3. On a number line, draw an arrow starting at the origin to repre- **[3-2]**
   sent $^-2$.

4. On a number line, draw an arrow ending at $^-3$ to represent 4.

Add.

5. $^-3.6 + ^-2.5$            6. $^-640 + ^-920$            **[3-3]**

Add.

7. $0.8 + ^-1.1$            8. $^-73 + 79$            **[3-4]**

Subtract.

9. $^-9 - 7$            10. $^-52 - ^-64$            **[3-5]**

Subtract.

11. $23.5 - 30.6$            12. $4.3 - ^-5.7$            **[3-6]**

Multiply.

13. $-8(24)$            14. $-30(-39)$            **[3-7]**

Multiply.

15. $9.6(-1.5)$            16. $-5.02(-4.7)$            **[3-8]**

Divide.

17. $5.1057 \div (-6.1)$            18. $-33.88 \div (-0.8)$            **[3-9]**

# Cumulative Review

Exercises 1–4 refer to the graph at the right.

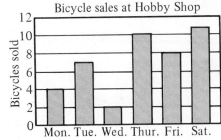

Bicycle sales at Hobby Shop

**1.** Which day had the fewest sales?

[Chap. 1]

**2.** Which day had the most sales?

**3.** On which day were 8 bicycles sold?

**4.** How many bicycles were sold in all during the week?

For the data at the right, find the

| Heights in cm of members of the tennis club |
|---|
| 160  162  160  165  162 |
| 163  155  162  162  159 |

**5.** range     **6.** mean
**7.** median     **8.** mode

Use one of the symbols < or > to make a true sentence.

**9.** 0.9 __?__ 0.4     **10.** 1.5 __?__ 2.3     **11.** 6.5 __?__ 5.6 [Chap. 2]

**12.** 3.4 __?__ 0.4     **13.** 9.9 __?__ 6.5     **14.** 0.3 __?__ 9.0

Compute the sum or difference.

**15.** $\begin{array}{r} 63.05 \\ +20.06 \end{array}$    **16.** $\begin{array}{r} 198.361 \\ +\ 47.555 \end{array}$    **17.** $\begin{array}{r} 89.54 \\ -16.45 \end{array}$    **18.** $\begin{array}{r} 133.73 \\ -\ 92.08 \end{array}$

Compute the product or quotient.

**19.** $\begin{array}{r} 38.02 \\ \times\ 0.6 \end{array}$    **20.** $\begin{array}{r} 165.09 \\ \times\ 3.12 \end{array}$    **21.** $18\overline{)53.6}$    **22.** $3.5\overline{)0.54}$

Compute the sum or difference.

**23.** $7.6 + {}^-9.2$     **24.** $^-0.5 + 12.2$     **25.** $^-3.4 + {}^+12.5$    [Chap. 3]

Compute the product or quotient.

**26.** $-4.23(3.5)$     **27.** $-12.3(-5.4)$     **28.** $18.2 \div (-0.91)$

# 4

# Rational Numbers

## 4-1 Positive Fractions

**Objective** To use terms and properties concerning positive fractions.

The table at the right reviews some important terms concerning fractions. As with decimals, fractions can be graphed on the number line. The figure below shows the graphs of several positive fractions.

In this figure, the fractions $\frac{2}{4}$ and $\frac{1}{2}$ have the same graph. Fractions which have the same graph are called equal fractions. Thus, $\frac{2}{4}$ and $\frac{1}{2}$ are equal fractions. Can you find three other sets of equal fractions in the figure above?

| **proper fraction** |
| $\frac{3}{5}$ ←——numerator ←——denominator numerator less than denominator |
| **improper fraction** |
| $\frac{7}{2}$  numerator greater than or equal to denominator |
| **mixed number** |
| $3\frac{1}{2}$  whole number and a fraction |

**105**

Calculations involving fractions depend on several important patterns. For instance, some basic properties of $\frac{1}{5}$ are as follows:

$$\underbrace{\frac{1}{5} + \frac{1}{5} + \frac{1}{5} + \frac{1}{5} + \frac{1}{5}}_{\text{5 addends}} = 1 \qquad 5 \times \frac{1}{5} = 1 \qquad 1 \div 5 = \frac{1}{5}$$

Fractions such as $\frac{1}{5}$, which have the numerator 1, are called **unit fractions.** All unit fractions follow the same patterns.

---

**properties**

**Properties of $\frac{1}{b}$**

If $b$ is a positive integer ($b \neq 0$), then $\frac{1}{b}$ represents the unique (one and only) number such that

$$\underbrace{\frac{1}{b} + \frac{1}{b} + \cdots + \frac{1}{b}}_{b\ \textbf{addends}} = 1 \qquad b \times \frac{1}{b} = 1 \qquad 1 \div b = \frac{1}{b}$$

---

Fractions with numerators other than 1 have similar properties:

$$\frac{3}{7} = \frac{1}{7} + \frac{1}{7} + \frac{1}{7} \qquad \frac{5}{9} = 5 \times \frac{1}{9} \qquad 31 \div 40 = \frac{31}{40}$$

---

**properties**

**Properties of $\frac{a}{b}$**

If $a$ and $b$ are integers ($b \neq 0$), then $\frac{a}{b}$ represents the unique number such that

$$\underbrace{\frac{1}{b} + \frac{1}{b} + \cdots + \frac{1}{b}}_{a\ \textbf{addends}} = \frac{a}{b} \qquad a \times \frac{1}{b} = \frac{a}{b} \qquad a \div b = \frac{a}{b}$$

The fact that $a \div b = \frac{a}{b}$ enables us to write whole numbers in fractional form:

$$\text{Since } 28 \div 7 = 4, \ \frac{28}{7} = 4.$$

$$\text{Since } 100 \div 5 = 20, \ \frac{100}{5} = 20.$$

$$\text{Since } 8 \div 1 = 8, \ \frac{8}{1} = 8.$$

$$\text{Since } 6 \div 6 = 1, \ \frac{6}{6} = 1.$$

We use fractional forms of whole numbers when we change mixed numbers to improper fractions:

$$2\frac{5}{6} = \frac{2}{1} + \frac{5}{6} = \frac{2 \times 6}{1 \times 6} + \frac{5}{6} = \frac{(2 \times 6) + 5}{6} = \frac{17}{6}$$

$$7\frac{1}{4} = \frac{7}{1} + \frac{1}{4} = \frac{7 \times 4}{1 \times 4} + \frac{1}{4} = \frac{(7 \times 4) + 1}{4} = \frac{29}{4}$$

or improper fractions to mixed numbers:

$$\frac{18}{7} = \frac{(7 \times 2) + 4}{7} = \frac{7 \times 2}{7} + \frac{4}{7} = \frac{2}{1} + \frac{4}{7} = 2\frac{4}{7}$$

$$\frac{106}{9} = \frac{(9 \times 11) + 7}{9} = \frac{9 \times 11}{9} + \frac{7}{9} = \frac{11}{1} + \frac{7}{9} = 11\frac{7}{9}$$

## Class Exercises

State the fractions whose graphs are shown in Exercises 1–8.

*Example*

*Solution*   **A is the graph of $\frac{2}{7}$ and B is the graph of $\frac{6}{7}$.**

**1.**

**2.**

**3.**

**4.**

**5.**

**6.**

**7.**

**8.**

## Exercises

Complete.

*Example* | $5 \times$ ___?___ $= 1$

*Solution* | $5 \times \frac{1}{5} = 1$

**A**  **1.** ___?___ $\times \frac{1}{6} = 1$         **2.** $7 \times \frac{1}{7} =$ ___?___

**3.** $\frac{1}{4} \times$ ___?___ $= \frac{3}{4}$         **4.** $\frac{1}{5} \times 5 =$ ___?___

**5.** ___?___ $\times 3 = 1$         **6.** ___?___ $\times 5 = 1$

**7.** $3 \div 7 =$ ___?___         **8.** $6 \div 5 =$ ___?___

*Example* | $2\frac{2}{3} = \frac{?}{3}$

*Solution* | $2\frac{2}{3} = \frac{(3 \times 2) + 2}{3} = \frac{6 + 2}{3} = \frac{8}{3}$

**9.** $1\frac{2}{5} = \frac{?}{5}$         **10.** $3\frac{1}{2} = \frac{?}{2}$         **11.** $4\frac{3}{4} = \frac{?}{4}$

**12.** $2\frac{5}{7} = \frac{?}{7}$         **13.** $1\frac{7}{10} = \frac{?}{10}$         **14.** $3\frac{13}{20} = \frac{?}{20}$

For each improper fraction, give an equal whole number or mixed number.

*Example* | $\frac{21}{5}$

*Solution* | $\frac{21}{5} = \frac{(4 \times 5) + 1}{5} = 4\frac{1}{5}$

**15.** $\frac{17}{3}$         **16.** $\frac{15}{7}$         **17.** $\frac{31}{10}$         **18.** $\frac{22}{11}$         **19.** $\frac{70}{5}$         **20.** $\frac{41}{4}$

# 4-2 Negative Fractions

**Objective** To use terms and properties concerning negative fractions.

The figure below shows the graphs of several negative fractions.

Do you see that $-\frac{2}{4}$ and $-\frac{1}{2}$ are equal fractions?

Patterns for negative fractions are the same as those for positive fractions:

$$\left(-\frac{1}{5}\right) + \left(-\frac{1}{5}\right) + \left(-\frac{1}{5}\right) + \left(-\frac{1}{5}\right) + \left(-\frac{1}{5}\right) = -1,$$

$$5 \times \left(-\frac{1}{5}\right) = -1.$$

In Section 3-9, we saw that the quotient of a positive decimal and a negative decimal is a negative decimal. Since $1 \div 5 = \frac{1}{5}$, it seems reasonable to assume that

$$1 \div (-5) = \frac{1}{-5} = -\frac{1}{5}, \quad \text{and} \quad (-1) \div 5 = \frac{-1}{5} = -\frac{1}{5}.$$

That is,

$$\frac{1}{-5} = \frac{-1}{5} = -\frac{1}{5}.$$

*Example 1* | **Express $-\frac{1}{7}$ in two other ways.**

*Solution* | $-\frac{1}{7} = \frac{1}{-7} = \frac{-1}{7}$

Negative fractions may have numerators other than 1:

$$-\frac{5}{7} = \frac{-5}{7} = \frac{5}{-7} \quad \text{and} \quad -\frac{3}{10} = \frac{-3}{10} = \frac{3}{-10}$$

The fact that $\frac{a}{b} = a \times \frac{1}{b}$ enables us to write

$$-\frac{5}{8} = \frac{5}{-8} = 5 \times \left(\frac{1}{-8}\right) = 5 \times \left(-\frac{1}{8}\right).$$

*Example 2* | **Express** $-\frac{7}{3}$ **in two other ways.**

*Solution* | $-\frac{7}{3} = -7 \times \frac{1}{3} = 7 \times \left(-\frac{1}{3}\right)$

A negative mixed number may be expressed as a negative improper fraction:

$$-3\frac{1}{3} = -\left[\frac{(3 \times 3) + 1}{3}\right] = -\frac{10}{3} \qquad\qquad -5\frac{3}{4} = -\left[\frac{(4 \times 5) + 3}{4}\right] = -\frac{23}{4}$$

Also, a negative improper fraction may be expressed as a negative mixed number:

$$-\frac{32}{5} = -\left(\frac{30 + 2}{5}\right) = -6\frac{2}{5} \qquad\qquad -\frac{24}{17} = -\left(\frac{17 + 7}{17}\right) = -1\frac{7}{17}$$

Since we now have numerators and denominators that are integers, rather than simply whole numbers, we are working with a new set of numbers called *rational numbers.* Any number that can be represented by a fraction $\frac{a}{b}$, where $a$ and $b$ are integers and $b$ is not 0, is a **rational number.**

## Class Exercises

State the fractions whose graphs are shown.

*Example* |

*Solution* | **A is the graph of** $-\frac{3}{6}$ **and B is the graph of** $-\frac{7}{6}$.

1.

2.

3.

4.

5.

6.

7.

8.

## Exercises

Write each fraction in two other ways.

*Example* $\quad \dfrac{1}{-6}$

*Solution* $\quad \dfrac{1}{-6} = \dfrac{-1}{6} = -\dfrac{1}{6}$

**A**
1. $-\dfrac{1}{8}$ 　　　　 2. $-\dfrac{1}{10}$ 　　　　 3. $\dfrac{-1}{12}$ 　　　　 4. $\dfrac{-1}{11}$

5. $\dfrac{1}{-3}$ 　　　　 6. $\dfrac{1}{-5}$ 　　　　 7. $-\dfrac{1}{25}$ 　　　　 8. $\dfrac{-1}{100}$

Write each fraction in two other ways.

*Example* $\quad \dfrac{-5}{11}$

*Solution* $\quad \dfrac{-5}{11} = \dfrac{5}{-11} = -\dfrac{5}{11}$

9. $\dfrac{3}{-17}$ 　　　　 10. $\dfrac{-5}{23}$ 　　　　 11. $-\dfrac{7}{17}$ 　　　　 12. $\dfrac{3}{-22}$

13. $\dfrac{-11}{3}$ 　　　　 14. $-\dfrac{15}{7}$ 　　　　 15. $\dfrac{-5}{2}$ 　　　　 16. $\dfrac{31}{-6}$

Write each mixed number as an improper fraction.

*Example* $\quad -5\dfrac{1}{8}$

*Solution* $\quad -5\dfrac{1}{8} = -\left(\dfrac{(8 \times 5) + 1}{8}\right) = -\dfrac{41}{8}$

17. $-3\dfrac{1}{3}$ 　　　　 18. $-4\dfrac{2}{5}$ 　　　　 19. $-5\dfrac{7}{8}$ 　　　　 20. $-5\dfrac{5}{9}$

21. $-8\dfrac{3}{7}$ 　　　　 22. $-10\dfrac{2}{9}$ 　　　　 23. $-11\dfrac{5}{8}$ 　　　　 24. $-20\dfrac{3}{5}$

Write each improper fraction as a mixed number.

*Example* $\quad -\dfrac{27}{5}$

*Solution* $\quad -\dfrac{27}{5} = -\left(\dfrac{25 + 2}{5}\right) = -5\dfrac{2}{5}$

25. $-\dfrac{8}{5}$ 　　　　 26. $-\dfrac{12}{7}$ 　　　　 27. $-\dfrac{18}{11}$ 　　　　 28. $-\dfrac{24}{5}$

29. $-\dfrac{32}{7}$ 　　　　 30. $-\dfrac{37}{6}$ 　　　　 31. $-\dfrac{53}{5}$ 　　　　 32. $-\dfrac{29}{10}$

# 4-3 Equal Fractions

**Objective** To use the equal-fractions rule.

In Sections 4-1 and 4-2 we saw that equal fractions have the same graph on the number line. We can calculate fractions equal to a given fraction using the following rule:

---

**rule**

**Equal-Fractions Rule**

For all integers $a$, $b$, and $c$ ($b \neq 0$, $c \neq 0$),

$$\frac{a}{b} = \frac{a \times c}{b \times c} \quad \text{and} \quad \frac{a}{b} = \frac{a \div c}{b \div c}$$

---

**Example 1**   Find three fractions equal to the given fraction.

   **a.** $\frac{5}{7}$   **b.** $\frac{12}{36}$   **c.** $-\frac{1}{8}$

**Solution**   Many solutions are possible. For instance:

   **a.** $\frac{5}{7} = \frac{5 \times 2}{7 \times 2} = \frac{10}{14}$;   $\frac{5}{7} = \frac{5 \times 3}{7 \times 3} = \frac{15}{21}$;   $\frac{5}{7} = \frac{5 \times 12}{7 \times 12} = \frac{60}{84}$

   **b.** $\frac{12}{36} = \frac{12 \div 2}{36 \div 2} = \frac{6}{18}$;   $\frac{12}{36} = \frac{12 \div 12}{36 \div 12} = \frac{1}{3}$;   $\frac{12}{36} = \frac{12 \times 5}{36 \times 5} = \frac{60}{180}$

   **c.** $-\frac{1}{8} = -\frac{1 \times 7}{8 \times 7} = -\frac{7}{56}$;   $-\frac{1}{8} = -\frac{1 \times 100}{8 \times 100} = -\frac{100}{800}$;

   $-\frac{1}{8} = -\frac{1 \times 125}{8 \times 125} = -\frac{125}{1000}$

If the numerator and denominator of a fraction have a common factor, then we can use the equal-fractions rule to *reduce* the fraction to an equal fraction:

$$\frac{40}{100} = \frac{40 \div 2}{100 \div 2} = \frac{20}{50}$$

$$\frac{20}{50} = \frac{20 \div 5}{50 \div 5} = \frac{4}{10}$$

$$\frac{4}{10} = \frac{4 \div 2}{10 \div 2} = \frac{2}{5} \quad \textbf{STOP!}$$

We can no longer reduce a fraction when the numerator and denominator have no common factor except 1. We say that the fraction is in *lowest terms*. In the preceding example, $\frac{40}{100}, \frac{20}{50}, \frac{4}{10}$, and $\frac{2}{5}$ are all equal, but only $\frac{2}{5}$ is in lowest terms.

*Example 2* | **Reduce $\frac{42}{28}$ to lowest terms.**

*Solution* | $\dfrac{42}{28} = \dfrac{42 \div 2}{28 \div 2} = \dfrac{21}{14}, \quad \dfrac{21}{14} = \dfrac{21 \div 7}{14 \div 7} = \dfrac{3}{2}$

**We often indicate the reduction process by using slashes:**

$$\dfrac{\overset{\overset{3}{\cancel{21}}}{\cancel{42}}}{\underset{\underset{2}{\cancel{14}}}{\cancel{28}}} = \dfrac{3}{2}$$ **The black slashes indicate "divide by 2."**
**The red slashes indicate "divide by 7."**

We can reduce a fraction to lowest terms in a single step by dividing both members by their *greatest* common factor (GCF).

*Example 3* | **Reduce the fraction to lowest terms.**

**a. $\dfrac{42}{28}$    b. $-\dfrac{90}{100}$**

*Solution* | **a. The greatest common factor of 42 and 28 is 14.**

$$\dfrac{42}{28} = \dfrac{42 \div 14}{28 \div 14} = \dfrac{3}{2}, \quad \text{or} \quad \dfrac{42}{28} = \dfrac{\overset{3}{\cancel{42}}}{\underset{2}{\cancel{28}}} = \dfrac{3}{2}$$

**b. The GCF of 90 and 100 is 10.**

$$-\dfrac{90}{100} = -\dfrac{90 \div 10}{100 \div 10} = -\dfrac{9}{10},$$

$$\text{or} \quad -\dfrac{90}{100} = -\dfrac{\overset{9}{\cancel{90}}}{\underset{10}{\cancel{100}}} = -\dfrac{9}{10}$$

In some cases, the GCF is easy to find and the fraction may be reduced to lowest terms in one step. For other fractions, it is easier to reduce in several steps.

*Example 4* | **Reduce $\frac{84}{140}$ to lowest terms.**

*Solution* | $\frac{84 \div 2}{140 \div 2} = \frac{42 \div 2}{70 \div 2} = \frac{21 \div 7}{35 \div 7} = \frac{3}{5}$

## Class Exercises

State two fractions that are equal to the given fraction.

**1.** $\frac{1}{6}$      **2.** $\frac{2}{3}$      **3.** $-\frac{3}{4}$      **4.** $-\frac{5}{6}$      **5.** $\frac{2}{7}$

**6.** $\frac{3}{2}$      **7.** $-\frac{5}{3}$      **8.** $-\frac{8}{5}$      **9.** $\frac{10}{3}$      **10.** $\frac{20}{7}$

Reduce to lowest terms.

**11.** $\frac{3}{6}$      **12.** $\frac{5}{15}$      **13.** $-\frac{2}{10}$

**14.** $-\frac{12}{3}$      **15.** $\frac{15}{20}$      **16.** $\frac{6}{9}$

## Exercises

Give two fractions equal to the given fraction.

**A**   **1.** $\frac{13}{14}$      **2.** $\frac{7}{25}$      **3.** $-\frac{11}{7}$      **4.** $-\frac{21}{13}$      **5.** $\frac{12}{25}$

    **6.** $-\frac{7}{30}$      **7.** $-\frac{21}{29}$      **8.** $\frac{13}{31}$      **9.** $\frac{37}{10}$      **10.** $-\frac{29}{41}$

Reduce each fraction to lowest terms.

**11.** $\frac{12}{36}$      **12.** $\frac{10}{35}$      **13.** $-\frac{14}{28}$      **14.** $-\frac{26}{39}$      **15.** $\frac{40}{80}$

**16.** $\frac{70}{100}$      **17.** $\frac{22}{55}$      **18.** $\frac{30}{45}$      **19.** $-\frac{21}{14}$      **20.** $-\frac{36}{9}$

**21.** $-\frac{48}{36}$      **22.** $-\frac{64}{36}$      **23.** $\frac{63}{84}$      **24.** $\frac{24}{148}$      **25.** $\frac{70}{105}$

**B**   **26.** $\frac{126}{210}$      **27.** $-\frac{48}{72}$      **28.** $-\frac{54}{63}$      **29.** $\frac{150}{210}$      **30.** $\frac{126}{252}$

# 4-4 Products of Fractions

**Objective** To use properties and rules of fractions to find products of fractions.

We can use the properties of numbers listed in Chapter 2 along with those introduced in this chapter to find products of fractions.

By recalling the rules of sign for products from Section 3-8, we can first concentrate on products of positive fractions, and then make adjustments for negative fractions as needed.

**Example 1** | Compute.

$$\textbf{a. } \tfrac{5}{3} \times 3 \qquad \textbf{b. } -\tfrac{3}{7} \times 7$$

**Solution**

$$\textbf{a. } \tfrac{5}{3} \times 3 = \left(5 \times \tfrac{1}{3}\right) \times 3 = 5\left(3 \times \tfrac{1}{3}\right) = 5(1) = 5$$

| Property | Commutative and | Property |
| --- | --- | --- |
| of $\frac{a}{b}$ | Associative Properties | of $\frac{1}{b}$ |

$\textbf{b. } -\tfrac{3}{7} \times 7$   Working with positive numbers only:

$$\tfrac{3}{7} \times 7 = \left(3 \times \tfrac{1}{7}\right) \times 7 = 3\left(7 \times \tfrac{1}{7}\right) = 3(1) = 3$$

Because one of the two factors is negative, the answer is $-3$.

**Example 2** | Compute $(5 \times 4) \times \left(\tfrac{1}{5} \times \tfrac{1}{4}\right)$.

**Solution**

$$(5 \times 4) \times \left(\tfrac{1}{5} \times \tfrac{1}{4}\right) = \left(5 \times \tfrac{1}{5}\right) \times \left(4 \times \tfrac{1}{4}\right) = 1 \times 1 = 1$$

| Commutative and Associative Properties | Property of $\frac{1}{b}$ |
| --- | --- |

Examples 1 and 2 suggest additional rules which simplify multiplication of fractions. From Example 1 we have the following rule.

> ## rule
>
> **For all integers $a$ and $b$ ($b \neq 0$),**
>
> $$\frac{a}{b} \times b = a$$

A closer look at Example 2 reveals a very important property of unit fractions:

$$(5 \times 4) \times \left(\frac{1}{5} \times \frac{1}{4}\right) = 20 \times \left(\frac{1}{5} \times \frac{1}{4}\right) = 1 \qquad \text{(Result of Example 2)}$$

Also,

$$20 \times \frac{1}{20} = 1 \qquad \left(\text{Property of } \frac{1}{b}\right)$$

Thus, we see that

$$\frac{1}{5} \times \frac{1}{4} = \frac{1}{20}, \quad \text{or} \quad \frac{1}{5} \times \frac{1}{4} = \frac{1}{5 \times 4}.$$

> ## rule
>
> ### Unit-Fraction Rule
>
> **For all integers $a$ and $b$ ($a \neq 0$, $b \neq 0$),**
>
> $$\frac{1}{a} \times \frac{1}{b} = \frac{1}{ab}$$

The unit-fraction rule and the property of $\frac{a}{b}$ can be used to derive the rule for multiplying any two fractions.

> ## rule
>
> **For all integers $a$, $b$, $c$, and $d$ ($b \neq 0$, $d \neq 0$),**
>
> $$\frac{a}{b} \times \frac{c}{d} = \frac{ac}{bd}$$

*Example 3* | Compute each product.

a. $\frac{1}{2} \times \frac{5}{6}$    b. $\frac{2}{5} \times \frac{3}{5}$    c. $-\frac{9}{2} \times \frac{3}{4}$    d. $\left(-\frac{3}{5}\right) \times \left(-\frac{3}{8}\right)$

*Solution*

a. $\frac{1}{2} \times \frac{5}{6} = \frac{1 \times 5}{2 \times 6} = \frac{5}{12}$    b. $\frac{2}{5} \times \frac{3}{5} = \frac{2 \times 3}{5 \times 5} = \frac{6}{25}$

c. $-\frac{9}{2} \times \frac{3}{4}$    **Note that the product is negative.**

$\frac{9}{2} \times \frac{3}{4} = \frac{9 \times 3}{2 \times 4} = \frac{27}{8}$    **Answer:** $-\frac{27}{8}$

d. $\left(-\frac{3}{5}\right) \times \left(-\frac{3}{8}\right)$    **Note that the product is positive.**

$\frac{3}{5} \times \frac{3}{8} = \frac{3 \times 3}{5 \times 8} = \frac{9}{40}$    **Answer:** $\frac{9}{40}$

When mixed numbers are involved in products, we first change each mixed number to an improper fraction and then multiply.

*Example 4* | Compute each product.

a. $4\frac{1}{8} \times 1\frac{1}{2}$    b. $-2\frac{2}{7} \times 3\frac{1}{3}$

*Solution*

a. $4\frac{1}{8} \times 1\frac{1}{2} = \frac{33}{8} \times \frac{3}{2} = \frac{99}{16} = 6\frac{3}{16}$

b. $-2\frac{2}{7} \times 3\frac{1}{3}$    **Note that the product is negative.**

$2\frac{2}{7} \times 3\frac{1}{3} = \frac{16}{7} \times \frac{10}{3} = \frac{160}{21} = 7\frac{13}{21}$    **Answer:** $-7\frac{13}{21}$

Whenever a product results in a fraction that is not in lowest terms, let us agree to reduce the fraction to lowest terms.

*Example 5* | $\frac{3}{4} \times \frac{6}{15}$

*Solution*

$\frac{3}{4} \times \frac{6}{15} = \frac{3 \times 6}{4 \times 15} = \frac{\overset{3}{\cancel{18}}}{\underset{10}{\cancel{60}}} = \frac{3}{10}$

Note that in Example 5 we could have divided by common factors *before* multiplying. Thus,

$$\frac{3}{4} \times \frac{6}{15} = \frac{3}{\underset{2}{\cancel{4}}} \times \frac{\overset{1}{\cancel{6}}}{\underset{5}{\cancel{15}}}^{3} = \frac{1 \times 3}{2 \times 5} = \frac{3}{10}.$$

## Class Exercises

Complete.

*Example* | $\underline{\quad?\quad} \times (-4) = 5$

*Solution* | $-\frac{5}{4} \times (-4) = 5$

**1.** $\frac{3}{5} \times 5 = \underline{\quad?\quad}$

**2.** $\frac{2}{3} \times \underline{\quad?\quad} = 2$

**3.** $\underline{\quad?\quad} \times (-6) = 7$

**4.** $-\frac{11}{13} \times \underline{\quad?\quad} = -11$

**5.** $\underline{\quad?\quad} \times \frac{3}{5} = -3$

**6.** $\frac{12}{17} \times 17 = \underline{\quad?\quad}$

**7.** $\frac{1}{2} \times \frac{3}{11} = \underline{\quad?\quad}$

**8.** $\frac{2}{3} \times \frac{4}{7} = \underline{\quad?\quad}$

**9.** $\frac{1}{2} \times \frac{7}{8} = \underline{\quad?\quad}$

**10.** $\frac{1}{3} \times \frac{5}{6} = \underline{\quad?\quad}$

**11.** $\left(-\frac{2}{5}\right) \times \frac{1}{7} = \underline{\quad?\quad}$

**12.** $\left(-\frac{3}{8}\right) \times \left(-\frac{5}{7}\right) = \underline{\quad?\quad}$

## Exercises

Compute each product. Give your result in lowest terms.

**A**

**1.** $\frac{4}{5} \times \frac{2}{7}$

**2.** $\frac{3}{7} \times \frac{6}{11}$

**3.** $-\frac{1}{4} \times \frac{2}{3}$

**4.** $-\frac{3}{2} \times \frac{5}{6}$

**5.** $\left(-\frac{7}{8}\right) \times \left(-\frac{4}{9}\right)$

**6.** $\left(-\frac{8}{15}\right) \times \left(-\frac{5}{16}\right)$

**7.** $\frac{7}{9} \times 0$

**8.** $0 \times \left(-\frac{5}{4}\right)$

**9.** $-\frac{8}{6} \times \frac{12}{4}$

**10.** $\frac{6}{10} \times \left(-\frac{5}{3}\right)$

**11.** $\frac{5}{16} \times \left(-\frac{4}{15}\right)$

**12.** $\frac{31}{32} \times \frac{16}{7}$

**13.** $8 \times -\frac{3}{4}$

**14.** $-\frac{7}{8} \times (-16)$

**15.** $2\frac{1}{3} \times -6$

**16.** $4\frac{1}{5} \times 10$

**17.** $-3\frac{1}{8} \times \left(-4\frac{1}{5}\right)$

**18.** $4\frac{2}{7} \times 5\frac{1}{6}$

**B**

**19.** $-\frac{3}{16} \times \left[\frac{2}{15} \times \left(-\frac{4}{3}\right)\right]$

**20.** $-\frac{11}{32} \times \left(-\frac{8}{7} \times \frac{2}{33}\right)$

**21.** $3\frac{1}{8} \times \left(-\frac{11}{4} \times 2\frac{1}{10}\right)$

**22.** $4\frac{3}{4} \times \left[-\frac{8}{15} \times \left(-3\frac{1}{4}\right)\right]$

## Problems

Solve.

**B**

1. Of 24 people who took a driving test, $\frac{7}{8}$ passed. Of those who passed, $\frac{2}{7}$ had failed the test previously. How many of those who passed had failed the test before?

2. Laura's usual work week is $37\frac{1}{2}$ hours long. Last week she worked $\frac{3}{5}$ as long as usual. How many hours did she work last week?

3. A restaurant uses $13\frac{1}{3}$ dozen eggs a day. How many dozen eggs will it use in $4\frac{1}{2}$ days?

4. Only $\frac{1}{5}$ of the downtown workers drive to work. Of those who do not drive, $\frac{3}{16}$ ride bicycles to work. What fraction of the workers ride bicycles to work?

# EXTRA!  Using Halves

An old method of multiplying two numbers makes use of doubling and halving. For example, to multiply 162 × 21, form two columns as shown below. Then double the numbers in the left column, and halve the numbers in the right column, dropping any remainders. Continue until you reach the number 1 in the right column. The product of 162 and 21 is the sum of the numbers in the left column that are opposite odd numbers in the right column.

This is often called the *Russian peasant* method of multiplication.

| Double | Halve |
|--------|-------|
| 162 | 21 (odd) |
| 324 | 10 |
| 648 | 5 (odd) |
| 1296 | 2 |
| 2592 | 1 (odd) |

$$
\begin{array}{r}
162 \\
648 \\
\underline{2592} \\
162 \times 21 = 3402
\end{array}
$$

## Self-Test

Words to remember:
numerator [p. 105]
denominator [p. 105]
proper fraction [p. 105]
improper fraction [p. 105]
mixed number [p. 105]

equal fractions [p. 105]
unit fractions [p. 106]
rational number [p. 110]
reduce a fraction [p. 112]
fraction in lowest terms [p. 113]

Complete.

1. $9 \times \underline{\quad?\quad} = 1$

2. $5\frac{5}{6} = \frac{?}{6}$           [4-1]

3. $4 \div 7 = \underline{\quad?\quad}$

4. $\frac{39}{5} = \underline{\quad?\quad}$

Write each negative fraction in two other ways.

5. $-\frac{2}{7}$

6. $\frac{-1}{4}$           [4-2]

Complete.

7. $-4\frac{5}{8} = \frac{?}{8}$

8. $-\frac{32}{5} = \underline{\quad?\quad}$

9. Give two fractions equal to $-\frac{11}{15}$.           [4-3]

Reduce each fraction to lowest terms.

10. $\frac{50}{34}$

11. $-\frac{42}{189}$

12. $\frac{75}{135}$

Compute each product. Give your result in lowest terms.

13. $-\frac{3}{4} \times \frac{2}{5}$

14. $\frac{21}{25} \times \frac{20}{56}$           [4-4]

15. $-\left(\frac{7}{18}\right) \times \left(-\frac{36}{49}\right)$

16. $4\frac{1}{16} \times 6\frac{2}{5}$

Self-Test answers and Extra Practice are at the back of the book.

# 4-5 Least Common Denominator

**Objective** To calculate the least common multiple (LCM) of two or more whole numbers and the least common denominator (LCD) of two or more fractions.

You may recall from previous work that a **multiple** of a whole number is any product of that number and a whole number. For example,

0, 2, 4, 6, 8, and so on are multiples of 2
0, 7, 14, 21, 28, and so on are multiples of 7

In calculations involving more than one fraction, it is sometimes necessary to replace fractions with equal ones so that all have the same denominator. We say that the fractions have a *common denominator*. A **common denominator** is a *common multiple* of the denominators of the fractions.

*Example 1* | **Replace the fractions with equal fractions having a common denominator.**

$$\frac{1}{2}, \ -\frac{3}{4}, \frac{1}{6}$$

*Solution*

$$\frac{1}{2} = \frac{1 \times 4 \times 6}{2 \times 4 \times 6} = \frac{24}{48}$$

$$-\frac{3}{4} = -\frac{3 \times 2 \times 6}{4 \times 2 \times 6} = -\frac{36}{48}$$

$$\frac{1}{6} = \frac{1 \times 2 \times 4}{6 \times 2 \times 4} = \frac{8}{48}$$

common denominator $= 2 \times 4 \times 6$

Example 1 above suggests that a common denominator can always be found by taking the *product* of all the denominators. It is often convenient, however, to find the *least common denominator (LCD)*. This number is the *least common multiple (LCM) of the denominators of the fractions.*

*Example 2* | **Find the least common multiple (LCM) of 10, 8, and 5.**

*Solution* | **Method 1**

multiples of 10: 10, 20, 30, (40), 50, 60, 70, 80, . . .
multiples of 8: 8, 16, 24, 32, (40), 48, 56, 64, . . .
multiples of 5: 5, 10, 15, 20, 25, 30, 35, (40), . . .
**The LCM is 40.**

Method 2

This method makes use of *prime factorizations.* A **prime** is a whole number greater than 0 having only two factors, itself and 1. For example, 2, 3, 5, 7, and 11 are primes.

prime factorization of 10: $\qquad$ 2 × 5
prime factorization of 8: $\underbrace{2 \times 2 \times 2}$
prime factorization of 5: $\qquad\qquad$ $\underbrace{5}$

The LCM must have $\qquad$ three factors $\quad$ one factor
$\qquad\qquad\qquad\qquad$ of 2 $\qquad\qquad$ of 5

Hence, the LCM is (2 × 2 × 2) × 5 = 40.

*Example 3*　Find the least common denominator of the fractions. Then calculate equal fractions having this LCD.

　　a. $\frac{5}{6}, -\frac{9}{8}$ 　　b. $\frac{1}{2}, \frac{3}{4}, \frac{1}{6}$

*Solution*　a. The LCD is the least common multiple of 6 and 8.

6, 12, 18, $\textcircled{24}$
8, 16, $\textcircled{24}$
The LCD is 24.

$$\frac{5}{6} = \frac{5 \times 4}{6 \times 4} = \frac{20}{24} \qquad -\frac{9}{8} = -\frac{9 \times 3}{8 \times 3} = -\frac{27}{24}$$

b. The LCD is the least common multiple of 2, 4, and 6.

2, 4, 6, 8, 10, $\textcircled{12}$
4, 8, $\textcircled{12}$
6, $\textcircled{12}$
The LCD is 12.

$$\frac{1}{2} = \frac{1 \times 6}{2 \times 6} = \frac{6}{12} \qquad \frac{3}{4} = \frac{3 \times 3}{4 \times 3} = \frac{9}{12} \qquad \frac{1}{6} = \frac{1 \times 2}{6 \times 2} = \frac{2}{12}$$

## Class Exercises

State the LCD of the given fractions.

1. $\frac{1}{2}, \frac{3}{4}$　　　2. $-\frac{1}{2}, \frac{5}{8}$　　　3. $\frac{2}{3}, \frac{5}{12}$　　　4. $\frac{1}{8}, \frac{3}{24}$

5. $-\frac{2}{3}, \frac{1}{2}$　　　6. $\frac{1}{3}, \frac{1}{4}$　　　7. $-\frac{1}{2}, -\frac{5}{7}$　　　8. $-\frac{3}{8}, \frac{5}{3}$

**9.** Examine the factorizations of 20 and 42 below.

$$20 = 2 \times 2 \times 5 \qquad 42 = 2 \times 3 \times 7$$

The LCM of 20 and 42 must have:

**a.** __?__ factor(s) of 2.            **b.** __?__ factor(s) of 3.
**c.** __?__ factor(s) of 5.            **d.** __?__ factor(s) of 7.

**10.** The LCM of 20 and 42 is __?__ .

**11. a.** Find the LCM of 20 and 42 by listing sets of multiples.
    **b.** Does your answer agree with that for Exercise 10?

**12.** Find the LCM of 30 and 36.         **13.** Find the LCM of 35 and 8.

## Exercises

Replace each set of fractions with equal fractions having the least common denominator (LCD).

**A**   **1.** $\frac{2}{3}, \frac{5}{9}$       **2.** $\frac{3}{2}, \frac{7}{6}$       **3.** $-\frac{3}{5}, \frac{7}{20}$       **4.** $-\frac{4}{7}, -\frac{18}{49}$

   **5.** $\frac{5}{3}, \frac{7}{5}$       **6.** $\frac{3}{5}, \frac{3}{7}$       **7.** $-\frac{8}{3}, \frac{9}{11}$       **8.** $-\frac{5}{7}, -\frac{12}{17}$

   **9.** $\frac{7}{3}, \frac{3}{4}$       **10.** $\frac{5}{4}, \frac{8}{5}$       **11.** $-\frac{3}{34}, -\frac{5}{39}$       **12.** $-\frac{5}{24}, \frac{8}{21}$

  **13.** $\frac{5}{54}, \frac{17}{42}$       **14.** $\frac{8}{45}, \frac{11}{75}$       **15.** $\frac{17}{32}, -\frac{3}{128}$       **16.** $\frac{7}{87}, \frac{4}{375}$

*Example*    $\dfrac{3}{4}, \dfrac{1}{6}, \dfrac{3}{30}$

*Solution*    **Find the LCM of 4, 6, and 30 by factoring:**

$$4 = 2 \times 2$$
$$6 = 2 \times \qquad 3$$
$$30 = 2 \times \qquad 3 \quad \times 5$$

two factors of 2    one factor of 3    one factor of 5

**The LCM is $2 \times 2 \times 3 \times 5 = 60$**

$$\frac{3}{4} = \frac{3 \times 15}{4 \times 15} = \frac{45}{60}, \qquad \frac{1}{6} = \frac{1 \times 10}{6 \times 10} = \frac{10}{60}, \qquad \frac{3}{30} = \frac{3 \times 2}{30 \times 2} = \frac{6}{60}$$

  **17.** $\frac{1}{2}, \frac{3}{4}, \frac{7}{8}$      **18.** $-\frac{2}{3}, \frac{3}{4}, -\frac{1}{20}$      **19.** $\frac{3}{16}, \frac{5}{18}, -\frac{1}{24}$      **20.** $\frac{5}{12}, \frac{3}{16}, \frac{7}{24}$

**B**   **21.** $\frac{2}{15}, -\frac{5}{12}, -\frac{4}{35}$      **22.** $\frac{7}{18}, \frac{5}{28}, -\frac{3}{56}$      **23.** $\frac{7}{30}, \frac{3}{35}, \frac{29}{60}$      **24.** $\frac{11}{24}, -\frac{19}{54}, \frac{13}{72}$

# 4-6 Sums and Differences of Fractions

**Objective** To apply the rules for adding and subtracting fractions and mixed numbers.

If two or more fractions have the same denominator, sums and differences may be calculated easily. The following rules can be justified using a property of $\frac{a}{b}$ and the distributive property.

---

## rules

For all integers $a$, $b$, and $c$ $(c \neq 0)$,

1. $\dfrac{a}{c} + \dfrac{b}{c} = \dfrac{a+b}{c}$

2. $\dfrac{a}{c} - \dfrac{b}{c} = \dfrac{a-b}{c}$

---

**Example 1** | Calculate and reduce to lowest terms.

**a.** $\dfrac{3}{8} + \dfrac{1}{8}$    **b.** $\dfrac{3}{8} - \dfrac{1}{8}$    **c.** $\dfrac{5}{9} - \dfrac{1}{9} + \dfrac{2}{9}$    **d.** $-\dfrac{2}{5} + \dfrac{3}{5}$

*Solution*

**a.** $\dfrac{3}{8} + \dfrac{1}{8} = \dfrac{3+1}{8} = \dfrac{\overset{1}{\cancel{4}}}{\underset{2}{\cancel{8}}} = \dfrac{1}{2}$

**b.** $\dfrac{3}{8} - \dfrac{1}{8} = \dfrac{3-1}{8} = \dfrac{\overset{1}{\cancel{2}}}{\underset{4}{\cancel{8}}} = \dfrac{1}{4}$

**c.** $\dfrac{5}{9} - \dfrac{1}{9} + \dfrac{2}{9} = \dfrac{5-1+2}{9} = \dfrac{\overset{2}{\cancel{6}}}{\underset{3}{\cancel{9}}} = \dfrac{2}{3}$

**d.** $-\dfrac{2}{5} + \dfrac{3}{5} = \dfrac{-2}{5} + \dfrac{3}{5} = \dfrac{-2+3}{5} = \dfrac{1}{5}$

These rules can also be used to add mixed numbers whose fractions have the same denominator.

*Example 2* | Calculate and reduce to lowest terms.

**a.** $5\frac{3}{5} + 2\frac{4}{5}$  **b.** $5\frac{3}{5} - 2\frac{4}{5}$  **c.** $2\frac{1}{3} - \left(-1\frac{2}{3}\right)$

*Solution* | **Method 1: Convert to improper fractions.**

**a.** $5\frac{3}{5} + 2\frac{4}{5} = \frac{28}{5} + \frac{14}{5} = \frac{42}{5}$, or $8\frac{2}{5}$

**b.** $5\frac{3}{5} - 2\frac{4}{5} = \frac{28}{5} - \frac{14}{5} = \frac{14}{5}$, or $2\frac{4}{5}$

**c.** $2\frac{1}{3} - \left(-1\frac{2}{3}\right) = \frac{7}{3} - \left(-\frac{5}{3}\right) = \frac{7}{3} + \frac{5}{3} = \frac{\overset{4}{\cancel{12}}}{\underset{1}{\cancel{3}}} = 4$

**Method 2: Add or subtract in columns.**

**a.** $\begin{array}{r} 5\frac{3}{5} \\ +2\frac{4}{5} \\ \hline 7\frac{7}{5} = 8\frac{2}{5} \end{array}$  **b.** $\begin{array}{r} 5\frac{3}{5} = \quad 4\frac{8}{5} \\ -2\frac{4}{5} = -2\frac{4}{5} \\ \hline 2\frac{4}{5} \end{array}$  **c.** $\begin{array}{r} 2\frac{1}{3} = \quad 2\frac{1}{3} \\ -\left(-1\frac{2}{3}\right) = +1\frac{2}{3} \\ \hline 3\frac{3}{3} = 4 \end{array}$

If two or more fractions have different denominators, we must first find equal fractions with a common denominator. Then we can add or subtract according to the rules on page 124.

*Example 3* | Calculate and reduce to lowest terms.

**a.** $\frac{3}{4} + \frac{5}{6}$  **b.** $\frac{7}{8} - \frac{2}{5} + \frac{1}{5}$

*Solution* | **a.** The LCD of $\frac{3}{4}$ and $\frac{5}{6}$ is 12.

$\frac{3}{4} = \frac{3 \times 3}{4 \times 3} = \frac{9}{12}$          $\frac{3}{4} + \frac{5}{6}$

$\frac{5}{6} = \frac{5 \times 2}{6 \times 2} = \frac{10}{12}$          $\frac{9}{12} + \frac{10}{12} = \frac{19}{12}$, or $1\frac{7}{12}$

**b.** The LCD of $\frac{7}{8}$, $\frac{2}{5}$, and $\frac{1}{5}$ is 40.

$\frac{7}{8} = \frac{7 \times 5}{8 \times 5} = \frac{35}{40}$          $\frac{7}{8} - \frac{2}{5} + \frac{1}{5}$

$\frac{2}{5} = \frac{2 \times 8}{5 \times 8} = \frac{16}{40}$

$\frac{1}{5} = \frac{1 \times 8}{5 \times 8} = \frac{8}{40}$          $\frac{35}{40} - \frac{16}{40} + \frac{8}{40} = \frac{27}{40}$

## Class Exercises

Express the sum or difference in lowest terms.

1. $\frac{3}{7} + \frac{1}{7}$

2. $\frac{5}{13} + \frac{7}{13}$

3. $\frac{6}{11} - \frac{1}{11}$

4. $\frac{16}{17} - \frac{5}{17}$

5. $\frac{3}{4} + \frac{1}{4}$

6. $-\frac{3}{6} + \frac{1}{6}$

7. $-\frac{3}{4} - \frac{3}{4}$

8. $\frac{4}{3} - \frac{2}{3}$

9. $\frac{5}{2} + \frac{3}{2} - \left(-\frac{1}{2}\right)$

10. $\frac{7}{3} - \frac{1}{3} + \left(-\frac{2}{3}\right)$

11. $2\frac{5}{16} - 1\frac{1}{16}$

12. $3\frac{7}{8} - 2\frac{3}{8}$

## Exercises

Express the sum or difference as a proper fraction in lowest terms or as a mixed number with fraction in lowest terms.

**A**

1. $\frac{3}{8} + \frac{5}{6}$

2. $\frac{5}{9} + \frac{1}{6}$

3. $\frac{7}{8} + \frac{1}{12}$

4. $\frac{3}{4} + \frac{4}{5}$

5. $\frac{5}{12} - \frac{3}{16}$

6. $\frac{11}{12} - \frac{11}{18}$

7. $\frac{7}{48} - \frac{3}{40}$

8. $\frac{16}{35} - \frac{3}{14}$

9. $\frac{11}{48} + \left(-\frac{18}{64}\right)$

10. $\frac{17}{27} + \left(-\frac{5}{24}\right)$

11. $-\frac{15}{32} - \frac{3}{40}$

12. $-\frac{12}{15} - \frac{5}{21}$

13. $1\frac{1}{4} + \frac{3}{8}$

14. $-2\frac{3}{4} + 1\frac{5}{18}$

15. $-3\frac{5}{12} + 1\frac{15}{16}$

16. $3\frac{5}{8} + 1\frac{2}{7}$

17. $4\frac{5}{12} - 2\frac{15}{16}$

18. $2\frac{5}{35} - 1\frac{5}{14}$

19. $2\frac{3}{8} - \frac{7}{12}$

20. $4\frac{11}{14} - \left(-\frac{20}{21}\right)$

21. $12\frac{3}{7} + \left(-8\frac{11}{42}\right)$

22. $10\frac{9}{48} + 8\frac{3}{20}$

23. $21\frac{11}{16} - 12\frac{1}{2}$

24. $15\frac{5}{8} - 11\frac{13}{30}$

**B**

25. $\frac{1}{2} + \frac{2}{3} + \frac{3}{4}$

26. $\frac{3}{8} + \frac{7}{15} - \frac{5}{18}$

27. $6\frac{1}{2} + 5\frac{3}{4} - 2\frac{1}{3}$

28. $\frac{7}{8} + 2\frac{2}{3} - 1\frac{5}{12}$

## Problems

Solve.

**A**  1. Nancy and Gary paddled upstream for $2\frac{7}{15}$ hours. Their return trip took $1\frac{2}{3}$ hours. How much faster was the trip downstream?

**B**  2. Anthony has a part-time job. One week he worked $2\frac{1}{3}$ hours Monday, $3\frac{1}{2}$ hours Tuesday, $1\frac{3}{4}$ hours Wednesday, $4\frac{5}{6}$ hours Thursday, $2\frac{2}{3}$ hours Friday, and $7\frac{2}{3}$ hours Saturday. How many hours did he work that week?

**C**  3. The west side of town is divided into three precincts. About $\frac{1}{12}$ of the voters live in the first precinct, about $\frac{3}{20}$ of the voters live in the second precinct, and about $\frac{4}{25}$ of the voters live in the third precinct. What part of the town's voters live on the west side of town?

4. It takes Lisa $\frac{4}{5}$ of a minute to play the first half of a march on her trumpet. The second half takes $\frac{7}{16}$ of a minute. How long does it take to play the march if both halves are played twice?

5. A teacher assigned a class a set of mathematics exercises. After two days $\frac{3}{7}$ of the class had completed them. After another day an additional $\frac{4}{9}$ had finished. What part of the class still had not completed the exercises?

## *EXTRA!* Fractions and Exponents

Just as we have used exponents to show powers of 10, so can we use exponents to show powers of other positive numbers. Thus we may have, for example

$$2^2 = 2 \times 2 = 4 \qquad 2^3 = 2 \times 2 \times 2 = 8$$
$$3^2 = 3 \times 3 = 9 \qquad 3^3 = 3 \times 3 \times 3 = 27$$
$$4^1 = 4 \qquad\qquad 4^3 = 4 \times 4 \times 4 = 64$$

We saw in Chapter 2 that we could find the product of two powers of 10 by adding exponents. Thus,

$$10^2 \times 10^3 = 10^{2+3} = 10^5$$

In general,

$$10^a \times 10^b = 10^{a+b}$$

In the same way, using 4 as a base, we can see that

$$4^1 \times 4^3 = 4 \times (4 \times 4 \times 4) = 4^{1+3} = 4^4$$

or $$4^a \times 4^b = 4^{a+b}$$

In Chapter 3, we explored the use of zero and negative integers for exponents. Can we extend the use of exponents to fractions? For example, can we find a meaning for $4^{\frac{1}{2}}$?

If $4^{\frac{1}{2}}$ names a number, and if it is true that

$$4^{\frac{1}{2}} \times 4^{\frac{1}{2}} = 4^{\frac{1}{2}+\frac{1}{2}} = 4^1 = 4$$

then $4^{\frac{1}{2}}$ must be one of two equal factors of 4; that is,

$$\left(4^{\frac{1}{2}}\right)^2 = 4$$

This means that $4^{\frac{1}{2}}$ must be equal to 2 or to $-2$, since these are the only numbers whose squares are 4. Because we do not wish to use the same symbol for two different numbers, we agree that $4^{\frac{1}{2}}$ stands for 2, and we call $4^{\frac{1}{2}}$, or 2, a **square root** of 4. (Square roots will be studied in more detail in Chapter 12.) In general, if $a$ stands for zero or a positive number, then

$$\left(a^{\frac{1}{2}}\right)^2 = a$$

We say that

$$a^{\frac{1}{2}} \text{ is the square root of } a$$

or $$a \text{ is the square of } a^{\frac{1}{2}}.$$

To find the value of $16^{\frac{1}{2}}$, we may ask, "What positive number multiplied by itself equals 16?" Since $4 \times 4 = 16$,

$$16^{\frac{1}{2}} = 4$$

Find the indicated square root.

**1.** $100^{\frac{1}{2}}$ **2.** $4^{\frac{1}{2}}$ **3.** $25^{\frac{1}{2}}$ **4.** $9^{\frac{1}{2}}$ **5.** $81^{\frac{1}{2}}$ **6.** $49^{\frac{1}{2}}$

**7.** Explore the use of fractions other than one half as exponents.

For example, what meaning would you give to $8^{\frac{1}{3}}$?

# 4-7 Quotients of Fractions

**Objective** To use a rule for dividing fractions.

To find a rule for dividing fractions, we use the relationship between multiplication and division:

$$\frac{3}{5} \div \frac{2}{7} = n \quad \text{means} \quad n \times \frac{2}{7} = \frac{3}{5}$$

It is easy to verify that substituting $\left(\frac{3}{5} \times \frac{7}{2}\right)$ for $n$ makes the multiplication sentence true.

$$\left(\frac{3}{5} \times \frac{7}{2}\right) \times \frac{2}{7} = \frac{3 \times \overset{1}{\cancel{7}} \times \overset{1}{\cancel{2}}}{5 \times \cancel{2} \times \cancel{7}} = \frac{3}{5}$$

In general:

┌─ **rule** ─────────────────────────────────────┐

**For all integers $a$, $b$, $c$, and $d$ ($b \neq 0$, $c \neq 0$, $d \neq 0$),**

$$\frac{a}{b} \div \frac{c}{d} = \frac{a}{b} \times \frac{d}{c}$$

└────────────────────────────────────────────────┘

*Example 1* | Calculate $\frac{8}{5} \div \frac{4}{5}$ and reduce to lowest terms.

*Solution* | $\dfrac{8}{5} \div \dfrac{4}{5} = \dfrac{\overset{2}{\cancel{8}}}{\underset{1}{\cancel{5}}} \times \dfrac{\overset{1}{\cancel{5}}}{\underset{1}{\cancel{4}}} = \dfrac{2}{1} = \mathbf{2}$

*Example 2* | Calculate $-\frac{5}{6} \div 2\frac{1}{2}$ and reduce to lowest terms.

*Solution* | Convert $2\frac{1}{2}$ to an improper fraction: $2\frac{1}{2} = \frac{5}{2}$

$$-\frac{5}{6} \div 2\frac{1}{2} = -\frac{5}{6} \div \frac{5}{2} = -\frac{\overset{1}{\cancel{5}}}{\underset{3}{\cancel{6}}} \times \frac{\overset{1}{\cancel{2}}}{\underset{1}{\cancel{5}}} = -\frac{1}{3}$$

We may state the rule for dividing fractions as follows:

┌─ **rule** ─────────────────────────────────────┐

**To divide by a fraction $\frac{c}{d}$, multiply by $\frac{d}{c}$.**

└────────────────────────────────────────────────┘

The rule for division works because the product of $\frac{c}{d}$ and $\frac{d}{c}$ is 1. We note this special relationship by calling $\frac{c}{d}$ and $\frac{d}{c}$ **reciprocals.** For all rational numbers $a$ and $b$, if $a \times b = 1$, then $a$ is the *reciprocal* of $b$ and $b$ is the *reciprocal* of $a$. A property of $\frac{1}{b}$, namely, $b \times \frac{1}{b} = 1$, tells us that $\frac{1}{b}$ and $b$ are reciprocals.

*Example 3* | Find the reciprocal of each number.

a. $\frac{3}{7}$    b. $-\frac{19}{12}$    c. $-8$    d. $\frac{1}{8}$

*Solution* | a. $\frac{7}{3}$ is the reciprocal of $\frac{3}{7}$.    b. $-\frac{12}{19}$ is the reciprocal of $-\frac{19}{12}$.

c. $-\frac{1}{8}$ is the reciprocal of $-8$.    d. 8 is the reciprocal of $\frac{1}{8}$.

Of course, 0 has no reciprocal, and division by 0 is impossible.

## Class Exercises

State the reciprocal of each given rational number.

**1.** 6      **2.** $\frac{1}{9}$      **3.** $-3$      **4.** $-\frac{2}{7}$      **5.** $\frac{3}{8}$      **6.** $\frac{5}{2}$      **7.** $-\frac{21}{11}$      **8.** $\frac{11}{15}$

Complete.

**9.** $\frac{2}{3} \div \frac{1}{5} = \frac{2}{3} \times$ _____

**10.** $\frac{1}{4} \div \frac{3}{8} = \frac{1}{4} \times$ _____

**11.** $-\frac{7}{2} \div \frac{2}{3} =$ _____ $\times \frac{3}{2}$

**12.** $-\frac{3}{5} \div \left(-\frac{1}{5}\right) = -\frac{3}{5} \times$ _____

**13.** $\frac{3}{8} \div$ _____ $= \frac{3}{8} \times \frac{7}{5}$

**14.** $\frac{2}{5} \div$ _____ $= \frac{2}{5} \times \frac{3}{4}$

## Exercises

Divide. Express all results in lowest terms.

A    **1.** $\frac{3}{5} \div \frac{6}{15}$        **2.** $\frac{4}{7} \div \frac{3}{14}$        **3.** $-\frac{4}{5} \div \left(-\frac{4}{5}\right)$        **4.** $-\frac{7}{16} \div \frac{7}{16}$

**5.** $-\frac{5}{16} \div \frac{11}{8}$        **6.** $-\frac{3}{32} \div \left(-\frac{9}{16}\right)$        **7.** $-8 \div \frac{16}{21}$        **8.** $\frac{14}{15} \div (-7)$

**9.** $\frac{24}{20} \div \frac{18}{15}$        **10.** $-\frac{32}{20} \div \left(-\frac{8}{30}\right)$        **11.** $2\frac{1}{5} \div 5\frac{1}{2}$        **12.** $4\frac{1}{3} \div 3\frac{1}{4}$

**13.** $-2\frac{3}{4} \div 3\frac{1}{8}$        **14.** $2\frac{3}{5} \div \left(-1\frac{11}{15}\right)$        **15.** $3\frac{2}{9} \div 29$        **16.** $-4\frac{4}{5} \div (-12)$

**17.** $12 \div 2\frac{2}{5}$        **18.** $-15 \div 2\frac{1}{2}$        **19.** $-4\frac{2}{7} \div \left(-1\frac{1}{14}\right)$        **20.** $-1\frac{7}{15} \div 3\frac{2}{3}$

**B** **21.** $\left(-\frac{18}{5} \div \frac{9}{35}\right) \times \frac{3}{7}$    **22.** $\frac{12}{25} \times \left[-\frac{5}{7} \div \left(-\frac{9}{14}\right)\right]$    **23.** $\left(-1\frac{2}{3} \times 4\frac{2}{3}\right) \div 6\frac{1}{9}$

## Problems

Solve.

**A**  **1.** A gardener uses $8\frac{1}{3}$ packets of seeds in planting $3\frac{3}{4}$ rows of cabbage. How many packets of seeds are needed for 1 row of cabbage?

**2.** A stamping machine can stamp 250 envelopes in $1\frac{2}{3}$ minutes. How many envelopes can the machine stamp in 1 minute?

# An Educator

Every year when Charlotte Hawkins Brown (1882–1961) was a child, she would visit her native North Carolina with her parents. As she grew older, she became particularly concerned about the poor conditions of the schools in her hometown. With the help of Alice F. Palmer, Brown attended the Salem Normal School and Wellesley College, where she studied to become a teacher. The opportunity for Brown to assist her native region came, and she accepted the position to teach in a small school near Sedalia, North Carolina. The school, however, was forced to close due to lack of funds. Brown, aware of the neighborhood's urgent need, decided to remain in Sedalia and establish her own school. In two years, she raised enough money to begin the construction of what was later to become Palmer Memorial Institute.

**Research Activity** Find out when the first public school was opened in this country. What subjects were taught? What is meant by a "one-room school"?

**Career Activity** In some places, teachers must be certified to teach a certain grade level. Find out what it means to be "certified." What types of certification are needed in your school?

# 4-8 Fractions and Decimals

**Objective** To find equal fractions and decimals.

Any decimal can be transformed into an equal fraction or mixed number as shown in Example 1, below.

*Example 1* | Convert **1.85** to a mixed number.

*Solution* | $1.85 = \frac{185}{100} = \frac{185 \div 5}{100 \div 5} = \frac{37}{20}$, or $1\frac{17}{20}$

A property of $\frac{a}{b}$, namely $\frac{a}{b} = a \div b$, tells us that we can convert a fraction into a decimal by dividing.

*Example 2* | Convert $\frac{15}{40}$ to a decimal.

*Solution*

$$
\begin{array}{r}
0.375 \\
40\overline{)15.000} \\
\underline{12\ 0}\ \ \ \ \ \\
3\ 00\ \ \ \\
\underline{2\ 80}\ \ \ \\
200 \\
\underline{200} \\
0
\end{array}
$$

So, $\frac{15}{40} = 0.375$

In Example 2, we reach a remainder of 0 and the division process ends. We say that $\frac{15}{40}$ is equal to the *terminating decimal* 0.375. Every terminating decimal is equal to a fraction that has a power of 10 as its denominator. For example, $0.375 = \frac{375}{10^3}$.

Sometimes when we convert a fraction into a decimal, the division process does not end.

*Example 3* | Convert $\frac{5}{33}$ to a decimal.

*Solution*

$$
\begin{array}{r}
0.1515 \\
33\overline{)5.0000} \\
3\,3 \\
\hline
1\,70 \\
1\,65 \\
\hline
50 \\
33 \\
\hline
170 \\
165 \\
\hline
5
\end{array}
$$

So, $\frac{5}{33} = 0.1515 \ldots$

In Example 3, we see that $\frac{5}{33}$ is equal to the *repeating decimal* 0.1515 . . . . We may write this decimal as $0.\overline{15}$, where the bar indicates the **repetend** 15.

Examples 2 and 3 represent a general property of rational numbers:

## property

Every rational number can be represented either by a terminating decimal number or by a repeating decimal number.

There is a simple test we can make to determine whether the decimal for a fraction will terminate or repeat:

1. Express the fraction in lowest terms.
2. If the denominator then has only powers of 2 or 5, the decimal for the fraction terminates.
3. If the denominator includes powers of any numbers other than 2 or 5, the decimal form repeats.

## Class Exercises

Complete.

**1.** $81 = \frac{81}{?}$     **2.** $23.6 = \frac{236}{?}$     **3.** $7.07 = \frac{707}{?}$     **4.** $1.309 = \frac{1309}{?}$

State as a fraction in which the numerator is an integer and the denominator is a power of ten.

*Example* | **56.1**

*Solution* | $\frac{561}{10}$

**5.** 23.11          **6.** 5.213          **7.** $-0.021$          **8.** $-1.0032$

State the terminating decimal for each fraction.

**9.** $\frac{1}{10}$          **10.** $\frac{3}{10}$          **11.** $\frac{1}{4}$          **12.** $\frac{1}{2}$

**13.** $-\frac{3}{4}$          **14.** $-\frac{1}{5}$          **15.** $-2\frac{2}{5}$          **16.** $-\frac{9}{10}$

State the repetend for each decimal.

**17.** $\frac{1}{6} = 0.1\overline{6}$          **18.** $\frac{1}{18} = 0.0\overline{5}$          **19.** $\frac{3}{11} = 0.\overline{27}$

**20.** $\frac{3}{7} = 0.\overline{428571}$          **21.** $\frac{12}{11} = 1.0\overline{9}$          **22.** $\frac{1}{13} = 0.\overline{076923}$

# Exercises

For each decimal, write a fraction in which the numerator is an integer and the denominator is a power of 10.

A     **1.** 3.5          **2.** 6.25          **3.** $-0.45$          **4.** $-1.54$

**5.** 2.023          **6.** 0.0011          **7.** 201.3          **8.** 402.112

Express as a fraction in lowest terms.

**9.** 2.75          **10.** 6.125          **11.** $-0.375$          **12.** $-1.025$

**13.** 1.625          **14.** 2.213          **15.** 0.416          **16.** 0.036

Find a terminating decimal for the given fraction.

**17.** $\frac{5}{4}$          **18.** $\frac{7}{2}$          **19.** $\frac{3}{20}$          **20.** $\frac{6}{25}$          **21.** $\frac{3}{8}$

**22.** $\frac{7}{8}$          **23.** $\frac{5}{16}$          **24.** $\frac{4}{40}$          **25.** $-\frac{1}{80}$          **26.** $-\frac{6}{125}$

Find a repeating decimal for the given fraction. Use a bar to show the repetend.

**27.** $\frac{4}{3}$        **28.** $\frac{7}{6}$        **29.** $\frac{5}{9}$        **30.** $\frac{7}{12}$        **31.** $-\frac{7}{11}$

**32.** $-\frac{3}{22}$        **33.** $\frac{5}{7}$        **34.** $\frac{8}{21}$        **35.** $\frac{1}{13}$        **36.** $\frac{5}{13}$

Tell whether the decimal for the fraction is terminating or repeating.

*Example*   |   $\frac{12}{15}$

*Solution*   |   In lowest terms, $\frac{12}{15} = \frac{4}{5}$. The denominator has no factors other than 2 or 5, so the decimal will terminate.

**37.** $\frac{2}{7}$      **38.** $\frac{1}{4}$      **39.** $\frac{5}{12}$      **40.** $\frac{3}{16}$      **41.** $\frac{8}{25}$      **42.** $\frac{9}{15}$

**B**    **43.** Divide 1 by the given integer and state the number of digits to the right of the decimal point in the decimal that results.

     **a.** 2
     **b.** $2 \times 2$, or 4
     **c.** $2 \times 2 \times 2$, or 8
     **d.** $2 \times 2 \times 2 \times 2$, or 16

   **44.** Study your results in Exercise 43 and guess the number of digits to the right of the decimal point in the terminating decimal for

$$\frac{1}{2 \times 2 \times 2 \times 2 \times 2 \times 2}.$$

Check your guess by dividing 1 by 64.

**C**    **45.** A terminating decimal for $\frac{1}{4}$ is 0.25. Suppose that in dividing 1 by 4, there was a failure to notice that $20 \div 4 = 5$ and $40 \div 4 = 10$ so that the steps shown at the right were taken. We now have a repeating decimal for $\frac{1}{4}$, namely, $0.24\overline{9}$. Do you think that every terminating decimal has an equivalent repeating decimal with repetend $\overline{9}$? Try to explain.

$$
\begin{array}{r}
0.24\overline{9} \\
4\overline{)1.000} \\
8 \\
\hline
20 \\
16 \\
\hline
40 \\
36 \\
\hline
4
\end{array}
$$

# EXTRA! Fractions for Repeating Decimals

We have seen that every terminating decimal can be converted into a fraction. Thus, every terminating decimal represents a rational number.

Does every *repeating* decimal represent a rational number? The answer is "Yes!" The example below shows a method for finding the rational number represented by a repeating decimal.

*Example* | Find the fraction in lowest terms that represents $2.\overline{18}$.

*Solution* | Suppose first that there is such a fraction naming a rational number $n$. Then

$$n = 2.\overline{18} = 2.18\overline{18}.$$

Since there are 2 digits in the repetend 18, we multiply both members of $n = 2.18\overline{18}$ by $10^2$, or 100, getting

$$100n = 218.\overline{18}$$
Subtract: $\quad n = \quad\; 2.\overline{18}$
$$99n = 216$$

$$n = \frac{216}{99} = \frac{24 \times 9}{11 \times 9} = \frac{24}{11}.$$

Thus, if there *is* a rational number $n$ represented by $2.\overline{18}$, then $n = \frac{24}{11}$. The division below shows that, in fact, $\frac{24}{11} = 2.\overline{18}$. Therefore, $2.\overline{18} = \frac{24}{11}$.

$$
\begin{array}{r}
2.18 \\
11\overline{)24.00} \\
22 \phantom{.00} \\
\hline
2\,0 \phantom{0} \\
1\,1 \phantom{0} \\
\hline
90 \\
88 \\
\hline
2
\end{array}
$$

Find a fraction in lowest terms for the repeating decimal.

1. $0.\overline{4}$
2. $0.\overline{7}$
3. $2.\overline{1}$
4. $1.\overline{3}$
5. $1.\overline{21}$
6. $2.\overline{42}$
7. $0.2\overline{3}$
8. $5.2\overline{13}$

## Self-Test

Words to remember:

least common denominator (LCD) [p. 121]     reciprocals [p. 130]
prime factorization [p. 122]

Replace each set of fractions with equal fractions having the least common denominator (LCD).

**1.** $\frac{4}{5}, \frac{2}{9}$

**2.** $-\frac{5}{6}, -\frac{1}{15}$          [4-5]

**3.** $\frac{7}{18}, \frac{5}{12}, \frac{1}{15}$

**4.** $\frac{3}{4}, \frac{4}{7}, -\frac{1}{6}$

Express the sum or difference as a proper fraction in lowest terms or as a mixed number with fraction in lowest terms.

**5.** $\frac{5}{8} + \left(-\frac{1}{6}\right)$

**6.** $-\frac{8}{15} - \frac{7}{40}$          [4-6]

**7.** $3\frac{5}{6} - 2\frac{7}{10}$

**8.** $\frac{1}{4} + 3\frac{2}{9} + 2\frac{5}{12}$

Divide. Express all results in lowest terms.

**9.** $\frac{3}{7} \div \frac{6}{21}$

**10.** $-\frac{11}{12} \div \left(-\frac{7}{8}\right)$          [4-7]

**11.** $-12 \div 3\frac{3}{4}$

**12.** $1\frac{1}{6} \div \left(-4\frac{2}{3}\right)$

Express as a fraction in lowest terms.

**13.** 1.78

**14.** $-0.325$          [4-8]

Express as a terminating or repeating decimal.

**15.** $\frac{23}{24}$

**16.** $-\frac{258}{125}$

Self-Test answers and Extra Practice are at the back of the book.

# Chapter Review

Write the letter that labels the correct answer.

**1.** $\underline{\ \ ?\ \ } \times 4 = 1$

    **A.** 1          **B.** $-3$        **C.** $-4$        **D.** $\frac{1}{4}$      [4-1]

**2.** $1\frac{3}{20} = \frac{?}{20}$

    **A.** 23        **B.** 61        **C.** 13        **D.** 203

**3.** $\frac{-2}{3} = \underline{\ \ ?\ \ }$

    **A.** $\frac{3}{-2}$        **B.** $\frac{2}{3}$        **C.** $\frac{2}{-3}$        **D.** $-1$      [4-2]

**4.** $-\frac{23}{7} = \underline{\ \ ?\ \ }$

    **A.** $-2\frac{3}{7}$        **B.** $\frac{23}{7}$        **C.** $-3\frac{2}{7}$        **D.** $-16$

**5.** $\frac{2}{5} = \underline{\ \ ?\ \ }$

    **A.** $\frac{4}{25}$        **B.** $\frac{5}{15}$        **C.** $\frac{12}{30}$        **D.** $-\frac{8}{20}$      [4-3]

**6.** $-\frac{56}{80}$ in lowest terms is $\underline{\ \ ?\ \ }$.

    **A.** $\frac{7}{10}$        **B.** $\frac{28}{40}$        **C.** $-\frac{28}{40}$        **D.** $-\frac{7}{10}$

**7.** In lowest terms, $\left(-\frac{3}{8}\right) \times \left(-\frac{1}{5}\right) = \underline{\ \ ?\ \ }$.

    **A.** $-\frac{3}{13}$        **B.** $\frac{3}{40}$        **C.** $\frac{15}{8}$        **D.** $\frac{8}{15}$      [4-4]

**8.** In lowest terms, $-12 \times \frac{5}{6} = \underline{\ \ ?\ \ }$.

    **A.** $-\frac{5}{72}$        **B.** 10        **C.** $-10$        **D.** $-\frac{60}{6}$

Name the set of equal fractions having the least common denominator (LCD).

9. $-\frac{5}{7}, \frac{15}{28}$ [4-5]

   A. $-\frac{33}{35}, \frac{22}{35}$     B. $-\frac{140}{196}, \frac{105}{196}$     C. $-\frac{40}{56}, \frac{30}{56}$     D. $-\frac{20}{28}, \frac{15}{28}$

10. $\frac{8}{3}, \frac{4}{5}$

   A. $\frac{40}{15}, \frac{12}{15}$     B. $\frac{20}{15}, \frac{14}{15}$     C. $\frac{13}{8}, \frac{7}{8}$     D. $\frac{80}{30}, \frac{24}{30}$

11. $\frac{5}{2} + \frac{2}{3} = \underline{\quad?\quad}$ [4-6]

   A. $\frac{19}{6}$     B. $\frac{7}{6}$     C. $\frac{7}{5}$     D. $\frac{19}{12}$

12. $3\frac{1}{8} - 2\frac{7}{10} = \underline{\quad?\quad}$

   A. $5\frac{33}{40}$     B. $\frac{17}{40}$     C. $1\frac{17}{40}$     D. $1\frac{23}{40}$

13. In lowest terms, $\frac{2}{3} \div \frac{7}{9} = \underline{\quad?\quad}$. [4-7]

   A. $\frac{14}{27}$     B. $\frac{6}{7}$     C. $\frac{18}{21}$     D. $\frac{7}{6}$

14. In lowest terms, $-5\frac{2}{5} \div \left(-\frac{9}{20}\right) = \underline{\quad?\quad}$.

   A. $12$     B. $\frac{243}{100}$     C. $-\frac{243}{100}$     D. $-12$

15. In lowest terms, $1.375 = \underline{\quad?\quad}$. [4-8]

   A. $1\frac{75}{200}$     B. $\frac{1375}{1000}$     C. $1\frac{1}{375}$     D. $1\frac{3}{8}$

16. In decimal form, $-\frac{13}{6} = \underline{\quad?\quad}$.

   A. $-0.21\overline{6}$     B. $-2.\overline{16}$     C. $-2.1\overline{6}$     D. $2.16$

# Nonrepeating Decimals

We have seen that every rational number is represented either by a terminating decimal or by a repeating decimal. But what about decimals that are nonterminating and nonrepeating? An example of such a decimal is

$$0.535533555333 \ldots ,$$

in which the digits after the decimal point are first one 5 and one 3, then two 5's and two 3's, and so on. It is neither terminating nor repeating. We know, then, that it does not represent a rational number.

Does the decimal expression given above represent any number $n$? If so, then $n$ must be:

greater than 0.5 . . . . . but less than 0.6,
greater than 0.53 . . . . but less than 0.54,
greater than 0.535 . . . . but less than 0.536,

and so on.

The figure indicates that the sequence of graph points is closing in from both sides to some point $P$. We say that $P$ is the graph of the *irrational* number 0.535533555333 . . . . An **irrational number** is a number represented by a nonterminating, nonrepeating decimal. The set of rational numbers together with the set of irrational numbers is called the set of **real numbers.**

It is easy to find other nonterminating and nonrepeating decimal numerals. Here are two:

0.101001000100001 . . .
0.123456789101112 . . .

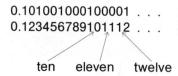

## Research Activity

1. Write a decimal number which, when added to 0.535533555333 . . . will make a sum of 0.777777777777 . . . , or $0.\overline{7}$. Is the number you wrote rational or irrational? Is the sum rational or irrational?

2. Use a pattern of your own making to write a decimal for an irrational number between 0 and 1. Write another decimal which when added to your first decimal will make a sum of $0.\overline{9}$. Are the addends rational or irrational? Is the sum rational or irrational?

3. Experiment with finding the sums of other pairs of irrational numbers. Can you come to any conclusions about the sum of two irrational numbers? Is the sum always rational, always irrational, or may it be either one or the other?

Not all irrational numbers have decimals with digits arranged in a pattern. A famous irrational number with which you may be familiar is $\pi$ (pi), the quotient of the circumference of a circle and its diameter. Its decimal representation begins 3.14159, but there is no simple rule for continuing the sequence of the digits.

From antiquity, mathematicians have searched for methods to determine better and better approximations to the value of $\pi$. The Greek mathematician, Archimedes, who lived in the 3rd century B.C., calculated that $\pi$ was greater than $3\frac{10}{71}$ and less than $3\frac{1}{7}$.

In more recent times, some formulas have been developed to express $\pi$. In 1655, an English mathematician, John Wallis, found the following:

$$\pi = 2\left(\frac{2}{1} \cdot \frac{2}{3} \cdot \frac{4}{3} \cdot \frac{4}{5} \cdot \frac{6}{5} \cdot \frac{6}{7} \cdot \frac{8}{7} \cdot \frac{8}{9} \cdot \cdots \right)$$

The three dots at the right inside the parentheses indicate that the pattern continues without end.

Another nice formula for $\pi$ was developed by a German mathematician, Gottfried Wilhelm von Leibniz, in 1674:

$$\pi = 4\left(1 - \frac{1}{3} + \frac{1}{5} - \frac{1}{7} + \frac{1}{9} - \frac{1}{11} + \cdots \right)$$

Another irrational number is

$\sqrt{2} = 1.41428 \ldots$ (read "the positive square root of 2"),

the positive number whose square is 2. (In the Extra! on page 128 we used the exponent $\frac{1}{2}$ to indicate square root, thus $\sqrt{2} = 2^{\frac{1}{2}}$.) Many square roots of positive integers are irrational; in fact, the square root of a positive integer is either another positive integer or it is an irrational number.

## Chapter Test

Complete.

**1.** $\underline{\ \ ?\ \ } \times \frac{1}{7} = 1$      **2.** $2 \div 5 = \underline{\ \ ?\ \ }$      **3.** $2\frac{3}{8} = \frac{?}{8}$      **[4-1]**

Write each negative fraction in two other ways.

**4.** $\frac{3}{-4}$                 **5.** $-\frac{29}{100}$      **[4-2]**

Complete.

**6.** $-6\frac{2}{9} = \frac{?}{9}$           **7.** $-\frac{59}{8} = \underline{\ \ ?\ \ }$

Reduce each fraction to lowest terms.

**8.** $\frac{60}{48}$      **9.** $\frac{378}{630}$      **10.** $-\frac{147}{168}$      **[4-3]**

Compute each product. Give your result in lowest terms.

**11.** $\frac{7}{5} \times \left(-\frac{20}{21}\right)$      **12.** $-1\frac{1}{5} \times \left(-7\frac{3}{11}\right)$      **13.** $\frac{15}{36} \times \frac{2}{33}$      **[4-4]**

Replace each set of fractions with equal fractions having the least common denominator (LCD).

**14.** $\frac{2}{3}, \frac{5}{4}$      **15.** $\frac{7}{33}, -\frac{4}{275}$      **16.** $\frac{1}{3}, \frac{2}{15}, -\frac{22}{27}$      **[4-5]**

Express the sum or difference as a proper fraction in lowest terms or as a mixed number with fraction in lowest terms.

**17.** $\frac{5}{6} + \frac{7}{15}$      **18.** $-\frac{11}{16} + \frac{17}{20}$      **19.** $5\frac{5}{12} - 2\frac{7}{18}$      **[4-6]**

Divide. Express all results in lowest terms.

**20.** $\frac{9}{10} \div \left(-\frac{9}{10}\right)$      **21.** $-1\frac{5}{27} \div \left(-1\frac{7}{9}\right)$      **22.** $-\frac{6}{19} \div \frac{9}{38}$      **[4-7]**

Express as a fraction in lowest terms.

**23.** $-4.125$               **24.** $0.628$      **[4-8]**

Express as a terminating or repeating decimal.

**25.** $-\frac{55}{12}$               **26.** $\frac{21}{32}$

## Skill Review

Add. Give your result in lowest terms.

**1.** $\frac{3}{5} + \frac{1}{5}$  **2.** $-\frac{3}{8} + \frac{2}{8}$  **3.** $\frac{1}{5} + \frac{2}{5}$  **4.** $-\frac{1}{4} + \frac{2}{4}$

**5.** $2\frac{1}{3} + 3\frac{1}{3}$  **6.** $-5\frac{2}{7} + 3\frac{3}{7}$  **7.** $12\frac{5}{6} + \left(-8\frac{4}{6}\right)$  **8.** $25\frac{3}{8} + 6\frac{3}{8}$

**9.** $\frac{1}{2} + \frac{2}{3}$  **10.** $\frac{1}{3} + \left(-\frac{1}{4}\right)$  **11.** $-\frac{2}{5} + \left(-\frac{1}{2}\right)$  **12.** $\frac{1}{10} + \frac{3}{5}$

**13.** $7\frac{1}{4} + 2\frac{1}{2}$  **14.** $12\frac{2}{3} + 11\frac{3}{4}$  **15.** $-6\frac{2}{5} + 3\frac{1}{3}$  **16.** $34\frac{1}{2} + \left(-12\frac{5}{6}\right)$

Subtract. Give your result in lowest terms.

**17.** $\frac{5}{6} - \frac{2}{6}$  **18.** $\frac{7}{8} - \frac{3}{8}$  **19.** $\frac{9}{10} - \frac{7}{10}$  **20.** $-\frac{4}{5} - \frac{3}{5}$

**21.** $8\frac{3}{4} - 5\frac{1}{4}$  **22.** $-2\frac{1}{7} - 3\frac{2}{7}$  **23.** $8\frac{1}{3} - 9\frac{2}{3}$  **24.** $12\frac{5}{6} + \left(+2\frac{1}{6}\right)$

**25.** $\frac{3}{4} - \frac{1}{8}$  **26.** $-\frac{1}{5} - \frac{3}{10}$  **27.** $\frac{8}{9} - \left(-\frac{1}{3}\right)$  **28.** $\frac{1}{2} - \frac{5}{8}$

Multiply. Give your result in lowest terms.

**29.** $\frac{3}{5} \times 5$  **30.** $7 \times \frac{5}{7}$  **31.** $-\frac{3}{8} \times 8$  **32.** $-4 \times \frac{1}{4}$

**33.** $\frac{1}{3} \times \frac{1}{4}$  **34.** $\frac{3}{8} \times \frac{1}{2}$  **35.** $-\frac{4}{5} \times \frac{5}{6}$  **36.** $-\frac{2}{3} \times \left(-\frac{5}{8}\right)$

**37.** $5\frac{1}{2} \times 4\frac{2}{3}$  **38.** $-8\frac{1}{8} \times 3\frac{1}{5}$  **39.** $12\frac{1}{2} \times \left(-5\frac{1}{3}\right)$  **40.** $9\frac{3}{4} \times 5\frac{2}{9}$

Divide. Give your result in lowest terms.

**41.** $3 \div \frac{1}{2}$  **42.** $\frac{3}{4} \div 2$  **43.** $-5 \div \frac{1}{8}$  **44.** $-\frac{1}{4} \div (-5)$

**45.** $\frac{2}{3} \div \frac{1}{2}$  **46.** $\frac{5}{8} \div \frac{1}{4}$  **47.** $\frac{2}{9} \div \left(-\frac{2}{3}\right)$  **48.** $-\frac{4}{5} \div \frac{8}{15}$

**49.** $5\frac{5}{6} \div 2\frac{1}{3}$  **50.** $-8 \div 3\frac{3}{7}$  **51.** $10 \div \left(-4\frac{3}{8}\right)$  **52.** $-12\frac{1}{2} \div \left(-1\frac{7}{8}\right)$

# 5

# Ratio, Proportion, Percent

## 5-1 Ratio

**Objective** To compare two numbers by use of a ratio expressed as a fraction, as a division, or with a ratio sign.

The **ratio** of a number $c$ to another number $d$ ($d$ cannot be zero) is the quotient of the first number divided by the second, or $\frac{c}{d}$. A ratio compares one quantity with another.

We can write a ratio in several ways. For example, the ratio 5 to 10 can be expressed as follows:

"NEW" MICROWAVE OVEN
FASTER BY A RATIO OF 5:10
NEW OVEN - 5 MIN.
OLD OVEN - 10 MIN.

$$\frac{5}{10} \qquad\qquad 5 \div 10 \qquad\qquad 5{:}10$$

as a
fraction

with a
division sign

with a
ratio sign

We may express a ratio in lowest terms:

$5 \text{ to } 10 = 1 \text{ to } 2 \qquad \frac{5}{10} = \frac{1}{2} \qquad 5 \div 10 = 1 \div 2 \qquad 5{:}10 = 1{:}2$

**145**

*Example 1*

There are **12 boys** and **8 girls** in the Art Club. Express in three ways the ratio of
**a. boys to girls,** and
**b. girls to club members.**
Then give a fraction in lowest terms for each ratio.

*Solution*

**a.** $\begin{array}{c}\text{boys} \longrightarrow 12 \\ \text{girls} \longrightarrow 8\end{array}$, or **12 ÷ 8,** or **12:8**

In lowest terms, $\frac{12}{8} = \frac{3}{2}$.

**b.** $\begin{array}{c}\text{girls} \rightarrow 8 \\ \text{club members} \rightarrow 20\end{array}$, or **8 ÷ 20,** or **8:20.**

In lowest terms, $\frac{8}{20} = \frac{2}{5}$.

When forming a ratio of quantities of the same kind, be sure to use the same unit of measure for each quantity.

*Example 2*

Express the ratio of **20 g to 3 kg** as a fraction in lowest terms.

*Solution*

**3 kg = 3000 g**

$\frac{20}{3000} = \frac{1}{150}$

A ratio can be used to compare quantities of different kinds. Such a ratio is sometimes called a **rate.** We say the roses are selling at a rate of 41¢ for 2 or 41¢ per pair. The word **per** indicates division.

We may write the rate as a ratio:

$$\frac{41}{2}, \text{ or } 41 \div 2, \text{ or } 41{:}2.$$

*Example 3*

Blueberries are selling at the rate of 89¢ for 2 boxes.
**a.** Write this information as a ratio.
**b.** Write a ratio to show the cost of 6 boxes of blueberries; of 10 boxes.

*Solution*

**a.** **89¢ for 2 boxes;** $\frac{89}{2}$

**b.** $\frac{3 \times 89}{3 \times 2} = \frac{267}{6}$; **6 boxes cost $2.67**

$\frac{5 \times 89}{5 \times 2} = \frac{445}{10}$; **10 boxes cost $4.45**

It is often useful to show a rate as a ratio per unit.

*Example 4*

**Apples cost 96¢ per dozen.**
**a.** **Write this rate as a ratio.**
**b.** **Write a ratio showing the rate of cost per *one* apple.**
**c.** **What is the cost of 5 apples? 8 apples? 14 apples?**

*Solution*

**a.** **96¢ per 12 apples;** $\frac{96}{12}$

**b.** $\frac{96 \div 12}{12 \div 12} = \frac{8}{1}$; **one apple costs 8¢**

**c.** **5 × 8¢ = 40¢**

    **8 × 8¢ = 64¢**

    **14 × 8¢ = 112¢, or $1.12**

## Class Exercises

Compare the two quantities by stating the ratio of the first to the second.

1. One dozen and 20.

2. A pair and a half dozen.

3. Number of days in a week and number of days in June.

4. Number of states in the United States today and number when George Washington became president.

5. Number of legs on a snake and number of legs on a chicken.

6. Number of hours in a Monday and number of hours in a week.

7. Number of windows in your classroom and number of doors in your classroom.

8. Number of elephants in your classroom and number of students in your classroom.

Write each ratio three ways.

**9.** 2 to 1      **10.** 3 to 4      **11.** 5 to 7      **12.** 1 to 4

**13.** 9 to 10      **14.** 5 to 6      **15.** 2 to 3      **16.** 7 to 9

## Exercises

Write each ratio as a fraction in lowest terms.

**A**   **1.** 10 to 4      **2.** 5 to 20      **3.** $\frac{8}{30}$      **4.** 45 ÷ 9

  **5.** 7 ÷ 21      **6.** 51:17      **7.** 25 ÷ 5      **8.** $\frac{3}{4}$ to $\frac{1}{3}$

  **9.** 3 dollars to 78 cents      **10.** 8 months to 2 years

  **11.** 50 minutes to 1 hour      **12.** 2 kL to 75 L

  **13.** 14 cm to 1 m      **14.** 700 m to 2 km

Platt's Pet Palace has 24 puppies and 16 kittens for sale. Compare each pair of quantities by writing a ratio as a fraction in lowest terms.

**15.** Number of puppies to number of kittens.

**16.** Number of kittens to total of kittens and puppies.

**17.** Total of kittens and puppies to number of puppies.

## Problems

Solve.

**A**   **1.** Jessie bought 3 cans of cat food for 66¢. Write a ratio to show the rate of cost per can. What is the cost of 6 cans? 9 cans? 21 cans?

**B**   **2.** A toy car travels 6 m per second. Write a ratio to show the rate of travel per minute. How far does the car travel in 2 minutes? 2.5 minutes? 5 seconds?

  **3.** In a recent election the ratio of "Yes" votes to "No" votes on a zoning amendment was 4 to 3. What fraction of the votes were "Yes" votes? "No" votes? More than half the votes were required for passage. Was the amendment passed?

**C**   **4.** A Ferris wheel turns 9 times in 3 minutes. Write a ratio to show how long it takes to make one turn.

# 5-2 Proportion

**Objective** To set up and solve proportions.

A **proportion** is a statement of equality of two ratios such as

$$\frac{3}{4} = \frac{18}{24} \qquad \text{or} \qquad 3\overset{\text{means}}{:}4 = 18\overset{}{:}24$$

extremes

The numbers 3, 4, 18, and 24 are called the **terms** of the proportion. The numbers 3 and 24 are called the **extremes** of the proportion, and the numbers 4 and 18 are called the **means**. From what we know about fractions, we have:

$$\frac{3}{4} = \frac{18}{24}$$

$$96 \times \frac{3}{4} = \frac{18}{24} \times 96$$

$$\overset{24}{\cancel{96}} \times \frac{3}{\underset{1}{\cancel{4}}} = \frac{18}{\underset{1}{\cancel{24}}} \times \overset{4}{\cancel{96}}$$

extremes $\longrightarrow 24 \times 3 = 18 \times 4 \longleftarrow$ means

$$72 = 72$$

Thus we see that the product of the extremes is equal to the product of the means. This property is true for any proportion, that is,

## property

If $\frac{a}{b} = \frac{c}{d}$, where $b$ and $d$ are not zero, then $ad = bc$.

We can use this property to help determine whether the two ratios in a proportion are indeed equal.

**Example 1** | Are these proportions correct?

**a.** $\frac{9}{16} = \frac{17}{31}$    **b.** $\frac{8}{25} = \frac{4}{12.5}$

*Solution* | **a.** Since $9 \times 31 = 279$ and $16 \times 17 = 272$, the proportion is not correct.

**b.** Since $25 \times 4 = 100$ and $8 \times 12.5 = 100$, the proportion is correct.

We can also use the property just stated to find one term of a proportion when we know the other three terms. This is called *solving the proportion.*

*Example 2*  |  Solve $\frac{10}{n} = \frac{60}{24}$ for $n$.

*Solution*  |  Since $\frac{10}{n} = \frac{60}{24}$, we have.

$$n \times 60 = 10 \times 24$$
$$60n = 240$$
$$n = 4$$

We can sometimes use proportions to solve word problems involving ratios or rates. The following steps are helpful.

**1.** Determine what quantity is to be found.
**2.** Determine whether the given facts involve any ratios or rates.
**3.** Write the ratios or rates involved as a proportion.
**4.** Solve the proportion.

*Example 3*  |  Maria spends 17 hours in a 2-week period practicing on the guitar. How many hours does she practice in 5 weeks?

*Solution*  |  **1.** The problem asks for the number of hours practiced in 5 weeks.

**2.** The given facts include the rate of 17 h in (per) 2 weeks, and the unknown number of hours in 5 weeks.

**3.** The proportion is $\frac{17}{2} = \frac{n}{5}$.

**4.** $2n = 5 \times 17$

$$n = \frac{85}{2}$$

$$n = 42\frac{1}{2}$$

Therefore, in 5 weeks Maria practices $42\frac{1}{2}$ hours.

## Class Exercises

Name the means and the extremes of the proportion.

**1.** $2:3 = 4:6$

**2.** $1:5 = 3:15$

**3.** $4:9 = 8:18$

**4.** $7:21 = 3:9$

**5.** $\frac{1}{2} = \frac{2}{4}$

**6.** $\frac{12}{16} = \frac{3}{4}$

**7.** $\frac{b}{3} = \frac{45}{27}$

**8.** $\frac{n}{6} = \frac{9}{54}$

**9.** $\frac{13}{19.5} = \frac{r}{1.5}$

**10.** $\frac{4.8}{12} = \frac{s}{3}$

**11.** $\frac{f}{g} = \frac{j}{k}$

**12.** $\frac{x}{y} = \frac{v}{w}$

Write a proportion for the situation described.

**13.** 5 m in one hour; 15 m in $h$ hours

**14.** 4 L of paint for 160 m²; 0.25 L for $x$ m²

**15.** 480 km on one tank of gas; 960 km on $x$ tanks.

**16.** 49¢ for 2 lemons; $1.47 for $n$ lemons

## Exercises

Use the property of proportions to tell whether or not the proportion is correct.

**A** **1.** $\frac{2}{3} = \frac{18}{27}$

**2.** $\frac{8}{5} = \frac{24}{15}$

**3.** $\frac{3}{12} = \frac{4}{14}$

**4.** $\frac{6}{5} = \frac{42}{35}$

**5.** $\frac{50}{32} = \frac{26}{16}$

**6.** $\frac{34}{15} = \frac{17}{8}$

**7.** $\frac{70}{90} = \frac{17}{22}$

**8.** $\frac{0}{112} = \frac{0}{65}$

Solve the proportion.

**9.** $\frac{n}{7} = \frac{15}{21}$

**10.** $\frac{18}{12} = \frac{6}{n}$

**11.** $\frac{n}{8} = \frac{2}{32}$

**12.** $\frac{24}{3} = \frac{n}{12}$

**13.** $\frac{n}{21} = \frac{9}{27}$

**14.** $\frac{19}{n} = \frac{57}{3}$

**15.** $\frac{16}{3} = \frac{n}{12}$

**16.** $\frac{n}{3.4} = \frac{2}{17}$

**17.** $\frac{13}{42} = \frac{65}{n}$

**18.** $\frac{3}{7} = \frac{n}{200}$

**19.** $\frac{35}{100} = \frac{7}{n}$

**20.** $\frac{1.21}{11} = \frac{5.5}{n}$

**21.** $\frac{2}{n} = \frac{12.5}{2.5}$

**22.** $\frac{9.6}{1.6} = \frac{n}{3}$

**23.** $\frac{2.7}{n} = \frac{8.1}{4.5}$

**24.** $\frac{n}{1.7} = \frac{5.1}{6.8}$

# EXTRA! Two Teasers

1. If 9 sopranos can sing 3 songs in 12 minutes, how long will it take 27 sopranos to sing the same 3 songs?

2. If a cat and a half catches a mouse and a half in a day and a half, how long will it take 6 cats to catch 6 mice?

## Problems

Solve.

A 1. Art can type 75 words in 2 minutes. At this rate how many words can he type in 12 minutes?

2. Mr. Roberts mixes 3 bags of sand with every 2 bags of cement. How many bags of cement should he mix with 8 bags of sand?

3. A fruit punch contains 5 parts of apple juice to 2 parts of cranberry juice. If 12 L of apple juice are used, how much cranberry juice should be used?

B 4. A recipe calls for 2 spoonfuls of butter for each egg used. One egg is used for every 3 servings to be made. How much butter is needed for 6 servings?

5. The Athletic Department bought a dozen cans of tennis balls at $2.50 each, and 3 tennis rackets. If the ratio of the price of one can of balls to the price of one racket was 1:14, what was the total cost?

## Self-Test

Words to remember:
ratio [p. 145]          rate [p. 146]          proportion [p. 149]
extremes [p. 149]       means [p. 149]

Write each ratio as a fraction in lowest terms.

**1.** 3 to 12      **2.** $\frac{9}{15}$      **3.** 30 cm to 5 m      **4.** 10 km to 50 m          [5-1]

Tell whether or not the proportion is correct.

**5.** $\frac{2}{3} = \frac{5}{6}$                    **6.** $\frac{4}{14} = \frac{2}{7}$          [5-2]

Solve the proportion.

**7.** $\frac{n}{3} = \frac{12}{9}$                    **8.** $\frac{21}{n} = \frac{9}{12}$

Self-Test answers and Extra Practice are at the back of the book.

# 5-3 Percent

**Objective** To express percents as fractions and as decimals, and to solve problems involving percent.

The word **percent** (symbol: %) means divided by 100, or hundredths. For example, 85% means 85 divided by 100, which is the same as the ratio 85:100, or $\frac{85}{100}$. Another way to name 85% is to use a decimal.

$$85\% = \frac{85}{100} = 0.85.$$

Similarly, $3\% = \frac{3}{100} = 0.03$. Note that $1.00 = \frac{100}{100} = 100\%$; that is, 100% is another name for 1. Percents greater than 100% name numbers greater than 1; for example, $246\% = \frac{246}{100} = 2.46$.

**Example 1** | Copy and complete the table. Give each fraction in lowest terms.

|   | Percent | Fraction | Decimal |
|---|---------|----------|---------|
| **a.** | 70% | ? | ? |
| **b.** | ? | $\frac{7}{8}$ | ? |
| **c.** | ? | ? | 0.025 |
| **d.** | 0.2% | ? | ? |

*Solution*

**a.** $70\% = \frac{70}{100} = \frac{7}{10} = 0.7$

**b.** $\frac{7}{8} = \frac{n}{100}$

$8n = 7 \times 100$

$n = 700 \div 8 = 87.5$

$\frac{7}{8} = \frac{87.5}{100} = 87.5\% = 0.875$

**c.** $0.025 = \frac{25}{1000} = \frac{2.5}{100} = 2.5\%$

$\frac{25}{1000} = \frac{1}{40}$

**d.** $0.2\% = \frac{0.2}{100} = \frac{2}{1000} = 0.002$

$\frac{2}{1000} = \frac{1}{500}$

The following table shows some of the more commonly used percents and the fractions and decimals equal to them.

| Percent | $12\frac{1}{2}\%$ | $16\frac{2}{3}\%$ | 20% | 25% | $33\frac{1}{3}\%$ | 50% |
|---------|---------|---------|-----|-----|---------|-----|
| Decimal | 0.125 | $0.16\frac{2}{3}$ | 0.20 | 0.25 | $0.33\frac{1}{3}$ | 0.50 |
| Fraction | $\frac{1}{8}$ | $\frac{1}{6}$ | $\frac{1}{5}$ | $\frac{1}{4}$ | $\frac{1}{3}$ | $\frac{1}{2}$ |

In the word phrase "5% of 40," the word "of" indicates multiplication. We can use this fact in solving problems involving percent.

*Example 2*

**What is 60% of 30?**

*Solution*

**Let $x$ represent the number we are to find. Express 60% as a decimal: 60% = 0.60. Then,**

$$x = 0.60 \times 30$$
$$x = 18$$

**So 18 is 60% of 30.**

*Example 3*

**10 is what percent of 30?**

*Solution*

**Let $n$ represent the percent. Then**

$$10 = n \times 30$$
$$n = \frac{10}{30} = 0.33\frac{1}{3}$$
$$n = 33\frac{1}{3}\%$$

**So 10 is $33\frac{1}{3}\%$ of 30.**

*Example 4*

**12 is 8% of what number?**

*Solution*

**Let $n$ = the number we are to find. Express 8% as a decimal: 0.08. Then, 12 = 0.08 $\times$ n**

$$n = \frac{12}{0.08} = 150$$

**So 12 is 8% of 150.**

## Class Exercises

Express as an equal fraction with a denominator of 100.

**1.** $\frac{1}{4}$        **2.** $\frac{4}{25}$        **3.** $\frac{3}{50}$        **4.** $\frac{3}{10}$        **5.** $\frac{7}{20}$

**6.** $\frac{5}{8}$        **7.** $\frac{1}{200}$        **8.** $\frac{3}{200}$        **9.** $\frac{1}{1000}$        **10.** $\frac{25}{1000}$

For Problems 11–13, let $n =$ the number you are to find, then set up an equation that fits the problem.

**11.** In a class of 30 students 25 are on the honor roll. What percent is this?

**12.** Of those who tried out for the baseball team, 65% made it. If 13 players made the team, how many tried out?

**13.** Sally's score on a test was 75%. If there were 28 questions on the test, how many did she answer correctly?

**14.** Here are the results of a class survey on color preferences.

| Student | Favorite Color |
|---------|----------------|
| Bob | red |
| Jane | blue |
| Maria | red |
| Bill | yellow |
| Jim | green |
| Barbara | blue |
| Ralph | red |
| Ken | blue |
| Margo | yellow |
| Eric | blue |

**a.** How many students took part in the survey?

**b.** What percent are boys?

**c.** What percent are girls?

**d.** What percent favor yellow?

**e.** What percent favor red?

**f.** What percent do not favor yellow?

**g.** What percent of the girls favor blue?

**h.** What percent are boys that favor yellow?

## Exercises

Copy the table and complete it.

A·

|  | 1. | 2. | 3. | 4. | 5. | 6. | 7. | 8. | 9. | 10. |
|---|---|---|---|---|---|---|---|---|---|---|
| Percent | 36% | 75% | ? | ? | ? | ? | ? | 1.25% | ? | 0.02% |
| Fraction | $\frac{9}{25}$ | ? | ? | $\frac{1}{5}$ | $\frac{3}{2}$ | ? | $\frac{3}{8}$ | ? | ? | ? |
| Decimal | ? | ? | 0.9 | ? | ? | 0.15 | ? | 0.0125 | 2.48 | ? |

Express as a percent.

**11.** 0.92  **12.** 0.405  **13.** $3\frac{1}{2}$  **14.** 0.001

**15.** 0.33  **16.** 1.01  **17.** 0.0403  **18.** $4\frac{7}{10}$

Find the percent or number.

B
**19.** What is 24% of 50?  **20.** 15 is what percent of 40?

**21.** What is 12% of 32?  **22.** 20 is 10% of what number?

**23.** 80 is what percent of 100?  **24.** 250 is 500% of what number?

**25.** 35 is what percent of 50?  **26.** 27 is 81% of what number?

**27.** What is 51% of 600?  **28.** 210 is what percent of 210?

## Problems

Solve.

A  **1.** Roger had 27 out of 30 mathematics problems correct. What was his percent of correct problems?

**2.** The Crown Ice Cream store gave 5% of its customers free cones one Saturday. That day they had 480 customers. How many received free ice cream cones?

**3.** Jeff saved $25 of the $80 he earned one month. What percent of his earnings did he save?

**4.** Of all those who responded to a survey, 390 were under 18 years of age. If 20% were under 18, how many responded to the survey?

5. The sales tax is 5% in Little Falls. What would be the tax on a purchase of $89.50?

**B** 6. Pat missed 7 words on a spelling test for a result of 86% correct. How many words were on the test?

7. Ten cartons were damaged in shipment. If this number was 1.6% of the cartons, how many were shipped?

Problems 8–12 refer to the table at the right.

8. What percent of the students are in the seventh grade?

9. What percent of the eighth grade students are boys?

10. Which grade has the smallest percent of girls?

11. Of the ninth grade students, 44% were under 14 years of age on December 1. How many is this?

12. Morley Junior High School has 40% of the total junior high school enrollment in the city. How many junior high school students are enrolled in the city?

| Enrollments at Morley Junior High School | | | |
|---|---|---|---|
| Grade | Girls | Boys | Total |
| 7 | 130 | 112 | 242 |
| 8 | 116 | 135 | 251 |
| 9 | 108 | 117 | 225 |
| Total | 354 | 364 | 718 |

# Application

**Computer Activity** You can use the BASIC computer program given below to make a table of some fractions and the percents that are equal to them.

```
10 PRINT "FRACTION", "PERCENT"
20 FOR A=1 TO 15
30 FOR B=1 TO 15
40 IF B<A THEN 60
50 PRINT A; "/"; B, 100×A/B; "%"
60 NEXT B
70 NEXT A
80 END
```

# 5-4 Percent Increase and Decrease

**Objective** To solve word problems involving a percent increase or decrease.

Many everyday problems are concerned with percents. One important use of percent is to express relative amounts of change.

*Example 1*  | Last year 84 students at Agawam Junior High School belonged to the Science Club. This year there are 25% more students in the club. How many students belong to the club this year?

*Solution*  | 1. Find the size of the increase.

Let $x$ represent the increase.
$$x = 0.25 \times 84 = 21$$

2. Add the increase to the original number.
$$84 + 21 = 105$$

Therefore, there are 105 students in the Science Club.

*Example 2*  | In 1975 the price of a Fastadder pocket calculator was $25. In 1979 the same model calculator sold for $7.50. What was the percent of decrease in the price?

*Solution*  | **Method 1** Find the amount of decrease:
$$25 - 7.50 = 17.50.$$
Let $n$ represent the percent.
$$n \times 25 = 17.50$$
$$n = \frac{17.50}{25} = 0.70 = 70\%$$

Thus the decrease is 70%.

**Method 2** Find what percent 7.50 is of 25.
$$n \times 25 = 7.50$$
$$n = \frac{7.50}{25} = 0.30 = 30\%$$

Since the price in 1979 is 30% of the price in 1975, the percent of decrease is $100\% - 30\% = 70\%$.

Note that when you are looking for a percent increase or decrease, you always base your calculation on the *original amount*.

---
**rule**

$$\text{percent of change} = \frac{\text{amount of change}}{\text{original amount}}$$

---

*Example 3* | The price of Maria Gomez's new car with extra equipment was $572 over the base price of the car. This amounted to 13% of the base price. What was the base price? How much did the car with the extra equipment cost?

*Solution* | Let *b* represent the base price of the car. Then

$$0.13 = \frac{572}{b}$$

$$0.13 \times b = 572$$

$$b = \frac{572}{0.13} = 4400$$

The base price was $4400. Equipped with extras the car cost $4400 + $572 = $4972.

## Problems

Solve.

**A** 1. In a recent year, 31 million airline passengers used O'Hare Airport in Chicago. About 18% more passengers are expected to use the airport in 1990. About how many passengers may use it in that year?

2. A Boeing 707 airliner can carry 185 passengers. The capacity of a 747 airliner exceeds the 707 capacity by about 170%. About how many passengers can a 747 carry?

3. The stock of Supco Industries sold for $14 a share six months ago. Today its price is $21 a share. What is the percent of increase?

4. Colleen is selling calendars door-to-door to raise money for the gymnastic team. Last week she sold 15 calendars. This week she sold 18. What is the percent of increase in sales?

5. Fred Aho had 120 customers on his newspaper route. Now he is down to 90 customers. What is the percent of decrease?

6. The Slap-It-On paint store sold 1800 L of paint last week. This week 2250 L of paint was sold. What is the percent of increase?

7. Ann Raymond earned $175 per week. With a promotion her salary became $200 per week. What was the percent of increase?

8. The Farriers' heating bill went down 15% after they insulated their house. They paid $450 for a winter's heating before insulating. How much did they pay after insulating?

9. When Leo Hong's car was new he could make 15 round trips between home and work on one tank of gas. Now he can make only $13\frac{1}{2}$ round trips on one tank of gas. What is the percent of decrease in trips per tank of gas?

10. Lyn has made a New Year's resolution to spend an average of 5% less pocket money each week than she did last year. Her average weekly expenditure last year was $17. What will her average weekly expenditure be this year if she keeps her resolution?

**B** 11. Jon went to the store with the exact amount of cash to buy a $169 bicycle. He had forgotten the sales tax, though, so he was $6.76 short. What percent of the price was the tax?

12. After a drop of 15% in the depth of the water in the Sullivan Reservoir, the depth gauge read 37.5 m. What was the original depth?

**C** 13. Sam's mathematics grade for this six weeks increased by 25% over his grade for the previous six weeks. His grade is now 95. What was it for the previous six weeks?

# 5-5 Commissions, Discounts, Budgets

**Objective** To solve problems involving commissions, discounts, and budgets.

A wide variety of problems in business and consumer settings involve percents.

Salespersons are often paid a *commission* in addition to a salary. A **commission** is usually a certain percent of sales. For example, a salesperson who works for a commission of 25%, and who sells $800 worth of goods, would earn 25% of $800, or $200. Sometimes the percent of sales that determines the commission is called the **rate** of the commission.

| | |
|---|---|
| *Example 1* | A furniture salesperson worked for a commission rate of 8.25% of sales. Last year, total sales were $216,850. Find the salesperson's commission for the year. |
| *Solution* | Let $x$ represent the commission. Then |

$$x = 0.0825 \times 216,850$$
$$x = 17,890.125$$

The salesperson's commission for the year was $17,890.13.

Stores sometimes sell merchandise at a **discount.** An advertisement that says "All appliances will be sold at a discount of 10%" means, for example, that a toaster originally marked $15.00 will sell at a discount of 10% of $15.00, or $1.50. The **sale price** or **net price** is $15.00 − $1.50, or $13.50.

| | |
|---|---|
| *Example 2* | A top-selling record album usually sells for $7.95. Sound World is selling it at a 20% discount. What is the sale price? |
| *Solution* | Let $x$ represent the amount of discount. Then |

$$x = 0.20 \times 7.95$$
$$x = 1.59$$

Original price − discount = sale price
$7.95 − $1.59 = $6.36

A budget is a plan one makes to be sure that one's income will be enough to cover expenses. It is a list of estimates of both income and expenses, usually for a year. One way to show a budget is with a **circle graph.**

*Example 3*

The circle graph shows the Glover family's budget for a year. If their yearly income is $17,000, how much do they plan to spend on food in a year?

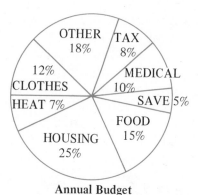

OTHER 18%
TAX 8%
12% CLOTHES
MEDICAL 10%
HEAT 7%
SAVE 5%
FOOD 15%
HOUSING 25%

**Annual Budget**

*Solution*

From the graph, the Glovers expect to spend 15% of their income on food. Letting *n* be the amount they will spend,

$n = 0.15 \times 17,000$

$n = 2550$

The Glovers plan to spend $2550 on food.

## Problems

Solve.

**A** 1. Sid Romney earns a commission of 12% on what he sells. Last month his sales totaled $15,400. How much did he earn?

2. Paula Jeffrey sells automobiles and earns a 6% commission. Last year she earned $21,000 in commissions. What was the dollar value of her total sales?

3. A real estate salesperson received $1000 as a commission for selling a $40,000 house. What percent of the sale price was the commission?

**B** 4. The Monroe Zeppelins, a rock group, earned $94,500 last year in royalty income from their hit single *Flash Flood.* If the total sales of *Flash Flood* last year were $3,150,000, what was the group's royalty rate?

Copy and complete the table.

|  | 5. | 6. | 7. | 8. | 9. | 10. |
|---|---|---|---|---|---|---|
| Item | Kitchen Tool Set | Toaster | Calculator | Mixer | Blender | Fan |
| Regular Price | $4.95 | $21.95 | $69.00 | $26.50 | ? | ? |
| Discount Rate | 50% | 15% | ? | ? | 10% | ? |
| Discount | ? | ? | $24.15 | ? | $3.99 | $9.70 |
| Sale Price | ? | ? | ? | $21.20 | $35.91 | $29.10 |

11. Hair dryers are on sale for $12.50. They are marked as being 20% off. What was the regular price?

12. Kay Mitsui sells women's clothing. She earns a base salary of $400 per month plus a commission of 3% on all her sales. In a recent month her income was $986.50. What were her total sales?

13. The Randolph family pays $546 per year for medical insurance. This amounts to 40% of the cost of all their insurance, and 5% of their annual income. How much does all their insurance cost and how much is their annual income?

14. Tim and Sally Wright are looking for an apartment. If they want to spend no more than 25% of their combined monthly take-home pay of $1375, what is the largest monthly rent they can afford?

15. The Roark family has a total income of $11,250. They budget $2400 for food and $2640 for shelter. What percent of the family budget goes for food and shelter?

Use the circle graph at the right for Problems 16 and 17.

16. What percent does savings interest contribute to the family's total income?

17. What percent do Madge's business earnings contribute to the family's total income?

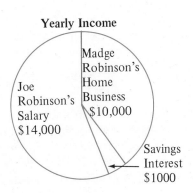

**Yearly Income**

Madge Robinson's Home Business $10,000

Joe Robinson's Salary $14,000

Savings Interest $1000

Use the circle graphs on the preceding page and at the right for Problems 18 and 19.

**C   18.** What amount is budgeted for Madge's business expenses?

**19.** What is the net income of Madge's business before taxes? (Net income = gross (total) income − expenses)

**20.** Dick Hart received a 25% discount on a coat during a sale. He also received a 5% discount on the sale price for paying cash. He paid $79.56. What was the regular price of the coat?

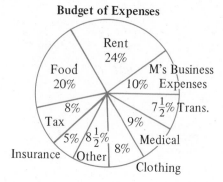

**Budget of Expenses**

Rent 24%

Food 20%

M's Business 10% Expenses

$7\frac{1}{2}$% Trans.

8%

9%

Tax

5%   $8\frac{1}{2}$%

8%   Medical

Insurance   Other

Clothing

Paper Bag Machine

# An Inventor

Margaret E. Knight (1838–1914) probably thought of her first invention when she was 12 years old. She was watching a loom in operation when one of the shuttles fell out and injured someone. Knight designed a stop-motion device that would hinder such accidents. In 1870, Knight received her first patent for a machine that folded square-bottomed paper bags. Her other inventions included a clasp for holding robes, a machine for cutting shoes, a window frame and sash, and a numbering mechanism. In 1902 she turned her efforts to rotary engines and motors. Her specific contribution was the invention of a sleeve-valve engine.

**Research Activity** Find out who invented the bicycle, the game of basketball, the transistor.

**Career Activity** Find out what a patent is and how to obtain one. For how long are patents effective? Some libraries have records of patents that have been issued. Can you find a copy of a patent?

## Self-Test

Words to remember:
percent [p. 153]          commission [p. 161]          discount [p. 161]
budget [p. 162]           net price [p. 161]            circle graph [p. 162 ]

Find the percent or number.

1. What is 8% of 20?

2. What is 25% of 72?          [5-3]

3. 12 is what percent of 60?

4. 8 is 30% of what number?

Solve.

5. The school play drew an audience of 255 persons on Friday. On          [5-4]
   Saturday, 51 more persons attended than on Friday. What was
   the percent of increase?

6. Sarah had 25 goldfish in her aquarium. She gave 3 of them away.
   What was the percent of decrease in the number of goldfish?

7. The Hobby Shop sold 16 10-speed bicycles in February and 25%
   more than that in March. How many did they sell in March?

8. Of 460 entrants in a marathon race, 23 did not finish. What was
   the percent of decrease between the number of entrants and the
   number who finished the race?

9. An auctioneer receives a commission of 15% of sales. At one          [5-5]
   auction, the sales were $12,856. What was the commission?

10. An artist pays an art gallery 30% commission to sell her paintings.
    One painting sold for $235. What commission did she pay the
    art gallery?

11. The Baffin Bay Boat Yard pays a sales commission of 6% to its
    salespersons. What would the commission be on a cabin cruiser
    selling for $18,600?

12. A jewelry store pays its salespersons a commission of 14%.
    During one week the total sales were $173,000. How much
    did the store pay in commissions?

Self-Test answers and Extra Practice are at the back of the book.

## Chapter Review

Write the letter that labels the correct answer.

1. Expressed as a fraction in lowest terms, the ratio 12 to 9 is __?__ .  [5-1]

    **A.** $\frac{3}{4}$　　　**B.** $\frac{4}{6}$　　　**C.** $\frac{4}{3}$　　　**D.** $\frac{2}{3}$

2. Expressed as a fraction in lowest terms, the ratio of 25 m to 5 km is __?__ .

    **A.** $\frac{5}{1}$　　　**B.** $\frac{1}{200}$　　　**C.** $\frac{1}{5}$　　　**D.** $\frac{200}{1}$

3. Tickets to a rock concert are selling at a rate of 2 for $5. How much do 6 tickets cost?

    **A.** $15　　　**B.** $12　　　**C.** $6　　　**D.** $30

4. The ratio of polar bears to pandas in a zoo is 6 to 2. If there are 9 polar bears in the zoo, how many pandas are there?

    **A.** 5　　　**B.** 6　　　**C.** 4　　　**D.** 3

5. The means of the proportion $\frac{3}{8} = \frac{9}{24}$ are __?__ .  [5-2]

    **A.** 3 and 8　　**B.** 3 and 24　　**C.** 8 and 24　　**D.** 8 and 9

6. The extremes of the proportion $\frac{2}{5} = \frac{8}{20}$ are __?__ .

    **A.** 2 and 20　　**B.** 5 and 8　　**C.** 5 and 20　　**D.** 2 and 8

7. Which proportion is not correct?

    **A.** $\frac{2}{3} = \frac{6}{9}$　　**B.** $\frac{1}{5} = \frac{4}{20}$　　**C.** $\frac{5}{6} = \frac{10}{12}$　　**D.** $\frac{1}{3} = \frac{7}{24}$

8. In the proportion $\frac{n}{6} = \frac{2}{3}$, $n =$ __?__ .

    **A.** 4　　　**B.** 9　　　**C.** 12　　　**D.** 1

9. In decimal form 26% __?__ .  [5-3]

    **A.** 0.026　　**B.** 2.60　　**C.** 0.26　　**D.** 26.00

10. Written as a fraction in lowest terms, 60% = __?__ .

    **A.** $\frac{6}{10}$　　　**B.** $\frac{6}{100}$　　　**C.** $\frac{30}{50}$　　　**D.** $\frac{3}{5}$

11. 15% × 30 = __?__ .

    **A.** 4.5　　　**B.** 60　　　**C.** 45　　　**D.** 20

12. 35 is what percent of 140?

    **A.** 40%    **B.** 45%    **C.** 25%    **D.** 22%

13. The Marchands increased the size of their vegetable garden from    [5-4]
15 m² to 18 m². What was the percent of increase?

    **A.** $33\frac{1}{3}$%    **B.** $12\frac{1}{2}$%    **C.** 62%    **D.** 20%

14. Jack worked 5 hours on Saturday. Jan worked 20% longer. How many hours did Jan work?

    **A.** 6 hours    **B.** 7 hours    **C.** $6\frac{1}{2}$ hours    **D.** 8 hours

15. On Saturday, the Ski Club covered 8 km on a cross-country ski tour. On Sunday they traveled 10 km. What was the percent of increase?

    **A.** 25%    **B.** 40%    **C.** 20%    **D.** 10%

16. Jeremy was 160 cm tall. In the next year he grew 3% taller. How tall was he then?

    **A.** 163 cm    **B.** 174.8 cm    **C.** 164.8 cm    **D.** 164 cm

17. The Good Sport Shop pays a sales commission of 9%. How    [5-5]
much commission would they pay on sales of $52,364?

    **A.** $5230    **B.** $471.28    **C.** $852.36    **D.** $4712.76

18. Cameras selling for $19.95 are put on sale at a 15% discount. What is the sale price?

    **A.** $16.96    **B.** $14.96    **C.** $9.98    **D.** $12.95

19. Transistor radios are being sold at a discount of 25% of their original price, $12.59. How much would you save by buying one at the discount price?

    **A.** $3.15    **B.** $6.59    **C.** $4.15    **D.** $9.44

20. A family budgets 22% of their income for rent. If their annual income is $15,000, how much do they spend for rent in one year?

    **A.** $1330    **B.** $3300    **C.** $3100    **D.** $3000

# The Golden Ratio

To Leonardo da Vinci and other artists of the Renaissance, a rectangle was most pleasing to the eye when the ratio of its length to its width was the same as the ratio of their sum to its length. We write this as the proportion shown at the right.

$$\frac{l}{w} = \frac{l + w}{l}$$

If we let the width be one, the length of this rectangle is the continuing decimal 1.618 . . . . The ratio 1.618 . . . : 1 is called the *Golden Ratio.* A rectangle whose length and width are proportional to the Golden Ratio is a *Golden Rectangle.*

Golden Rectangles occur frequently throughout modern and classical art and architecture.

A Golden Rectangle fits neatly around the central figure in da Vinci's unfinished painting, *St. Jerome.*

A Golden Rectangle bounds the original outline of the ancient Greek Parthenon.

How many rectangles which appear to be Golden Rectangles can you find in Piet Mondrian's *Place de La Concorde* at right?

**Career Activity** Applications to most art schools and for many types of art-related jobs include the submission of a portfolio. Find out how many and what kinds of materials different types of portfolios should contain.

The Golden Ratio has a curious link to a sequence of numbers arising in the work of the medieval mathematician Leonardo of Pisa, nicknamed Fibonacci (son of Bonaccio). The infinite sequence of numbers 1, 1, 2, 3, 5, 8, 13, 21, . . . is called a *Fibonacci sequence*. To generate a Fibonacci sequence, we first pick any two integers as the first two *terms* of the sequence (in this case 1 and 1). Then each of the following terms is the sum of the previous two terms.

$$2 = 1 + 1$$

3rd term  2nd term  1st term

$$3 = 2 + 1$$

4th term  3rd term  2nd term

$$5 = 3 + 2$$

5th term  4th term  3rd term

The ratio of the sixth term to the fifth term of this sequence is 8:5 = 1.6:1. This is very close to the Golden Ratio 1.618 . . . :1. In fact, if we compute the ratios of consecutive terms farther and farther along in this sequence, we will see that they get closer and closer to the Golden Ratio.

## Research Activities

1. Write down the first several terms of the Fibonacci sequence which begins 2, 2, . . . .

   How do the terms of this sequence compare with the terms of the sequence we considered earlier?

   How do the ratios of consecutive terms compare with those of the sequence we considered earlier? Explain.

2. Botanists have discovered that numbers in a Fibonacci sequence (commonly called *Fibonacci numbers*) occur quite often in nature. For example, a pine cone has two sets of spirals, 8 spirals in one direction and 13 in the opposite direction, and 8 and 13 are Fibonacci numbers. Find some other instances of Fibonacci numbers in nature.

# **Application** Consumer Price Index

We live in a time of *inflation,* that is, money buys less and less as time goes by. One measure of inflation is the Consumer Price Index (CPI). Computation of the CPI starts with a selection of goods and services used by consumers (food, clothing, housing, and so on). The CPI is the ratio, expressed as a percent, between the total price *now* for this selection and the price during a *base year.* For example, a current CPI of 185 means that the total price of a selection of goods is 185% of the price during the base year.

**Research Activity** Go to your library and find a current CPI. What is the base year? Based on your findings, what would have been the cost of $100 worth of groceries (at today's prices) during the base year?

## Chapter Test

Write the ratio as a fraction in lowest terms.

**1.** 4 to 10          **2.** 80 cm to 1 m     [5-1]

**3.** Tell whether or not the proportion $\frac{12}{20} = \frac{3}{4}$ is correct.     [5-2]

**4.** Solve the proportion $\frac{n}{8} = \frac{9}{36}$.

Find the percent or number.

**5.** What is 5% of 40?       **6.** 18 is what percent of 90?     [5-3]

Solve.

**7.** The attendance at the Wheatland County Fair was 182,560 last year. This year it increased by 5%. What was the attendance this year?     [5-4]

**8.** During a two-month period, Jim increased his typing speed from 35 words per minute to 49 words per minute. What was the percent increase in his typing speed?

**9.** Typewriters are on sale at a discount of 12% of their original price of $129.95. What is their sale price?     [5-5]

**10.** A swimming-pool salesperson receives a commission of 9% of sales. What would the commission be for selling a $2300 pool?

# Skill Review

Express the ratio as a fraction in lowest terms.

**1.** 6 to 8

**2.** 14 to 35

**3.** 9 to 24

**4.** 56 to 16

**5.** 26 to 78

**6.** 34 to 18

**7.** 36 to 132

**8.** 69 to 42

**9.** 60 cm to 1 m

**10.** 520 m to 1 km

**11.** 300 mL to 1 L

**12.** 3 L to 900 mL

Solve the proportion.

**13.** $\dfrac{n}{6} = \dfrac{11}{3}$

**14.** $\dfrac{n}{8} = \dfrac{7}{4}$

**15.** $\dfrac{10}{n} = \dfrac{6}{33}$

**16.** $\dfrac{14}{n} = \dfrac{12}{42}$

**17.** $\dfrac{16}{5} = \dfrac{n}{30}$

**18.** $\dfrac{8}{18} = \dfrac{n}{27}$

**19.** $\dfrac{6}{45} = \dfrac{6}{n}$

**20.** $\dfrac{13}{14} = \dfrac{26}{n}$

**21.** $\dfrac{n}{3.3} = \dfrac{4}{6}$

**22.** $\dfrac{n}{9} = \dfrac{3.2}{4.8}$

**23.** $\dfrac{12.6}{n} = \dfrac{3.2}{8}$

**24.** $\dfrac{5.5}{n} = \dfrac{11}{4.2}$

**25.** $\dfrac{7.8}{6} = \dfrac{n}{3.4}$

**26.** $\dfrac{12.5}{0.15} = \dfrac{n}{6}$

**27.** $\dfrac{1.6}{9.6} = \dfrac{2.8}{n}$

**28.** $\dfrac{24.6}{1.2} = \dfrac{0.41}{n}$

Express as a percent.

**29.** $\dfrac{2}{5}$

**30.** $\dfrac{3}{4}$

**31.** $\dfrac{7}{10}$

**32.** $\dfrac{1}{8}$

**33.** $\dfrac{2}{3}$

**34.** $\dfrac{5}{6}$

**35.** $\dfrac{3}{8}$

**36.** $\dfrac{1}{12}$

**37.** $\dfrac{3}{5}$

**38.** $\dfrac{5}{4}$

**39.** $\dfrac{18}{10}$

**40.** $\dfrac{7}{3}$

**41.** 0.15

**42.** 0.36

**43.** 0.08

**44.** 1.6

**45.** 3.75

**46.** 2.02

**47.** $0.33\frac{1}{3}$

**48.** 0.125

**49.** 0.045

**50.** 2.125

**51.** 0.375

**52.** $0.66\frac{2}{3}$

Find the percent or number.

**53.** What is 4% of 32?

**54.** What is 15% of 80?

**55.** 6 is what percent of 48?

**56.** 25 is what percent of 75?

**57.** 35 is 20% of what number?

**58.** 17 is 9% of what number?

**59.** What is 5% of 85?

**60.** What is 93% of 400?

**61.** 18 is what percent of 72?

**62.** 50 is what percent of 300?

**63.** 14 is 75% of what number?

**64.** 48 is 30% of what number?

# 6

# Measurement and Geometry

## 6-1 Units of Length

**Objective** To name points, segments, rays, and lines, and to use metric units of length.

The diagram at the right contains several geometric figures: points, segments, rays, and a line.

A **point** is represented by a dot labeled with a capital letter. If two points $A$ and $B$ are joined by drawing along the edge of a ruler, we get a picture of **line segment** $AB$, denoted $\overline{AB}$. Points $A$ and $B$ are called **endpoints** of the segment.

$A$ • point $A$   $B$ • point $B$   $A$ •————————• $B$ segment $AB$

If $\overline{AB}$ is extended without end in just one direction, we obtain **ray** $AB$. Point $A$ is called the endpoint of the ray. If $\overline{AB}$ is extended without end in both directions, we get **line** $AB$. A line has no endpoints.

ray $AB$   line $AB$

**173**

In the diagram you should be able to locate:

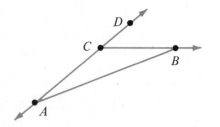

1. Segments: $\overline{AB}, \overline{CB}, \overline{CD}, \overline{CA}$, and $\overline{AD}$
2. Rays $CB$, $CD$, $CA$, $DC$, and $AC$. (Note ray $AC$ is the same as ray $AD$.)
3. Line $AC$. (This is the same as line $CD$ and line $AD$.)

The length of $\overline{XY}$ is denoted by the symbol $XY$. The diagram below shows that the length of $\overline{XY}$ is about 5.2 **centimeters (cm)**. Thus, we write $XY \approx 5.2$ cm. Since each centimeter is subdivided into 10 **millimeters (mm)**, we could also write $XY \approx 52$ mm.

The centimeter and millimeter are subdivisions of a **meter (m)**, the basic unit of length in the metric system. These and other metric units of length are shown in the table below. The units given in the non-shaded rows of the table are not used very often.

| Name of unit | Abbreviation | Multiple of a meter |
|---|---|---|
| millimeter | mm | 0.001, or $10^{-3}$ |
| centimeter | cm | 0.01 , or $10^{-2}$ |
| decimeter | dm | 0.1 , or $10^{-1}$ |
| meter | m | 1 , or $10^{0}$ |
| dekameter | dam | 10 , or $10^{1}$ |
| hectometer | hm | 100 , or $10^{2}$ |
| kilometer | km | 1000 , or $10^{3}$ |
| megameter | Mm | 1,000,000, or $10^{6}$ |

One of the nice things about the metric system is that it is easy to convert from one unit to another. You just move the decimal point.

$$5 \text{ mm} = 0.5 \text{ cm} = 0.005 \text{ m}$$
$$3500 \text{ m} = 3.5 \text{ km}$$

## Class Exercises

1. In the diagram, are $\overline{AB}$ and $\overline{BA}$ the same segment or different segments?

2. Is ray *OQ* the same as ray *QO?*

3. Name several segments in the diagram.

4. Name several rays in the diagram.

5. There is one line in the diagram. Name it in several ways.

6. What does the symbol *AB* stand for?

Complete.

7. 4800 m = _?_ km

8. 7.6 km = _?_ m

9. 340 cm = _?_ m

10. 340 cm = _?_ mm

11. 57 mm = _?_ cm

12. 800 mm = _?_ m

13. Estimate the length of this page in centimeters.

14. Estimate the length of your classroom in meters.

15. Look about your classroom to find an object about 50 cm long.

16. Look about your classroom to find an object about 2 m long.

17. Measure the width of your fingernails to find the one closest to 1 cm.

## Exercises

Complete.

**A**

|     | 1. | 2. | 3. | 4. | 5. | 6. | 7. | 8. |
|-----|-----|-----|-----|-----|-----|-----|-----|-----|
| mm  | 486 | 1200 | ? | ? | ? | ? | ? | ? |
| cm  | ? | ? | 58 | 4 | ? | ? | ? | ? |
| dm  | ? | ? | ? | ? | 93 | 72 | ? | ? |
| m   | ? | ? | ? | ? | ? | ? | 3.5 | 0.6 |

|     | 9. | 10. | 11. | 12. | 13. | 14. | 15. | 16. |
|-----|-----|-----|-----|-----|-----|-----|-----|-----|
| m   | 4000 | 715 | ? | ? | ? | ? | ? | ? |
| dam | ? | ? | 10 | 55 | ? | ? | ? | ? |
| hm  | ? | ? | ? | ? | 100 | 37 | ? | ? |
| km  | ? | ? | ? | ? | ? | ? | 5.9 | 15 |

In Exercises 17–20, find the lengths in centimeters and in millimeters.

**17.** *AB*          **18.** *CD*          **19.** *EF*          **20.** *GH*

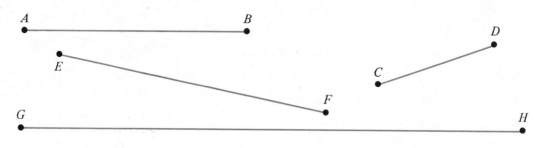

Complete.

**21.** 750 cm = __?__ m          **22.** 40 m = __?__ cm          **23.** 2 km = __?__ m

**24.** 500 m = __?__ km          **25.** 1 cm = __?__ km          **26.** 1 km = __?__ mm

C   **27.** Estimate the thickness of a page of this book.

# EXTRA!  Compass and Straightedge Constructions

In *compass and straightedge constructions,* a ruler may be used as a *straightedge* to draw straight lines, but it may not be used to measure lengths.

**How to copy a segment with a straightedge and compass**

Original Segment          Construction of New Segment

**1.** Draw a ray with endpoint O.

**2.** Spread your *compass* so the point is at *A* and the pencil tip is at *B*. Then put the point of your compass at *O* and draw an arc crossing the ray at *P*. Then *AB = OP*.

**Research Activity** Find out about other geometric constructions that use only a straightedge and compass.

# 6-2 Circles

**Objective** To identify parts of a circle and find its circumference.

The diagram shows a **compass** being used to draw a circle. The point of the compass is at the **center** of the circle. Any line segment joining the center to a point on the circle is called **a radius.** The length of such a segment is called **the radius** of the circle.

A **chord** of a circle is a segment joining two points of the circle. The diagram at the left below shows that a chord divides the circle into two **arcs.** If a chord contains the center of a circle, it is called **a diameter.** The arcs formed by a diameter are called **semicircles.**

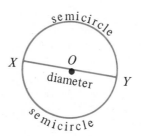

The length of a diameter is called **the diameter** of a circle, and the distance around the circle is called its **circumference,** or perimeter. The circumference and diameter of a circle are related by a very famous number called pi, denoted by the Greek letter $\pi$. Pi is defined as the ratio of a circle's circumference to its diameter.

$$\pi = \frac{\text{circumference}}{\text{diameter}}$$

If you measured the circumference and diameter of a record with a cloth tape measure, you would find:

$$\pi \approx \frac{94.6 \text{ cm}}{30.1 \text{ cm}} \approx 3.1$$

The value 3.1 is only an approximation for $\pi$. A better approximation is 3.14. Sometimes the fraction $\frac{22}{7}$ is used as an approximation.

## formula

**Circumference** $= \pi \times$ **diameter**
$$C = \pi \times d = \pi d$$

**Example 1** | The diameter of a circle is 12. Find its circumference
by using two different approximations for $\pi$:

**a.** $\pi \approx \frac{22}{7}$        **b.** $\pi \approx 3.14$

*Solution* | **a.** $C = \pi \times d$        **b.** $C = \pi \times d$

$\approx \frac{22}{7} \times 12$        $\approx 3.14 \times 12$

$= \frac{264}{7} = 37\frac{5}{7}$        $= 37.68$

The diameter of any circle is twice its radius, $r$. Therefore, if you
substitute $2r$ for $d$ in the formula $C = \pi \times d$, you get another formula
which relates the circumference $C$ and the radius $r$.

## formula

$$C = \pi \times 2r = 2\pi r$$

**Example 2** | The circumference of a circle is 62.8 cm. What is the
radius? Use $\pi \approx 3.14$.

*Solution* | $C = \quad 2 \times \pi \times r$

$62.8 = 2 \times 3.14 \times r$

$62.8 = 6.28 \times r$

$10 = r$, or $r = 10$ cm

## Class Exercises

The circle shown has center $O$.

**1.** Name a diameter of the circle.

**2.** Name two radii. (*Radii* is the plural of *radius*.)

**3.** If $OC = 5$, $AB = \underline{\ ?\ }$.

**4.** If $AB = 10$ cm, what is the circumference? (Use $\pi \approx 3.14$.)

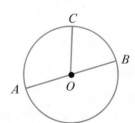

**5.** If you are told the circumference of a circle, how can you find the diameter?

**6.** Which is correct, $\pi = \frac{22}{7}$ or $\pi \approx \frac{22}{7}$?

## Exercises

Find the circumference of the circle described.
Use $\pi \approx 3.14$ for Exercises 1–6.

**A**
  **1.** diameter $= 100\,cm$

  **4.** radius $= 15\,cm$

  **2.** diameter $= 25\,cm$

  **5.** radius $= 1.7\,m$

  **3.** diameter $= 76\,mm$

  **6.** radius $= 2.18\,km$

Use $\pi \approx \frac{22}{7}$ for Exercises 7–12.

  **7.** diameter $= 210$

  **10.** radius $= 42$

  **8.** diameter $= 3\frac{1}{2}$

  **11.** radius $= \frac{42}{1000}$

  **9.** diameter $= 49$

  **12.** radius $= 1\frac{3}{11}$

Find the diameter of the circle whose circumference is given. Use $\pi \approx \frac{22}{7}$.

**13.** 220    **14.** 66    **15.** $\frac{77}{100}$    **16.** $8\frac{4}{5}$    **17.** 83.6    **18.** 2.42

**B** **19.** The curve shown is a semicircle. Which figure has the greater perimeter, the shaded figure or the unshaded one?

|←— 2 cm —→|←— 2 cm —→|

# Application   Circles and Power

One of the earliest mechanical discoveries was the **wheel.** It is much easier to pull a load on a wagon than to drag it along the ground. From this idea developed many of our modern transportation vehicles.

Circles are also used in **gears.** Gears usually have teeth of some kind that mesh with other gears. If the diameter of the large gear is twice that of the small gear, the circumference of the large gear is twice that of the small gear. In this case, the small gear will make two complete revolutions while the large gear is making one revolution.

A bicycle uses circles in both ways—as wheels and as gears.

**Research Activity** Find out how the gears on a bicycle work. Find out how the gears in an automobile work.

# 6-3 Measuring and Constructing Angles

**Objective** To measure and construct angles and identify special angles.

The diagram shows that an **angle** is the figure formed by two rays with the same endpoint. This endpoint is called the **vertex** of the angle, and the rays are called the **sides**.

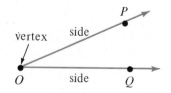

The diagrams below show various ways of naming angles.

angle $A$

angles 1 and 2

angle $RST$

The diagram at the left below shows a **protractor** being used to measure angles. The table at the right below shows how angles are classified according to their measures.

$\angle AOB = 35°$     $\angle AOC = 90°$

| Name | Measure |
|---|---|
| Acute | Between 0° and 90° |
| Right | 90° |
| Obtuse | Between 90° and 180° |

If the sum of *two* angles is 180°, the angles are called **supplementary angles.** If the sum of *two* angles is 90°, the angles are called **complementary angles.**

If two lines form a right angle, they are said to be perpendicular. In the diagram, line *l* is perpendicular to line *m*. This is abbreviated by writing $l \perp m$. The mark (⌐) shown in the diagram is frequently used to indicate a right angle.

Whenever two lines intersect, four angles are formed. In the diagram, angles 1 and 3 are called **vertical angles.** So are angles 2 and 4. To see that *a pair of vertical angles have the same measure,* notice that

$$\angle 1 + \angle 2 = 180°, \text{ and}$$
$$\angle 3 + \angle 2 = 180°.$$

From this you can conclude that $\angle 1 = \angle 3$. In the diagram, each pair of vertical angles is marked the same way to show that they have the same measure. Angles with the same measure are called **equal angles.**

Vertical angles are equal.
$\angle 1 = \angle 3$    $\angle 2 = \angle 4$

In the diagram at the right, ray *SZ* divides angle *RST* into two equal angles. We say that *SZ* **bisects** angle *RST.*

You can bisect an angle by using a protractor or by using a compass.

### How to bisect an angle with a compass

1. Suppose you want to bisect angle *AOB.* Draw an arc with center at point *O* and intersecting the sides of angle *AOB* at *X* and *Y.*

2. Draw an arc with center *X.* Then with center *Y* and the same radius, draw another arc intersecting the first one at *C.*

3. Join *O* to the point *C.* Now $\angle AOC = \angle BOC$, and ray *OC* bisects angle *AOB.*

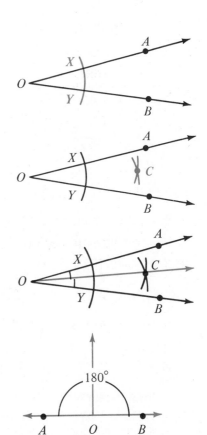

Now that you can bisect an angle, you can construct a right angle. The secret to this is to think of a straight line as forming a "180° angle." You then bisect this "angle" using the same three steps as before. This will give you two 90° angles. This method for constructing a right angle is given on the next page.

### How to construct a right angle using a compass

1. Draw a line, say line *AB*. Draw an arc with center at point *O* and intersecting line *AB* at points *X* and *Y*.

2. Spread the compass farther apart. Then draw two arcs with centers at *X* and at *Y*, intersecting at point *C*.

3. Join *O* to point *C*. Now angle *AOC* and angle *BOC* are right angles.

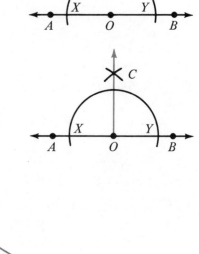

## Class Exercises

1. Name angle 1 using letters.

2. Name angle *QRT* using a number.

3. What is the vertex of angle 2?

4. Name an acute angle.

5. Name an obtuse angle.

6. Name two pairs of vertical angles.

7. Name three pairs of supplementary angles.

8. If $\angle 4 = 32°$, then $\angle 6 = $ ___?___ °.

9. If lines *PQ* and *QR* are perpendicular, name two right angles.

10. If you bisect a 24° angle, you get two angles, each with measure ___?___.

11. If you bisect a right angle, you get two angles, each with measure ___?___.

12. Draw an acute angle. Then bisect it using a compass.

13. Construct a right angle. Then use this angle to construct a 45° angle.

14. a. Fold a rectangular piece of paper so as to make a 45° angle.
    b. Fold it again to make a $22\frac{1}{2}°$ angle.

Use the diagram to find the measures of the following angles.

**15.** angle *DOE*          **16.** angle *BOC*

**17.** angle *COD*          **18.** angle *AOF*

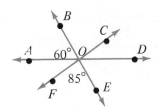

## Exercises

In the diagram, $\overline{BE} \perp \overline{CO}$ and $\angle AOB = 28°$.

**A**  **1.** Name two right angles.

**2.** Name two acute angles.

**3.** Name two obtuse angles.

**4.** Name a pair of vertical angles.

**5.** Name a pair of complementary angles.

**6.** $\angle DOE =$ __?__   **7.** $\angle COD =$ __?__   **8.** $\angle BOD =$ __?__

Use the diagram to find the measures of the following angles.

**9.** angle *RWS*          **10.** angle *TWU*

**11.** angle *TWS*          **12.** angle *PWQ*

In Exercises 13 and 14, ray *OX* bisets angle *AOB*.  Find:
**a.** $\angle AOB$          **b.** $\angle AOX$
**c.** The number on the protractor corresponding to ray *OX*.

**13.**                    **14.**

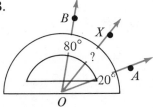

**15.** Draw an acute angle and bisect it using a compass.

**16.** Draw an obtuse angle and bisect it using a compass.

**17.** Construct a right angle.          **18.** Construct a 45° angle.

**B**  **19. a.** Draw an acute angle and its bisector.
**b.** Now extend the three rays in the opposite direction.
**c.** Must the two new acute angles formed be equal? Tell why or why not.

# *EXTRA!* Constructions

**Original Angle**

**Construction of New Angle**

**How to copy an angle with a compass**

1. Draw a ray with endpoint O.

2. Draw an arc with center A. Then with center O and the same radius, draw another arc.

3. Put your compass point at Y and spread your compass so you can draw an arc through X. Then with center C and this radius, draw an arc which intersects the first arc at B.

4. Draw ray OB.
   Now ∠ BOC = ∠ A.

Draw an obtuse angle and copy it.

# *EXTRA!* Angles Inscribed in Semicircles

Use a compass to draw several circles of different sizes. For each, draw a diameter $\overline{AB}$.

  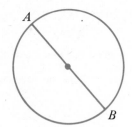

Locate a point C on each semicircle, and join C to A and to B. Angle ACB is **inscribed in** the semicircle. Measure angle ACB in each case. What do you discover?

# 6-4 **Parallel Lines**

**Objective** To identify special angles associated with parallel lines.

If two lines in a plane do not intersect, they are called **parallel lines.** In the diagram, we say that line *l* is parallel to line *m* and abbreviate this by writing *l* ∥ *m*.

Whenever two parallel lines are cut by a third line, called a **transversal,** several pairs of equal angles are formed. These pairs of equal angles are given special names as follows.

**alternate interior angles**

      angles 3 and 5

      angles 4 and 6

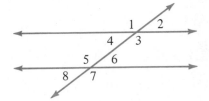

    **corresponding angles**

angles 1 and 5     angles 3 and 7

angles 2 and 6     angles 4 and 8

*Example* | In the diagram, lines *l* and *m* are parallel and ∠1 = 120°. Find the measures of the other angles.

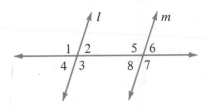

*Solution* | Angles 1 and 5 are corresponding angles, so ∠5 = 120°. Angles 5 and 3 are alternate interior angles, so ∠3 = 120°. Angles 3 and 7 are corresponding angles, so ∠7 = 120°. Since ∠1 = 120°,

$$\angle 2 = 180° - 120° = 60°.$$

**Do you also see that**

$$\angle 4 = \angle 6 = \angle 8 = 60°?$$

It is also true that if two lines are cut by a transversal so that pairs of angles are equal as described above, then the two given lines are parallel. We use this idea in the following construction, which is given on the next page.

### How to use a compass to construct a line parallel to a given line through a given point

1. Given line $m$ and point $A$. Draw line $t$ through $A$ cutting line $m$ at $B$.

2. At $A$, construct angle 2 equal to angle 1. Then lines $m$ and $n$ are parallel since they form equal corresponding angles with transversal $t$.

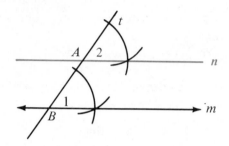

## Class Exercises

In the figure, $a \parallel b$.

1. Name two pairs of alternate interior angles.

2. Name four pairs of corresponding angles.

3. Name three angles equal to angle 1.

4. Name three angles equal to angle 2.

5. If $\angle 5 = 130°$, then $\angle 3 =$ __?__ and $\angle 4 =$ __?__ .

6. If $\angle 6 = 40°$, then $\angle 2 =$ __?__ and $\angle 1 =$ __?__ .

7. If $\angle 7 = 120°$, then $\angle 3 =$ __?__ and $\angle 1 =$ __?__ .

8. Draw a large diagram of two parallel lines cut by a third line. Use a protractor to measure a pair of alternate interior angles.

## Exercises

In the figure, $l \parallel m$.

A  1. Name two pairs of alternate interior angles.

2. Name four pairs of corresponding angles.

3. Name three angles equal to angle 8.

4. Name three angles equal to angle 7.

5. If $\angle 1 = 112°$, find the measures of the other seven angles.

6. If $\angle 4 = 55°$, find the measures of the other seven angles.

In the figure, $l \parallel m$ and $l \perp n$.

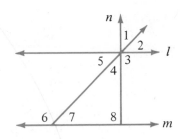

**7.** Angles 7 and __?__ are alternate interior angles.

**8.** Angles 7 and __?__ are corresponding angles.

**9.** If $\angle 1 = 55°$, find the measures of the other seven angles.

**10.** Is $m \perp n$?

**B** **11.** Use a ruler and compass to construct two parallel lines. Note that the ruler should be used only as a straightedge and not for measuring.

In Exercises 12 and 13, use a ruler and protractor to draw a figure like the one shown. Through point $B$, draw a line parallel to line $CA$. Through point $A$, draw a line parallel to line $CB$. These lines will meet at a point $D$. Use a protractor to find $\angle ADB$.

**12.**

**13.**

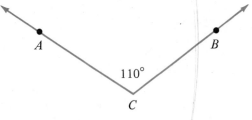

**14.** Draw two parallel lines cut by a third line. Now use a compass or a protractor to bisect the angles shown. Measure the angle at which the bisectors meet. Now repeat the experiment by drawing other parallel lines cut by a third line. What did you discover?

**C** **15.** Take a rectangular sheet and mark a point $A$ on it. By folding the paper, make a crease line which goes through $A$ and is parallel to the bottom edge of the sheet.

**16.** Take a sheet of paper which has just one straight edge (the bottom). Mark a point $B$ on the paper.
   **a.** By folding the paper, make a crease line which goes through $B$ and is perpendicular to the bottom edge of the sheet.
   **b.** Leave the paper folded, and make another fold which will pass through $B$ and be parallel to the bottom edge of the sheet.

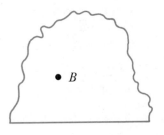

# **EXTRA!** Rays Intersecting Parallel Lines

**1.** On a sheet of lined paper, choose a point A on one line and draw two rays from A as shown. Measure the distances between parallel lines along one ray. Are they all the same? Measure the distances between parallel lines along the other ray. Are they the same? Are they equal to the distances along the first ray?

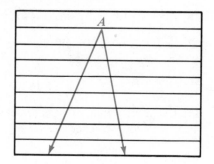

**2.** Draw a △ *ABC* so that *AB* = 6 cm. Locate *P* on $\overline{AB}$ so that *AP* = 4 cm and *PB* = 2 cm. Construct $\overline{PQ}$ parallel to $\overline{BC}$. Measure $\overline{AQ}$ and $\overline{QC}$. Find the ratio $\frac{AQ}{QC}$ and compare it with $\frac{AP}{PB}$. What do you notice? Locate point *X* on $\overline{AB}$ so that *AX* = 4.5 cm and *XB* = 1.5 cm. Construct $\overline{XY}$ parallel to $\overline{BC}$ (with *Y* on $\overline{AC}$). Measure $\overline{AY}$ and $\overline{YC}$. Find the ratio $\frac{AY}{YC}$ and compare it with $\frac{AX}{XB}$. What do you notice?

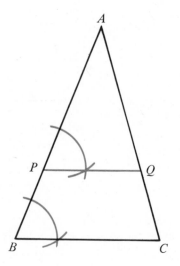

### How to divide a segment into equal segments

**3.** You can divide a given segment such as $\overline{AB}$ into any given number of equal segments, such as three. Draw a ray with endpoint *A*. Starting with point *A* and any convenient radius, construct three equal segments on the ray. Call the points *C*, *D*, and *E*. Draw $\overline{EB}$. At *C* and *D* construct angles equal to angle *AEB* with one side intersecting $\overline{AB}$ at *X* and *Y*. Are $\overline{CX}$ and $\overline{DY}$ parallel to $\overline{EB}$? Why? Are *AX*, *XY*, and *YB* equal? Why?

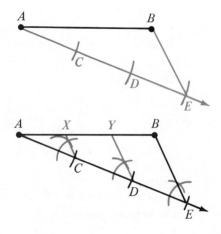

**4.** Draw $\overline{LM}$ and divide it into four equal segments.

## Self-Test

Symbols and words to remember:

$\overline{AB}$ [p. 173]  $XY$ [p. 174]  $\approx$ [p. 174]  $\pi$ [p. 177]  $\angle$ [p. 180]

° [p. 180]  $\perp$ [p. 180]  $\parallel$ [p. 185]

point [p. 173]  line segment [p. 173]  endpoint [p. 173]
ray [p. 173]  line [p. 173]  center [p. 177]
radius [p. 177]  chord [p. 177]  arc [p. 177]
diameter [p. 177]  semicircle [p. 177]  circumference [p. 177]
angle [p. 180]  acute, right, obtuse angles [p. 180]
supplementary, complementary angles [p. 180]  vertical angles [p. 181]
equal angles [p. 181]  bisect [p. 181]  parallel lines [p. 185]
alternate interior, corresponding angles [p. 185]

Complete.

1. A ray has __?__ endpoint(s).
2. A line has __?__ endpoint(s).    **[6-1]**
3. 35 m = __?__ cm
4. 200 mm = __?__ m

5. If a chord contains the center of a circle, it is called a __?__ .    **[6-2]**

6. If the radius of a circle is 40 cm, then the circumference of the circle is __?__ . (Use $\pi \approx 3.14$.)

7. If the diameter of a circle is 42, then the circumference of the circle is __?__ . (Use $\pi \approx \frac{22}{7}$.)

8. If the circumference of a circle is 17.6, then the radius of the circle is __?__ . (Use $\pi \approx \frac{22}{7}$).

9. If we bisect a right angle, each angle formed has measure __?__ .    **[6-3]**

10. A __?__ is used to measure angles.

11. Two supplementary equal angles each have measure __?__ .

12. If one of two vertical angles has measure 50°, the other angle has measure __?__ .

13. Lines in the same plane that do not intersect are called __?__ .    **[6-4]**

14. Whenever two parallel lines are cut by a third line, the corresponding angles are __?__ .

15. If one of the angles formed when two lines intersect is a 42° angle, the measures of the other three angles are __?__ .

16. If two lines in the same plane are both perpendicular to a third line, the two lines are __?__ .

Self-Test answers and Extra Practice are at the back of the book.

# 6-5 Special Triangles

**Objective** To classify triangles.

The figure formed by $\overline{AB}$, $\overline{AC}$, and $\overline{BC}$ is called triangle ABC, abbreviated △ABC.

**Classification by angles**

**Acute Triangle**
Three acute angles

**Right Triangle**
One right angle

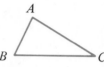

**Obtuse Triangle**
One obtuse angle

**Classification by sides**    (Small marks indicate sides of equal length.)

**Scalene Triangle**
No two sides
are equal

**Isosceles Triangle**
At least two sides
are equal.

**Equilateral Triangle**
All sides are equal.

## Class Exercises

1. Draw any kind of triangle (either acute, right, or obtuse) and measure its angles with a protractor. Add the three measures and compare your total with the totals of your classmates.

2. If you follow the instructions below, you will see why the sum of the angle measures in a triangle is 180°.
   **a.** Draw any △ABC. Then draw a line through B parallel to $\overline{AC}$.
   **b.** Give reasons for each statement below.
   **1.** $\angle 1 = \angle A$
   **2.** $\angle 2 = \angle C$
   **3.** $\angle 1 + \angle 3 + \angle 2 = 180°$
   **4.** $\angle A + \angle 3 + \angle C = 180°$

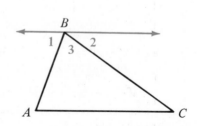

3. Suppose a friend drew a right triangle and told you that the measure of one angle was 40°. Could you tell the measures of the other two angles?

4. Draw a triangle which is both acute and isosceles. (This is called an acute isosceles triangle.) By measuring, see if any of the angles are equal. Which ones?

5. Draw an obtuse isosceles triangle. See if any of the angles are equal. Which ones?

6. Construct an equilateral triangle with a compass. If you work accurately, each angle should measure 60°.

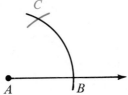

7. Use one of your 60° angles to construct a 30° angle.

---

### SUMMARY OF RESULTS FROM CLASS EXERCISES

1. In any triangle, the angle measures total 180°.

2. In an isosceles triangle, the angles opposite the equal sides are themselves equal.

3. In an equilateral triangle, all three angles measure 60°.

---

## Exercises

Refer to the triangles shown. Give the letter of each triangle which appears to be:

**A** 1. acute

2. obtuse

3. right

4. scalene

5. isosceles

6. equilateral

7. isosceles right

Without using a protractor, find the measure of each angle denoted by a question mark.

**8.**

**9.**

**10.**

**11.**

**12.**

**13.**

**14.** Draw an isosceles right triangle. Can you give the three angle measures without using a protractor?

Find the values of $x$ and $y$ in each diagram.

**B  15.**

**16.**

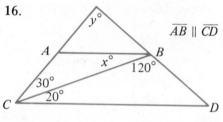

$\overline{AB} \parallel \overline{CD}$

**17.**

**18.**

**19.**

$\overline{AB} \parallel \overline{CD}$

**20.**

**C**   **21.** In $\triangle ABC$, $\angle C = 70°$. The bisectors of angles $A$ and $B$ meet at point $X$. How large is angle $AXB$? (Draw the figure.)

**22.** In $\triangle DEF$, $M$ is a point of $EF$ such that $ME = MF = MD$. How large is angle $EDF$?

# *EXTRA!* Paper Folding

**1.** Cut out a large $\triangle ABC$. By folding the paper, make a crease through $A$ perpendicular to $\overline{BC}$. Let $D$ be the point where the crease meets $\overline{BC}$. Now fold the paper so that $B$ coincides with $D$. Fold it again so that $C$ falls on $D$.

Finally, fold the paper so that $A$ coincides with $D$. What does this experiment show about $\angle A + \angle B + \angle C$?

**2.** Cut a large triangle out of a piece of paper. By folding the paper, make a crease that bisects the smallest angle.
Now make creases to bisect the other two angles. If you worked accurately, the three creases should meet in a point. Do they?
Put the point of your compass at the place where the three creases meet. Can you draw a circle that "just fits" inside the triangle?

**3.** Cut out a large triangle having three unequal, acute angles.
Fold corner $A$ onto corner $C$, as shown, so that $\overline{NA}$ falls on top of $\overline{NC}$.
Estimate the measure of the angle between the crease and $\overline{NC}$.
Check your estimate by measuring.
Now return $A$ to its original position and fold $B$ onto $C$.
Return $B$ to its original position and fold $A$ onto $B$.
If you worked carefully, your three creases should meet in a point. Do they?
Put the point of your compass at the place where the three creases meet. Can you draw a circle that goes through all three vertexes?

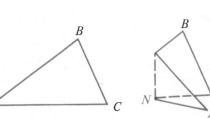

# 6-6 Special Quadrilaterals

**Objective** To identify some special quadrilaterals.

A **quadrilateral** is a four-sided closed figure. Some special quadrilaterals are shown below with some of their properties.

**Trapezoid**
Exactly two parallel sides

**Isosceles Trapezoid**
Two parallel sides
Other sides equal
Two pairs of equal angles (shown)

While a trapezoid has just one pair of parallel sides, a
parallelogram has two pairs of parallel sides. Each figure
shown below is a special kind of parallelogram.

**Parallelogram**
Opposite sides parallel
Opposite sides equal
Opposite angles equal

**Rhombus**
Opposite sides parallel
All sides equal
Opposite angles equal

**Rectangle**
Opposite sides parallel
Opposite sides equal
Four right angles

**Square**
Opposite sides parallel
All sides equal
Four right angles

*Example*

*ABCD* is a parallelogram.

Find:  **a.** *DC*    **b.** *AD*

        **c.** $\angle C$    **d.** $\angle D$

*Solution*

Since opposite sides are equal,
*DC* = 4 and *AD* = 9.

Since opposite angles are equal,
$\angle C = 55°$ and $\angle D = 125°$.

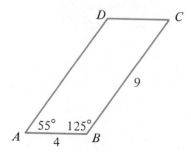

## Class Exercises

Refer to the quadrilaterals shown. Give the letter of each one which appears to be a:

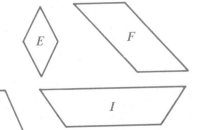

1. square

2. rectangle

3. rhombus

4. parallelogram

5. trapezoid

6. isosceles trapezoid

True or false?

7. All squares are rectangles.

8. All rectangles are squares.

9. All squares are rhombuses.

10. All rhombuses are squares.

Exercises 11–13 show why the opposite angles of a parallelogram must be equal.

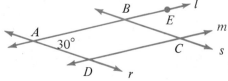

11. In the diagram, $l \parallel m$ and $r \parallel s$. What kind of figure is $ABCD$?

12. Suppose $\angle BAD = 30°$.
 a. Find $\angle EBC$.  b. Find $\angle BCD$.

13. Repeat Exercise 12 assuming that $\angle BAD = 40°$.

## Exercises

For each figure, supply the length or angle measure requested.

WXYZ is a parallelogram.

 **A**

1. $XY = \underline{\ ?\ }$  2. $YZ = \underline{\ ?\ }$

3. $\angle X = \underline{\ ?\ }$  4. $\angle W = \underline{\ ?\ }$

STAR is a rhombus.

5. $TA = \underline{\ ?\ }$  6. $AR = \underline{\ ?\ }$

7. $\angle A = \underline{\ ?\ }$  8. $\angle R = \underline{\ ?\ }$

FLAT is a rectangle.

9. FT = __?__    10. FL = __?__

11. ∠A = __?__    12. ∠FLT = __?__

TANK is an isosceles trapezoid.

13. NK = __?__

14. ∠TKN = __?__

15. ∠KAN = __?__

16. ∠ANK = __?__

ACEF and BCDG are parallelograms.

17. ∠C = __?__    18. ∠G = __?__

19. FE = __?__    20. DE = __?__

SLAM is a rectangle.  FLAK is a rhombus.

21. ∠SLF = __?__

22. ∠MAK = __?__

23. FK = __?__

24. SM = __?__

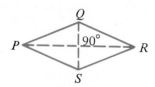

**B**  25. PQRS is a rhombus.  Its diagonals $\overline{PR}$ and $\overline{QS}$ are perpendicular.  Experiment and see if this is true of the diagonals of other rhombuses.

26. By drawing several rectangles, see if the diagonals of a rectangle are perpendicular.  Are they equal?

**C**  27. Rhombus ABCD has ∠A = 60° and CD = 12 cm.  Find the distance from B to D.

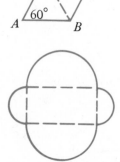

28. Four semicircles are constructed on the sides of a rectangle.  The total distance around the figure is 66.  If the length of the rectangle is twice its width, find the width.  Use $\pi \approx \frac{22}{7}$.

# 6-7 Polygons and Their Perimeters

**Objective** To identify some special polygons and find their perimeters.

A **polygon** is a closed figure formed by connecting segments at their endpoints. These endpoints are called the **vertexes** of the polygon, and the segments are called the **sides.** If all sides of a polygon are equal, the polygon is called **equilateral.**

Some polygons are given special names depending on the number of their sides.

| Sides | 3 | 4 | 5 | 6 | 8 | 10 |
|---|---|---|---|---|---|---|
| polygon | triangle | quadrilateral | pentagon | hexagon | octagon | decagon |

The **perimeter** of a polygon is the sum of the lengths of its sides.

6

Perimeter = 15

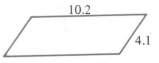

0.9 cm

Perimeter = 0.9 + 0.9 + 0.9 + 0.9 + 0.9 + 0.9
= 6 × 0.9 = 5.4 (cm)

Sometimes you can calculate the perimeter of a figure even if you are not told the length of each side.  Here are two examples.

*Example 1* | Find the perimeter of the parallelogram shown.

*Solution* | The opposite sides of a parallelogram are equal.

Thus, perimeter = 10.2 + 4.1 + 10.2 + 4.1
= 28.6

*Example 2* | Find the perimeter of the figure shown. All the angles are right angles.

*Solution* | Side *AF* must have length 8 − 3 = 5.

Side *FE* must have length 10 − 6 = 4.

Perimeter = 10 + 8 + 6 + 3 + 4 + 5
= 36

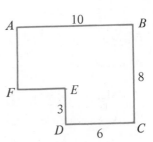

## Class Exercises

Find the perimeter of each figure.

**1.**

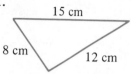

15 cm

8 cm    12 cm

**2.**

13 m

7 m

**3.**

3

4

**4.**

3.2

**5.** Estimate the perimeter of the floor in your classroom. Check your estimate by measuring.

In Exercises 6–9, all the angles in the figures are right angles. Find the perimeter of each.

**6.**

5

7

**7.**

4

3

2

5

**8.**

6

2

2    2

4

**9.**

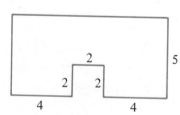

2

2    2

5

4    4

Tell how many sides each polygon has.

**10.** Quadrilateral

**11.** Octagon

**12.** Hexagon

**13.** Pentagon

**14.** What is an equilateral polygon?

**15.** An equilateral quadrilateral is usually called a __?__

## Exercises

Find the perimeter.

**A**   **1.**

64.3 mm

28.7 mm

56.2 mm

**2.**

2.74 cm

2.88 cm

6.08 cm

**3.**

$2\frac{1}{4}$

$4\frac{1}{2}$

**4.**

253 mm

17 cm

**5.** A STOP sign is an example of an equilateral ___?___ .

**6.** If one side of a STOP sign is 15 cm, find its perimeter.

**7.** If the perimeter of a STOP sign is 160 cm, find the length of each side.

**8.** Each side of a pentagon is 14.3 cm. What is its perimeter?

**9.** Each side of a hexagon is $6\frac{1}{4}$ units. What is its perimeter?

**10.** Two sides of a parallelogram have lengths 6.2 cm and 8.4 cm. Find the perimeter.

**11.** The perimeter of a rhombus is 26.8 cm. Find the length of each side.

**12.** The perimeter of an equilateral hexagon is 497.4 cm. Find the length of each side.

In Exercises 13 and 14, the adjacent sides of the figure form right angles. Find the perimeter.

**B**   **13.**

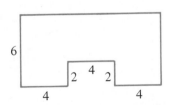

6

2   4   2

4         4

**14.**

3

5

4         4

3

**15.** The perimeter of an isosceles trapezoid is 64 cm. The lengths of its parallel sides are 14 cm and 24 cm. How long are the other two sides?

**16.** The figure at the right shows some walks through and around a park. If John and Sue start at the point marked, and if John takes the black path while Sue takes the red path, which one will travel the greater distance before returning to the starting point?

start

**C**   **17.** Four semicircles are constructed on the sides of a rhombus. If the total distance around the figure is 88 cm, what is the perimeter of the rhombus? Use $\pi \approx \frac{22}{7}$.

**18.** Which figure has the greater perimeter, the shaded figure or the unshaded one?

|←—1 m—→|←—1 m—→|

# EXTRA! Polygons Inscribed in a Circle

**1.** Use a compass to draw a circle with any radius. Using the same radius, put the point of your compass at any point *P* of the circle and draw an arc intersecting the circle. Call the point of intersection *A*. Move the compass point to *A* and mark another arc intersecting the circle at point *B*. Continue marking arcs.
How many points on the circle have you marked?
Connect the points in order. What kind of figure has been formed? It is **inscribed** in the circle.
What is the relationship of the perimeter of the polygon and the diameter of the circle?

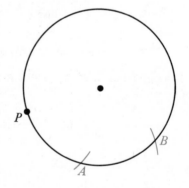

**2.** Using a protractor, mark 24 points equally spaced around a large circle. Use six differently colored pencils to show six different kinds of equilateral polygons which can be formed by connecting dots.

# 6-8 Congruent Polygons

**Objective** To identify congruent polygons and their corresponding parts.

If two polygons have the same size and shape, they are called **congruent** polygons. In the diagram below, $\triangle RST$ is congruent to $\triangle XYZ$. This statement can be abbreviated by writing

$$\triangle RST \cong \triangle XYZ.$$

Corresponding parts of congruent triangles are equal.

**Corresponding angles are equal**

$\angle R = \angle X$

$\angle S = \angle Y$

$\angle T = \angle Z$

**Corresponding sides are equal**

$RS = XY$

$ST = YZ$

$RT = XZ$

When referring to two congruent polygons, it is customary to list their corresponding vertexes in the same order. Thus, we write $\triangle RST \cong \triangle XYZ$ and *not* $\triangle RST \cong \triangle YZX$.

*Example* | **Suppose *ABCD* $\cong$ *HGFE*.**

**Then $\angle B =$ \_\_?\_\_ and *AD* = \_\_?\_\_ .**

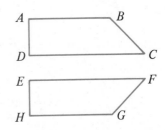

*Solution* | **Equal corresponding parts are listed in the same order. Thus, $\angle B = \angle G$ and *AD* = *HE*.**

You can tell whether two polygons are congruent by seeing whether or not you can match their vertexes in such a way that all the corresponding parts are equal. However, to see if two triangles are congruent, you do not have to check all three pairs of sides and three pairs of angles. You can use any of the methods listed on the following page.

**The side-angle-side (SAS) check for congruent triangles**
If two sides and the included angle of one
triangle are equal to two sides and the
included angle of another triangle, then the
triangles are congruent.

**The angle-side-angle (ASA) check for congruent triangles**
If two angles and the included side of one
triangle are equal to two angles and the
included side of another triangle, then
the triangles are congruent.

**The side-side-side (SSS) check for congruent triangles**
If three sides of one triangle are equal
to three sides of another triangle, then
the triangles are congruent.

# Class Exercises

Complete the statements below each pair of congruent polygons.

**1.** $\triangle RUN \cong$ __?__       **2.** $RN =$ __?__

**3.** $\angle U =$ __?__

**4.** $XY =$ __?__ cm       **5.** $LA =$ __?__ cm

**6.** $BT =$ __?__ cm       **7.** $\angle A =$ __?__

**8.** $\angle Y =$ __?__       **9.** $\angle C =$ __?__

Each pair of triangles below is marked to show equal sides and equal angles.
Tell whether or not the triangles in each pair are congruent. Also give
your reason why (SAS, ASA, or SSS).

**10.**         **11.**         **12.**

**13.**   **14.**   **15.**

*ABCD* is a parallelogram.

**16.** Explain how to use SSS to show △*ABD* ≅ △*CDB*.

**17.** Explain how to use SAS to show △*ABD* ≅ △*CDB*.

**18.** Explain how to use ASA to show △*ABD* ≅ △*CDB*.

# Exercises

Complete the statements below each pair of congruent polygons.

**A**  **1.** *WXYZ* ≅ __?__    **2.** ∠*X* = __?__    **4.** *ABCDE* ≅ __?__    **5.** *TN* = __?__ cm

**3.** *YZ* = __?__    **6.** *DE* = __?__ cm    **7.** ∠*Q* = __?__

**8.** ∠*N* = __?__    **9.** ∠*E* = __?__

Tell whether or not the triangles in each pair below are congruent. Also give your reason (SAS, ASA, or SSS).

**10.**     **11.**     **12.**

**13.**     **14.**     **15.**

*Hint:* $\overline{AB}$ is a side of both triangles.

*Hint:* Vertical angles are equal.

**B**  16. Draw a large triangle. Then join the midpoints of the three sides so that four smaller triangles are formed. Which of these four triangles are congruent?

17. Draw a large parallelogram *ABCD*. Then draw diagonals $\overline{AC}$ and $\overline{BD}$ intersecting at *O*, so that four small triangles are formed. Which of these triangles are congruent?

18. Repeat Exercise 17 for a rhombus *ABCD*.

19. *SLIM* is a rectangle. Name three triangles congruent to △*SLI*.

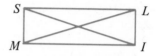

The figure shown is a cube. (All its edges are equal, and intersecting edges are perpendicular.)

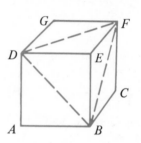

**C**  20. Why is △*ABD* ≅ △*CBF*?

21. Name other triangles congruent to △*ABD*.

22. What kind of triangle is △*BDF*?

# EXTRA!

## Constructing Congruent Triangles

| Side-angle-side (SAS) method of copying a triangle | Original Triangle | Construction of New Triangle |
|---|---|---|

1. Construct $\overline{XZ}$ so that *XZ* = *AC*.

2. At *X*, copy angle *A*.

3. Construct $\overline{XY}$ so that *XY* = *AB*. Connect *Y* and *Z*. Now △*XYZ* ≅ △*ABC*.

**Angle-side-angle (ASA) method of copying a triangle**

**Original Triangle**          **Construction of New Triangle**

1. Copy angle *P*. Call the new angle *J*.

2. On one side of angle *J*, construct $\overline{JK}$ so that *JK* = *PQ*.

3. At *K*, copy angle *Q*. Let *L* be the point where the sides of angles *J* and *K* intersect. Now △*JKL* ≅ △*PQR*.

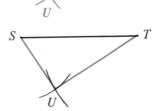

**Side-side-side (SSS) method of copying a triangle**

**Original Triangle**          **Construction of New Triangle**

1. Construct $\overline{ST}$ so that *ST* = *DE*.

2. Adjust your compass so the point is at *D* and the pencil is at *F*. Now put the point at *S* and draw an arc. Now adjust the compass so the point is at *E* and the pencil is at *F*. Now put the point at *T* and draw an arc. Let *U* be the point where the arcs intersect.

3. Draw $\overline{SU}$ and $\overline{TU}$. Now △*STU* ≅ △*DEF*.

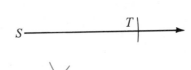

Use a compass and straightedge to make all constructions.
1. Draw a large triangle. Copy it using the three methods described in this section.
2. Draw a parallelogram like the one shown. Construct a copy of it. (*Hint:* Draw a diagonal.)

# 6-9 Similar Polygons

**Objective** To identify similar polygons and their corresponding parts.

Congruent polygons have the same shape and size. **Similar** polygons have the same shape, but do not necessarily have the same size. We use the symbol ~ to stand for "is similar to."

**Congruent Polygons**
$\triangle LMN \cong \triangle RST$
Corresponding angles are equal.
Corresponding sides are equal.

**Similar Polygons**
$\triangle LMN \sim \triangle XYZ$
Corresponding angles are equal.
Corresponding sides are proportional.

When we say that corresponding sides of similar triangles are proportional, we mean that the ratios of the lengths of corresponding sides are equal. For the similar triangles above, we have:

$$\frac{MN}{YZ} = \frac{LM}{XY} = \frac{LN}{XZ} \qquad \frac{4}{8} = \frac{5}{10} = \frac{6}{12}$$

It is customary to list the corresponding vertexes of similar polygons in the same order, just as we did for congruent polygons. Thus for the similar polygons below, we write:

$ABCD \sim EFGH$

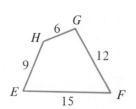

Notice again that the lengths of corresponding sides are proportional.

$$\frac{AB}{EF} = \frac{BC}{FG} = \frac{CD}{GH} = \frac{DA}{HE}$$

$$\frac{20}{15} = \frac{16}{12} = \frac{8}{6} = \frac{12}{9} \longleftarrow \text{Each of these ratios equals } \frac{4}{3}.$$

*Example* | If *MORT* ~ *NACK*, find:

a. ∠O    b. *KC*

*Solution* | **a. Since corresponding angles are equal,**

∠O = ∠A = **62°.**

**b. Since corresponding sides are proportional,**

$$\frac{KC}{8} = \frac{9}{6}$$

6 × KC = 8 × 9 = 72

KC = 12

## Class Exercises

Complete the statements given below each pair of similar polygons.

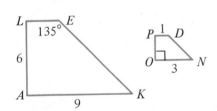

**1.** △*JOG* ~ __?__

**2.** ∠*G* = __?__

**3.** $\frac{RN}{JG}$ = __?__

**4.** *NU* = __?__

**5.** *RU* = __?__

**6.** *LAKE* ~ __?__

**7.** ∠*A* = __?__

**8.** ∠*D* = __?__

**9.** *LE* = __?__

**10.** *PO* = __?__

**11.** Are all squares similar?

**12.** Are all rectangles similar?

**13.** Give the length and width of some rectangle similar to *ABCD*.

# Exercises

Complete the statements given below each pair of similar polygons.

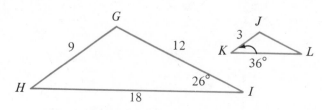

**A**

1. △ABC ~ △ __?__

2. ∠D = ∠ __?__

3. ∠E = __?__

4. DE = __?__

5. EF = __?__

6. △GHI ~ △ __?__

7. ∠L = __?__

8. ∠H = __?__

9. JL = __?__

10. KL = __?__

11. Are all equilateral triangles similar?    12. Are all rhombuses similar?

13. Two rhombuses each have a 60° angle. Must they be similar?

14. Two parallelograms each have a 60° angle. Must they be similar?

15. Two isosceles trapezoids each have a 100° angle. Must they be similar?

16. Two isosceles triangles each have a 100° angle. Must they be similar?

17. The length and width of a rectangle are 20 cm and 15 cm. The length and width of a similar rectangle are 12 cm and __?__ cm.

18. The length and width of one rectangle are twice the length and width of another rectangle. Are the rectangles similar?

19. The length and width of one rectangle are each 2 cm more than the length and width of another rectangle. Are they similar?

20. If two figures are congruent, are they also similar?

Find the lengths of sides indicated by letters in these similar polygons.

**B** **21.**

**22.**

## Self-Test

Symbols and words to remember:
△ [p. 190]          ≅ [p. 201]                      ~ [p. 206]
triangle [p. 190]          acute, right, obtuse triangles [p. 190]
scalene, isosceles, equilateral triangles [p. 190]          quadrilateral [p. 194]
trapezoid [p. 194]          isosceles trapezoid [p. 194]          parallelogram [p. 194]
rhombus [p. 194]          polygon [p. 197]          equilateral [p. 197]
congruent [p. 201]          corresponding angles, sides [p. 201]
SAS, ASA, SSS [p. 202]                      similar [p. 206]

1. If the measure of one angle of a right triangle is 30°, what are the          [6-5]
   measures of the other two angles?

2. Can three sides of an isosceles triangle be congruent?

3. What is the measure of each angle of an equilateral triangle?

4. How many acute angles does an obtuse triangle have?

True or false? Write T or F.
5. Every square is a rhombus.          [6-6]
6. An isosceles trapezoid has two pairs of equal sides.
7. Every quadrilateral is a parallelogram.
8. Opposite sides of a parallelogram are equal.
9. A hexagon has eight sides.          10. All decagons are equilateral.          [6-7]

11. What is the perimeter of a rhombus with one side 6 cm long?

12. If one side of a parallelogram is 3.8 cm long and the perimeter
    of the parallelogram is 15.6 cm, how long are the other sides of
    the parallelogram?

13. If three angles of one triangle are equal to three angles of another          [6-8]
    triangle, must the triangles be congruent?

Complete each statement for the congruent triangles.

14. △ABC ≅ _?_

15. ∠D = _?_

16. DF = _?_

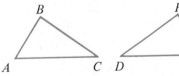

17. Are all congruent polygons also similar polygons?          [6-9]

18. Are all squares similar?          19. Are all rhombuses similar?

20. Are all isosceles triangles similar?

Self-Test answers and Extra Practice are at the back of the book.

# Chapter Review

Write the letter that labels the correct answer.

1. A line segment has __?__ endpoints(s).                          [6-1]
   **A.** 0          **B.** 1          **C.** 2          **D.** many

2. 6 km = __?__
   **A.** 600 m      **B.** 0.006 m    **C.** 600,000 m   **D.** 6000 m

3. 20 mm = __?__
   **A.** 0.002 m    **B.** 0.02 m     **C.** 2000 m      **D.** 0.2 m

4. A __?__ is used to draw a circle.                               [6-2]
   **A.** protractor  **B.** compass   **C.** straightedge  **D.** ruler

5. If the radius of a circle is 10 m, the circumference of the circle is approximately __?__.
   **A.** 31.4 m     **B.** 314 m      **C.** 62.8 m      **D.** 6.28 m

6. If the circumference of a circle is 154, the diameter of the circle is approximately __?__.
   **A.** 49         **B.** 484        **C.** 51          **D.** 0.5

7. If two lines form a right angle, they are said to be __?__.     [6-3]
   **A.** parallel                     **B.** perpendicular
   **C.** intersecting                 **D.** vertical

8. A pair of __?__ angles always have the same measure.
   **A.** complementary                **B.** acute
   **C.** supplementary                **D.** vertical

9. The supplement of a 30° angle has measure __?__.
   **A.** 60°        **B.** 30°        **C.** 150°        **D.** 180°

10. When two parallel lines are cut by a third line, alternate interior   [6-4]
    angles are __?__.
    **A.** corresponding               **B.** equal
    **C.** vertical                    **D.** supplementary

11. If lines $l$ and $m$ are parallel, we abbreviate this by writing __?__.
    **A.** $l \perp m$   **B.** $l \cong m$   **C.** $l \parallel m$   **D.** $l \sim m$

12. In a plane, two lines perpendicular to a third line are __?__ each other.
    **A.** perpendicular to            **B.** parallel to
    **C.** intersecting                **D.** equal to

13. In any triangle, the angle measures total __?__ .　　　　　[6-5]
    A. 360°　　　B. 90°　　　　C. 135°　　　D. 180°

14. A right triangle __?__ has two acute angles.
    A. always　　B. sometimes　C. never　　D. usually

15. In a(n) __?__ triangle, each angle measures 60°.
    A. acute　　B. isosceles　C. equilateral　D. scalene

16. A trapezoid is __?__ isosceles.　　　　　　　　　　　[6-6]
    A. always　　B. sometimes　C. never　　D. usually

17. A rhombus is __?__ a rectangle.
    A. always　　B. sometimes　C. never　　D. usually

18. A quadrilateral is __?__ a parallelogram.
    A. always　　B. sometimes　C. never　　D. usually

19. An octagon has __?__ sides.　　　　　　　　　　　　　[6-7]
    A. five　　　B. six　　　　C. eight　　　D. ten

20. If two sides of a parallelogram are 5 cm and 2 cm long, the perimeter of the parallelogram is __?__ .
    A. 7 cm　　B. 14 cm　　C. 28 cm　　　D. 3 cm

21. If the perimeter of an equilateral polygon is 24 cm and one side is 4 cm long, the polygon is a(n) __?__ .
    A. pentagon　B. hexagon　　C. octagon　　D. decagon

22. If $AB = DE, BC = EF$, and $\angle B = \angle E$, then $\triangle ABC \cong \triangle DEF$　　[6-8]
    by __?__ .
    A. SAS　　　B. ASA　　　C. AAA　　　D. SSS

23. If pentagon $JKLMN \cong$ pentagon $PQRST$, then __?__ .
    A. $JKLMN \cong TSRQP$　　　　B. $\angle J = \angle T$
    C. $\angle K = \angle Q$　　　　　　D. $JK = QR$

24. A method which is *not* used to check whether triangles are congruent is __?__ .
    A. SAS　　　B. ASA　　　C. AAA　　　D. SSS

25. If $ABCD \sim EFGH$, then __?__ .
    A. $AB = EF$　B. $CD = GH$　C. $\angle A = \angle E$　D. $\angle A = \angle H$　[6-9]

26. Two __?__ are always similar to each other.
    A. parallelograms　　　　B. rectangles
    C. squares　　　　　　　D. rhombuses

## *Mirror Geometry*

### GEOMETRY WITH ONE MIRROR

Can you read the word at the right? It is done in *mirror writing*. If you hold a mirror upright along the red line and look at the reflection of the word, you will be able to read it more easily. Sometimes this word is printed as shown here on the front of an ambulance. Why, do you think, is this so?

You can show your name in mirror writing by following these steps.

1. Write your name.

2. Hold a mirror upright alongside it as shown in the figure at the right.

3. Copy the reflection of your name in the mirror.

### Activities

1. In the diagram at the right, hold a mirror upright along the red line that cuts the angle. What kind of figure is formed by the angle and its reflection in the mirror? What happens to this figure as you move the mirror left and right?

2. In the diagram at the right, hold a mirror upright along the red line that cuts the angle. What kind of figure is formed by the angle and its reflection in the mirror? What happens to this figure as you move the mirror left and right?

In Activities 3–6 you are to draw a reflection as seen in a mirror. Ask a friend to help you by holding the mirror and the paper on which you are drawing.

3. Copy the figure at the right. With a mirror held upright along the red line, look *only* at the reflection of the dots and connect them to make an *X*.
4. Repeat Activity 3, but connect the dots to make an *N*.
5. With a mirror held upright along a line, draw a triangle by looking *only* at the reflection in the mirror.
6. Repeat Activity 5, but draw a circle.

GEOMETRY WITH TWO MIRRORS

Tape together two pocket mirrors so that they open like a book. Now open the mirrors to a 90° angle and set them down on a line drawn on a piece of paper as shown at the right.

## Activities

1. As you change the angle between the two mirrors, the reflection of the line will form different polygons. By experimenting, you can complete the following table.

| Angle | 90° | 120° | 60° | 45° | ? |
|---|---|---|---|---|---|
| Polygon | square | ? | ? | ? | pentagon |

2. Make a colored design on a piece of paper and set the open mirrors down on it. Watch what happens to the reflections as you change the angle between the mirrors.

# Chapter Test

1. Are ray AB and ray BA the same ray?  [6-1]

2. Are line CD and line DC the same line?

Complete.

3. If the radius of a circle is 6 cm, the circumference is __?__. (Use $\pi \approx 3.14$.)  [6-2]

4. If the circumference of a circle is 135.6, the diameter is __?__. (Use $\pi \approx \frac{22}{7}$.)

5. The measure of a(n) __?__ angle is between 0° and 90°.  [6-3]

6. The sum of two __?__ angles is 90°.

7. If you bisect a 48° angle, you get two angles each with measure __?__.

8. Two lines in a plane which do not intersect are called __?__.  [6-4]

9. Two lines in a plane which are perpendicular to a third line are __?__ to each other.

10. Whenever two parallel lines are cut by a third line, corresponding angles are __?__.

11. A triangle whose sides are three different lengths is called __?__.  [6-5]

12. In a(n) __?__ triangle, all three angles measure 60°.

13. If one angle of a parallelogram measures 60°, the angle opposite it measures __?__.  [6-6]

14. If all the sides of a parallelogram are equal, the parallelogram is called a(n) __?__.

15. An octagon has __?__ more side(s) than a pentagon has.  [6-7]

16. If two sides of a parallelogram are 11 cm and 9 cm long, the perimeter is __?__.

17. $\triangle ABC \cong$ __?__  [6-8]

18. The triangles are congruent by __?__.

19. Corresponding angles of similar polygons are __?__.  [6-9]

20. Corresponding sides of similar polygons are __?__.

# Cumulative Review

**1.** Name the fractions whose graphs are shown.  [Chap. 4]

Write each improper fraction as a mixed number.

**2.** $-\dfrac{11}{3}$  **3.** $\dfrac{51}{8}$  **4.** $\dfrac{17}{-6}$  **5.** $\dfrac{100}{9}$

Simplify. Express your answer in lowest terms.

**6.** $-2\dfrac{2}{3} \div \left(-1\dfrac{7}{16}\right) \times 3\dfrac{3}{8}$  **7.** $\dfrac{5}{8} - \dfrac{3}{4} + \left(-1\dfrac{1}{6}\right)$

Solve each proportion.

**8.** $\dfrac{n}{7} = \dfrac{3}{12}$  **9.** $\dfrac{2.4}{w} = \dfrac{0.7}{3.5}$  **10.** $\dfrac{1.44}{12} = \dfrac{q}{5}$  **11.** $\dfrac{0}{1.4} = \dfrac{y}{2.8}$  [Chap. 5]

**12.** If Jim rides his bicycle 90 km in 4 weeks, how far does he ride his bicycle in 7 weeks?

**13.** 12 is 40% of what number?  **14.** Change $\dfrac{7}{8}$ to a percent.

**15.** A radio normally selling for $32 is on sale for $28. What is the percent discount?

**16.** A salesclerk earns a $5\dfrac{1}{2}$% commission selling sporting goods. If she earned $13,000 in commissions last year, what was the value of her total sales?

Complete.

**17.** 3720 m = __?__ km  **18.** 32 mm = __?__ cm  [Chap. 6]

Find the circumference of the circle described. (Use $\pi \approx 3.14$.)

**19.** diameter = 32 cm  **20.** radius = 3.25 m

**21.** Use a ruler and compass to construct a $22\dfrac{1}{2}°$ angle.

**22.** Find the values of $x$ and $y$ in the diagram.

**23.** $\overline{AB} \| \overline{CD}$ and $AB = CD$. Does $AO = OD$? Explain.

Exercise 23

Exercise 22

**24.** A rectangle is 21 m long and 9 m wide. What is the perimeter of a similar rectangle 2.25 m wide?

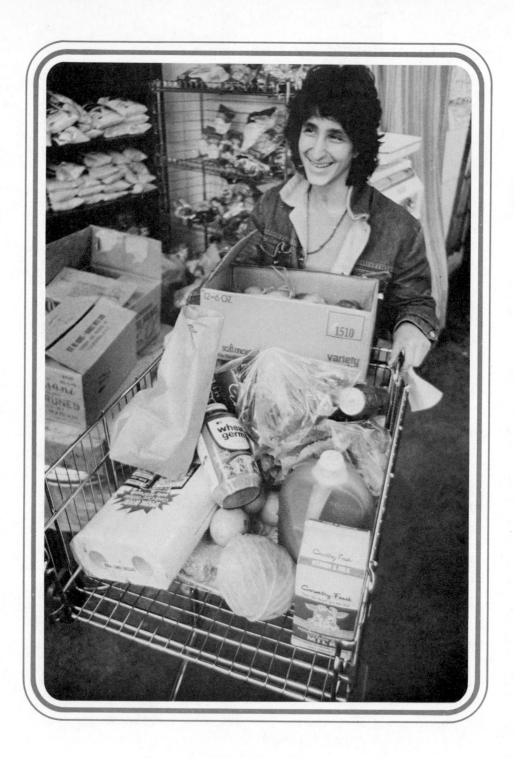

# 7

# Equations and Inequalities

## 7-1 Word Phrases and Numerical Expressions

**Objective** To translate word phrases describing numerical operations into numerical expressions, and vice versa.

The group of words

the sum of eight and four

is not a sentence, because it does not contain a verb. The group of words forms a word phrase. When we put this phrase into the mathematical form

$$8 + 4$$

we have a numerical expression that names the number twelve. The numerical expressions "12," "4 × 3," and "24 ÷ 2" also name the number twelve. Of course, "12" is the simplest name for twelve. Whenever we replace a numerical expression by its simplest name, we say that we have **simplified the expression.**

A numerical expression containing a variable is called a **variable expression.** Thus, the following are variable expressions:

$$6x \qquad 2y + 5 \qquad n \qquad 3(m - 4)$$

**Example 1** | Translate into a numerical expression: The product of nine and $b$.

Solution | $9b$

**Example 2** | Translate into a word phrase:

| **a.** $6 + 11n$ | **b.** $x - 3$ | **c.** $7(a + 5)$ | **d.** $\frac{r}{2}$

Solution | **a.** The sum of six and the product of eleven and $n$.
**b.** The difference when three is subtracted from $x$.
**c.** The product of seven and the sum of $a$ and five.
**d.** The quotient when $r$ is divided by two.

## Class Exercises

Translate the given word phrase into a numerical expression.

1. The product of negative four and two.

2. The sum of nineteen and negative twelve.

3. The difference when fourteen is subtracted from nine.

4. The quotient when eighteen is divided by negative six.

Translate into a word phrase.

| **5.** $8 + t$ | **6.** $15n$ | **7.** $3n - 8$ | **8.** $5(k - 4)$ |

Translate into a variable expression.

9. The product of fifteen and $n$.

10. $x$ divided by seven.

11. Eleven greater than $c$.

12. Nine less than $d$.

## Exercises

Write a variable expression for the word phrase.

**A** 1. Eight greater than $q$

2. Four less than $t$

3. The product of seven and $z$

4. The quotient when $m$ is divided by negative nineteen

**5.** The product of nine and the sum of $a$ and 3

**6.** The quotient when $x$ is divided by the sum of 2 and $n$

Match the word phrase with the numerical expression.

**7.** The difference when $y$ is subtracted from $x$

**8.** The sum of $x$ and twice $y$

**9.** Twice the sum of $x$ and $y$

**10.** The sum of 2 and the product of $x$ and $y$

**11.** The quotient when $x$ is divided by $y$

**12.** The quotient when $y$ is divided by $x$

**a.** $2 + xy$

**b.** $\frac{y}{x}$

**c.** $x - y$

**d.** $\frac{x}{y}$

**e.** $2(x + y)$

**f.** $x + 2y$

Write a word phrase for the variable expression.

**B**   **13.** $-5 + t$     **14.** $x - 9$     **15.** $2x + 7$     **16.** $-3z + 4$

**17.** $\frac{a}{2}$     **18.** $\frac{b - 2}{6}$     **19.** $\frac{1}{2}ab$     **20.** $\frac{-3 - n}{5}$

# EXTRA! Think of a Number . . .

You can use variable expressions to do a magic trick. Ask a friend to think of a number but not to tell you what it is. Then give the following directions. While your friend performs these operations, you perform them mentally on the variable $n$.

| Directions | You think | Your friend thinks (for example) |
|---|---|---|
| **1.** Think of a number. | $n$ | 4 |
| **2.** Add 3. | $n + 3$ | 7 |
| **3.** Multiply by 6. | $6n + 18$ | 42 |
| **4.** Subtract 8. | $6n + 10$ | 34 |
| **5.** Divide by 2. | $3n + 5$ | 17 |
| **6.** Subtract 5. | $3n$ | 12 |

Now you ask for the number your friend has arrived at. In this case it is 12. Since you know it is $3n$, or 3 times the original number, as if by magic you tell your friend the original number was 4.

**Research Activity** Try making up your own set of directions for "Think of a Number."

# 7-2 Evaluating Numerical Expressions

**Objective** To evaluate a variable expression for given values of each variable.

In Chapter 2 we learned that we can evaluate an expression such as $x + 3$ by replacing the variable $x$ with one of its values and doing the indicated arithmetic, or simplifying the expression. We say that we are **substituting** a value for $x$.

| | |
|---|---|
| *Example 1* | **Evaluate $3 + x$ if the value of $x$ is 2.** |
| *Solution* | **Substituting 2 for $x$ in $3 + x$, we obtain** |
| | $$3 + 2, \text{ or } 5$$ |

In evaluating expressions with grouping symbols such as parentheses or brackets, we perform the operation within the grouping symbols first. In evaluating expressions with fraction bars, we perform the operations indicated above and below the fraction bars first.

| | |
|---|---|
| *Example 2* | **Evaluate $4(1 - y)$ if $y = 5$.** |
| *Solution* | **Substituting 5 for $y$, we have** |
| | $$4(1 - 5) = 4(-4) = -16$$ |

| | |
|---|---|
| *Example 3* | **What is the value of $\dfrac{2n + 5}{3}$ when the value of $n$ is 17?** |
| *Solution* | **Replacing $n$ with 17, we obtain** |
| | $$\frac{(2 \times 17) + 5}{3} = \frac{34 + 5}{3} = \frac{39}{3} = 13$$ |

When there are no grouping symbols in an expression to indicate which operations should be done first, we agree to the following order:
1. Perform all multiplications and divisions in order from left to right.
2. Perform all additions and subtractions in order from left to right.

| | |
|---|---|
| *Example 4* | **Simplify $15 - 6 \div 3 + 4 \times 2$** |
| *Solution* | $15 - 6 \div 3 + 4 \times 2 = 15 - (6 \div 3) + (4 \times 2)$ |
| | $= 15 - 2 + 8$ |
| | $= 13 + 8 = 21$ |

## Class Exercises

Tell in which order the operations should be performed in simplifying the expression.

**1.** $(5 + 7) \times 2$

**2.** $5 + (7 \times 2)$

**3.** $3^2 - 4$

**4.** $\frac{4 - 2}{2}$

**5.** $\frac{6}{2 + 1}$

**6.** $13 - \frac{4 + 5}{3}$

Evaluate each expression when the value of $x$ is 3.

**7.** $x + 1$

**8.** $7x + 2$

**9.** $x^2 + 1$

**10.** $5x - x^2$

**11.** $\frac{1}{x}$

**12.** $\frac{x + 6}{-x}$

## Exercises

Evaluate each expression for the given value of the variable.

The value of $m$ is 1.

**A**

**1.** $12 + m$

**2.** $-4m$

**3.** $6 - m$

**4.** $2(m + 1)$

The value of $n$ is 2.

**5.** $n^2$

**6.** $-n$

**7.** $1 - n$

**8.** $3(5 - n)$

The value of $t$ is $-1$.

**9.** $\frac{t + 1}{2}$

**10.** $-2t$

**11.** $t^2$

**12.** $\frac{5}{t}$

The value of $x$ is 0.

**13.** $4x$

**14.** $x(x + 3)$

**15.** $\frac{x + 2}{2}$

**16.** $-x$

The value of $z$ is $-6$.

**B**

**17.** $z^2 + z$

**18.** $-z - 6$

**19.** $\frac{z + 6}{z}$

**20.** $\frac{1}{z} + z$

The value of $a$ is 2 and the value of $b$ is $-2$.

**21.** $3a + 4b$

**22.** $\frac{a - b}{a}$

**23.** $\frac{a^2 - b^2}{a - b}$

**24.** $\frac{1}{a} - \frac{1}{b}$

The value of $x$ is $\frac{1}{3}$ and the value of $y$ is $\frac{1}{4}$.

**C**

**25.** $\frac{x - y}{x}$

**26.** $\frac{x^2 + y^2}{-x^2}$

**27.** $\frac{1}{x}\left(\frac{1}{y} - \frac{1}{x}\right)$

**28.** $\frac{-x - y}{y^2}$

# 7-3 Word Sentences and Number Sentences

**Objective** To convert word sentences into number sentences and vice versa.

The group of words

> The sum of nine and five is fourteen

is a word sentence. When we put this sentence into the mathematical form

$$9 + 5 = 14$$

we have a *number sentence.* A **number sentence** consists of two numerical expressions, called **members of the sentence,** with a verb symbol between them. The verb symbol may be $=$ (is equal to), $\neq$ (is not equal to), or one of the symbols $>$, $<$ (is greater than, is less than). If the verb symbol is $=$, the sentence is an equation. If the verb symbol is an inequality symbol, the sentence is an inequality. For example, the number sentences

$$3 \neq 4, \quad 12 - 1 > 10, \quad \text{and} \quad 6 - 2 < 5$$

are inequalities.

Other symbols we use are

$\geq$ to mean "is greater than or equal to"
$\leq$ to mean "is less than or equal to"

Thus,

$$n \geq 3 \text{ means } "n > 3 \text{ or } n = 3"$$

A number sentence that contains one or more variables is called an **open number sentence** or, simply, an **open sentence.**

*Example* | Convert into a number sentence:

**a.** The difference when four is subtracted from $n$ is greater than six.

**b.** The product when five is multiplied by the sum of $x$ and two is less than or equal to twenty.

*Solution* | **a.** $n - 4 > 6$

**b.** $5(x + 2) \leq 20$

## Class Exercises

Convert into a word sentence.

**1.** $5 > 3$

**2.** $-1 < 0$

**3.** $4 + 2 = 6$

**4.** $2 + 1 \neq 4$

**5.** $\frac{1}{2} + \frac{1}{3} \neq \frac{1}{2+3}$

**6.** $\frac{2}{3} < \frac{3}{2}$

**7.** $m + 2 = 10$

**8.** $x - 1 = 2x + 2$

**9.** $\frac{1}{2}y - 3 \geq y - 4$

**10.** $\frac{n}{3} - 1 < n - 2$

Convert into a number sentence.

**11.** The sum of $x$ and two is less than negative four.

**12.** The product of two and the sum of $x$ and three is less than or equal to negative three.

**13.** The difference when nine is subtracted from seven is $t$.

**14.** The quotient when $m$ is divided by negative two is greater than ten.

**15.** The sum of $x$ and one third is less than or equal to negative one.

## Exercises

Match the word sentence with the number sentence.

**A**

**1.** Twice the sum of $x$ and four is less than two.

**2.** The sum of twice $x$ and four is greater than two.

**3.** The difference when four is subtracted from twice $x$ is less than two.

**4.** The sum of twice $x$ and four is less than two.

**5.** The product of two and the sum of $x$ and four is less than or equal to two.

**6.** Twice the difference when four is subtracted from $x$ is less than two.

**a.** $2(x + 4) \leq 2$

**b.** $2x + 4 > 2$

**c.** $2x + 4 < 2$

**d.** $2x - 4 < 2$

**e.** $2(x + 4) < 2$

**f.** $2(x - 4) < 2$

Write a number sentence.

**7.** The difference when seven is subtracted from $t$ is two.

**8.** The product of five and $z$ is greater than or equal to fifteen.

**9.** The quotient when $t$ is divided by eight is less than one half.

Write a number sentence.

**10.** A number *n* is the product of two thirds and five eighths.

**11.** The product of one half and *t* is less than or equal to eight.

**12.** A number *m* is the product of negative eleven and three fourths.

**13.** Negative one half is greater than the product of two and negative one.

**14.** The product of six and the sum of *x* and one is less than nine.

# A Rocket Pioneer

Robert Hutchings Goddard (1882–1945) was born in Worcester, Massachusetts. As a youngster he was often unable to attend school with his classmates because of health problems. Nevertheless, he kept up with his studies at home, and also did much additional reading in science.

As a research fellow at Princeton University in 1912, Dr. Goddard worked in radio electronics during the day, but at night he used his own time and money to study the fundamentals of rocketry. He was the first to prove that a rocket would work in a vacuum. In 1919, he published a paper entitled "A method of reaching extreme altitudes," in which he referred to the possibility of reaching the moon by rocket. The press ridiculed him as a "moon-man," but he continued his research. In New

Mexico in the early 1930's he designed and built the first prototypes of the rockets which now can land people on the moon and probe the outer solar system.

Dr. Goddard is considered the father of modern rocketry and received many honors after his death including the U.S. Congressional Gold Medal.

**Career Activity**  Find out what training is required to become an astronaut.

# 7-4 The Solution of an Open Sentence

**Objective** To decide whether or not a given value of a variable is a solution of a given open sentence.

The equation

$$x + 4 = 9$$

becomes a true statement if we replace $x$ with 5, because

$$5 + 4 = 9.$$

However, the equation is not true if $x = 8$, because

$$8 + 4 = 12 \quad \text{and} \quad 12 \neq 9.$$

We say that 5 is a **solution** of, or **satisfies,** the given equation.
   When we write

$$n + 2 \leq 15$$

we mean that

$$n + 2 < 15 \quad \text{or} \quad n + 2 = 15$$

Thus 6 and 13 are both solutions of $n + 2 \leq 15$ because

$$6 + 2 < 15 \quad \text{and} \quad 13 + 2 = 15$$

A solution of an open sentence in one variable is a value of the variable that makes the sentence a true statement.

*Example* | Find which of the two replacements for $n$ is a solution of
$$n - 6 > 11.$$
   **a.** $n = 25$        **b.** $n = 4$

*Solution* | **a.** Substituting 25 for $n$, we have
$$25 - 6 > 11, \text{ or } 19 > 11.$$
   Since $19 > 11$ is a true statement, **25** *is* a solution.

**b.** When $n = 4$, we have $4 - 6 > 11$, or $-2 > 11$.
   Since $-2 > 11$ is a false statement, $-2$ *is not* a solution.

## Class Exercises

Tell whether the statements are true or false.

**1.** $2 > 2$

**2.** $2 < 2$

**3.** $2 = 2$

**4.** $-1 > 0$

**5.** $-1 \geq -1$

**6.** $1 > 0$

**7.** $-3 \geq -3$

**8.** $-3 = -3$

**9.** $-1 \leq 0$

Tell whether or not the given value of the variable is a solution of the given sentence. Explain your answer.

*Example*  |  $t + 4 = 3; -1$

*Solution*  |  $-1$ **is a solution because** $-1 + 4 = 3$ **is a true statement.**

**10.** $x + 1 < 0; \frac{1}{2}$

**11.** $3x = 2; \frac{2}{3}$

**12.** $y - 1 > 0; \frac{1}{2}$

**13.** $m \geq 1; 1$

**14.** $3 - t = 4; -1$

**15.** $4z > 0; -1$

**16.** $2n = 1; 0$

**17.** $-x < 0; -1$

**18.** $-2t \leq 0; -1$

## Exercises

Replace the variable with the given value and tell whether the resulting statement is true or false.

**A**

**1.** $m + 1 = 0; -1$

**2.** $m + 1 \geq 0; -1$

**3.** $t - 3 > 0; 2$

**4.** $t - 3 \geq 0; 2$

**5.** $t - 3 \leq 0; 2$

**6.** $t - 3 < 0; 2$

**7.** $3x \leq 3; -1$

**8.** $3x \leq 3; 0$

**9.** $3x \leq 3; 1$

**10.** $3y \geq 0; 0$

**11.** $-3y \geq 0; 0$

**12.** $-n = 5; -5$

**13.** $-z = 1; -1$

**14.** $-m - 3 = 0; 3$

**15.** $-m - 3 = 0; -3$

Tell whether or not the given number is a solution of the given open sentence.

**16.** $x + 1 \geq -7; -6$

**17.** $3 - t = 2; 5$

**18.** $b + 4 = -3; -7$

**19.** $a - \frac{2}{3} > 0; \frac{1}{3}$

**20.** $\frac{y}{-1} = -2; 2$

**21.** $2t < 3; 1$

**B**

**22.** $5n \leq 2; -\frac{2}{5}$

**23.** $2x - 1 \geq 0; \frac{1}{2}$

**24.** $-8k > 9; -\frac{3}{4}$

**25.** $3x + 1 > 2x - 1; -1$

**26.** $x < 2x + 2; -2$

**27.** $3 - t \leq 4t; 1$

**28.** $-z + 8 = z - 8; 8$

**29.** $\frac{4x - 5}{3} \geq 0; 8$

**30.** $\frac{-n + 2}{7} < 1; 5$

# 7-5 The Solution Set of an Open Sentence

**Objective** To find the solution set of an open sentence in one variable whose replacement set is given.

To **solve** an open sentence in one variable, we look for all the solutions of the sentence. Of course, we have to know the replacement set (page 37) of the variable.

It sometimes helps in finding solutions to begin by drawing a graph.

*Example 1* | If the replacement set for $x$ is the set of whole numbers, find all solutions of

$$x \le 5.$$

*Solution*

the whole numbers

From the figure, you can see that there are just six solutions, 0, 1, 2, 3, 4, and 5, because they are the only *whole numbers* that are equal to or less than 5.

*Example 2* | If the replacement set for $y$ is the set of whole numbers, find all solutions of

$$3y = 7.$$

*Solution* | Since $y$ is a member of the set of whole numbers, $\{0, 1, 2, 3, \ldots\}$, $3y$ is a member of $\{3 \times 0, 3 \times 1, 3 \times 2, 3 \times 3, \ldots\}$ or $\{0, 3, 6, 9, \ldots\}$. The equation $3y = 7$ has *no* solution in the given replacement set.

The **solution set** of an open sentence consists of all the values in the given replacement set of the variable that make the sentence true. Thus the solution set in Example 1 is $\{0, 1, 2, 3, 4, 5\}$. In Example 2, the solution set has no members. The set with no members is called the **empty set** and is denoted by the symbol $\varnothing$.

## Class Exercises

Given the replacement set for $x$, $\{-2, -1, 0, 1, 2\}$, find the solution set of the given open sentence.

1. $x \leq 2$

2. $x < 2$

3. $x < 0$

4. $x > 0$

5. $x + 1 = 2$

6. $x + 2 = 0$

7. $x = -5$

8. $x - 5 = -3$

9. $x - 2 = 0$

Match the open sentence with the graph which represents its solution set. The replacement set for $x$ is $\{-1, 0, 1, 2, 3\}$.

10. $x < 0$

11. $x \geq 0$

12. $x > 0$

13. $x \leq 3$

## Exercises

Graph the solution set. The replacement set for $x$ is $\{-3, -2, -1, 0, 1, 2, 3\}$.

**A**

1. $x + 1 = 2$

2. $x < -1$

3. $x \geq 0$

4. $2x = 0$

5. $2x - 1 \leq 4$

6. $x + 3 = 10$

7. $7 - x \leq 5$

8. $x + 7 \leq 5$

9. $x - 4 = 5$

10. $x - 5 > -4$

11. $-x \geq 3$

12. $3x + 3 = 0$

Give the solution set if the replacement set for $x$ is the set of integers.

*Example*  | $x + 1 > -3$

*Solution*  | $\{-3, -2, -1, \ldots\}$

13. $x < 0$

14. $x > 4$

15. $x \geq 4$

16. $x < -3$

17. $x - 1 \geq 2$

18. $2x - 1 > 0$

Give the solution set. The replacement set for $x$ is given.

**B**  19. $-x + 2 \le -1$                  $\{-3, -2, -1, 0, 1, 2, 3\}$

    20. $3x - 5 > -7$                $\{-2, -1, 0, 1, 2, 3, 4\}$

    21. $\frac{x+1}{3} < 1$                     $\{0, 1, 2, 3, 4, 5\}$

    22. $4x - 3 \le 2$                  $\{-3, -2, -1, 0, 1, 2, 3\}$

**C**  23. $3x - 2 \le x + 2$            $\{-5, -4, -3, -2, -1, 0\}$

    24. $3 - 2x > x$                  $\{-3, -2, -1, 0, 1, 2, 3\}$

# *EXTRA!* Investigating Inequalities

1. Copy the number line shown below. Use a heavy dot to mark the graph of each solution of the inequality $x < 4$ if the replacement set for $x$ is $\{0, 1, 2, 3, 4, 5, 6, 7, 8\}$.

2. Make another copy of the number line shown above and use a heavy dot to mark the graph of each solution of the inequality $x + 1 < 5$, using the same replacement set for $x$ as in Step 1.

3. Repeat Step 2 for the inequality $x - 1 < 3$.

4. From your results for Steps 1, 2, and 3, what can you say about the solution sets of the inequalities

$$x < 4, \qquad x + 1 < 5, \qquad \text{and} \qquad x - 1 < 3$$

when the replacement set for $x$ is $\{0, 1, 2, 3, 4, 5, 6, 7, 8\}$?

5. What do Steps 1–4 suggest about the solution sets of the inequalities

$$x < a, \qquad x + 1 < a + 1, \qquad \text{and} \qquad x - 1 < a - 1$$

for a given replacement set for $x$?

6. What do you think might be true of the inequalities

$$x < a, \qquad x + b < a + b, \qquad \text{and} \qquad x - b < a - b$$

for a given replacement set for $x$?

## Self-Test

Words to remember:
numerical expression (p. 217)   variable expression (p. 217)
evaluate (p. 220)   number sentence (p. 222)
open sentence (p. 222)   solution (p. 225)
solve (p. 227)   solution set (p. 227)
empty set (p. 227)

Write a variable expression.

**1.** The sum of one and a number, $x$.

**2.** The product of twelve and a number, $n$.   [7-1]

Write a word phrase.

**3.** $13 - z$

**4.** $5z + 12$

Evaluate the expressions if $x = -5$.

**5.** $-7 + x$   **6.** $\frac{3}{5}x$   **7.** $-2x + 4$   **8.** $-\frac{1}{x}$   [7-2]

Translate into a number sentence.

**9.** The quotient when $y$ is divided by three is negative nine.   [7-3]

**10.** The product when two is multiplied by the sum of $n$ and four is fourteen.

Write a word sentence.

**11.** $3(y - 9) \le -8$   **12.** $-7x + 31 > 4$

Tell whether or not the given number is a solution of the given open sentence.

**13.** $x - 13 > -1;\ 5$   **14.** $4x - 7 = 5;\ -3$   [7-4]

**15.** $-4y \ge 16;\ y = -4$   **16.** $n < -2n - 3;\ -2$

Graph the solution set. The replacement set for $x$ is $\{-5, -4, -3, -2, -1, 0\}$.

**17.** $x + 4 > 0$   **18.** $x + 2 = 0$   [7-5]

**19.** $2x + 3 = -5$   **20.** $x - 3 \le -6$

Self-Test answers and Extra Practice are at the back of the book.

# 7-6 Properties of Equality

**Objective** To use the addition and multiplication properties of equality.

We use the addition property of equality and the multiplication property of equality to solve equations.

## properties

**Addition Property of Equality**
Given a true equation, we may add the same number to both members and the resulting equation will also be true.

$$4 + 3 = 7 \quad \text{and} \quad (4 + 3) + 5 = 7 + 5$$

In general, for any numbers $a$, $b$, and $c$:

If $a = b$, then $a + c = b + c$.

If $a + c = b + c$, then $a = b$.

---

**Multiplication Property of Equality**
Given a true equation, we may multiply both members by the same number and the resulting equation will also be true.

$$11 - 2 = 9 \quad \text{and} \quad (11 - 2)4 = (9)4$$

In general, for any numbers $a$, $b$, and $c$:

If $a = b$, then $ac = bc$.

If $ac = bc$ and $c \neq 0$, then $a = b$.

It is important to note that even though $a \times 0 = b \times 0$, we can still have $a \neq b$.

$$7 \times 0 = 4 \times 0 \quad \text{but} \quad 7 \neq 4$$

*Example* | Use one of the properties of equality to form a true sentence:

$$\text{If } y = 2, \text{ then } y + \underline{\ ?\ } = 11$$

*Solution* | Since $2 + 9 = 11$, by the addition property of equality we know that $y + 9 = 2 + 9$.

$$\text{If } y = 2, \text{ then } y + 9 = 11.$$

## Class Exercises

Use one of the properties of equality to form a true sentence.

**1.** If $t = 3$, then $t + 6 = \underline{\ ?\ }$

**2.** If $z = 1$, then $z + \underline{\ ?\ } = 9$

**3.** If $x = -1$, then $4x = \underline{\ ?\ }$

**4.** If $n = 6$, then $n - 7 = \underline{\ ?\ }$

**5.** If $x = 13$, then $2x = \underline{\ ?\ }$

**6.** If $m = 12$, then $8m = \underline{\ ?\ }$

**7.** If $a = -2$, then $a - 9 = \underline{\ ?\ }$

**8.** If $b = 7$, then $-3b = \underline{\ ?\ }$

**9.** If $t = 3$, then $t - 6 = \underline{\ ?\ }$

**10.** If $4n = -16$, then $n = \underline{\ ?\ }$

**11.** If $7d = 28$, then $d = \underline{\ ?\ }$

**12.** If $k = 9$, then $k + \underline{\ ?\ } = 4$

**13.** If $-3y = 12$, then $y = \underline{\ ?\ }$

**14.** If $m = 0$, then $m + \underline{\ ?\ } = -6$

## Exercises

Use one of the properties of equality to form a true sentence.

**A**

**1.** If $x = 7$, then $x + 11 = \underline{\ ?\ }$

**2.** If $n = -8$, then $n + 12 = \underline{\ ?\ }$

**3.** If $t = -1$, then $t - 3 = \underline{\ ?\ }$

**4.** If $y = 9$, then $y - 8 = \underline{\ ?\ }$

**5.** If $x = 0$, then $x + 4 = \underline{\ ?\ }$

**6.** If $a = 12$, then $5a = \underline{\ ?\ }$

**7.** If $c = -3$, then $2c = \underline{\ ?\ }$

**8.** If $b = 9$, then $-3b = \underline{\ ?\ }$

**9.** If $m = -11$, then $-3m = \underline{\ ?\ }$

**10.** If $t = -4$, then $-4t = \underline{\ ?\ }$

*Example* | If $t + 1 = 4$, then $t = \underline{\ ?\ }$

*Solution* | $t + 1 = 4$ and $4 = 3 + 1$

$t + 1 = 3 + 1$   so by the addition property of equality,

$t = 3.$

**B** **11.** If $x + 9 = 15$, then $x =$ ?

**12.** If $z + 1 = 9$, then $z =$ ?

**13.** If $4n = 16$, then $n =$ ?

**14.** If $3t = 21$, then $t =$ ?

**15.** If $-3a = 21$, then $a =$ ?

**16.** If $4k = -16$, then $k =$ ?

**17.** If $2b = -22$, then $b =$ ?

**18.** If $-8t = -24$, then $t =$ ?

**19.** If $z - 11 = 3$, then $z =$ ?

**20.** If $m - 3 = -2$, then $m =$ ?

**21.** If $-4a = -24$, then $a =$ ?

**22.** If $9 + z = 6$, then $z =$ ?

**C** **23.** If $\frac{2}{3}z = 16$, then $z =$ ?

**24.** If $-\frac{3}{5}n = 12$, then $n =$ ?

**25.** If $2n = 5$, then $4n - 2 =$ ?

**26.** If $4n = -3$, then $8n + 2 =$ ?

**27.** If $3t = -7$, then $6t + 5 =$ ?

**28.** If $3x = -4$, then $9x + 2 =$ ?

# Application
## Pricing by Quantity

Items in stores are frequently priced by quantity, such as "3 pens for 76¢." If you buy only one pen, you cannot pay the exact amount of 76¢ ÷ 3 = $25\frac{1}{3}$¢, so the store charges you 26¢. In general, the store charges you the number of cents which is the least integer greater than or equal to the exact price in cents.

**Computer Activity** The BASIC computer program below computes the price you pay on single items which are priced by quantity.

```
10 PRINT"QUANTITY=";
20 INPUTQ
30 PRINT"COST IN CENTS=";
40 INPUTC
50 PRINT"PRICE FOR SINGLE ITEM=";-INT(-C/Q);"CENTS"
60 END
```

Use this program to find the price of a single item which is priced at

**1.** 6 for 98¢          **2.** 5 for 89¢          **3.** 3 for 55¢

Which is the better buy?
**4.** 3 for $2.98 or 6 for $5.69
**5.** 5 for $12.29 or 15 for $35.98
**6.** $16.98 a dozen or 20 for $27.59

# 7-7 Solving Equations by Transformations

**Objective** To solve an equation in one variable by transforming it into one which can be solved by inspection.

Two equations are **equivalent** if they have the same solution. The usual way to solve an equation is to transform it into an equivalent equation in which one member is the variable and the other member is some number $c$.

$$x = c$$

Then the solution is simply $c$.

Here are some transformations, based on the properties of equality, that yield equivalent equations.

---

**a.** **Simplify numerical expressions in either member.**

$x + 3 = 4 + 7$ is equivalent to $x + 3 = 11$

**b.** **Exchange members.**

$-6 = 9 + x$ is equivalent to $9 + x = -6$

**c.** **Use the properties of addition and multiplication, for example, the distributive property.**

$2(x - 7) = 0$ is equivalent to $2x - 14 = 0$

**d.** **Add the same number to both members.**

$3x + 2 = 5$ is equivalent to $3x + 2 + (-2) = 5 + (-2)$

We can also subtract the same number from both members. This is equivalent to adding the opposite, as we did here.

**e.** **Multiply or divide both members by the same nonzero number.**

$4x = 13$ is equivalent to $\frac{4x}{4} = \frac{13}{4}$

---

Sometimes we have to use more than one transformation to obtain an equation of the form $x = c$.

*Example* | Solve $21 = 3(x - 4)$. The replacement set for $x$ is {the rational numbers}. Identify which transformations you use and check your solution in the original equation.

Transformation used

*Solution*

$$21 = 3(x - 4)$$
$$3(x - 4) = 21 \qquad \textbf{b}$$
$$3x - 12 = 21 \qquad \textbf{c}$$
$$3x - 12 + 12 = 21 + 12 \qquad \textbf{d}$$
$$3x = 33 \qquad \textbf{a}$$
$$x = 11 \qquad \textbf{e}$$

The solution set is $\{11\}$.

Check:

Substitute 11 for $x$ in $21 = 3(x - 4)$.

$$21 \stackrel{?}{=} 3(11 - 4)$$
$$21 = 3(7) = 21 \checkmark$$

# Class Exercises

Tell which transformation is used to obtain the second equation from the first.

1. $4x = 28;\ x = 7$

2. $12 = x + 9;\ x + 9 = 12$

3. $1 + t = -3;\ t + 1 = -3$

4. $y - 3 = 1;\ y = 4$

5. $z = 5 + (-9);\ z = -4$

6. $6(x - 2) = 3;\ 6x - 12 = 3$

Tell which transformation is used in each step.

7. $\quad \frac{2}{3}t - 4 = 4$

$\frac{2}{3}t - 4 + 4 = 4 + 4$

$\frac{2}{3}t = 8$

$3\left(\frac{2}{3}t\right) = 3(8)$

$2t = 24$

$t = 12$

8. $\quad -5 = 3z + 13$

$3z + 13 = -5$

$3z + 13 - 13 = -5 - 13$

$3z = -18$

$\frac{3z}{3} = \frac{-18}{3}$

$z = -6$

## Exercises

Solve. Check your solution.

A

1. $y - 9 = 3$

2. $t + 2 = 13$

3. $5x = 25$

4. $y - 3 = -8$

5. $\frac{3}{4}t = -15$

6. $-\frac{1}{2}x = \frac{24}{36} + \frac{1}{6} = \frac{5}{6}$

7. $-3 - 7 = x + 1$

8. $6x = -4 + (-18)$ ⌒22

9. $x(4 - 2) = 40$

10. $-y - (-2y) = 9$

11. $-3t = -1 + 4$

12. $5x - 2x = -18$

B

13. $5x - 2 = x + 10$

14. $-9y + (+y) = 5$

15. $\frac{2}{3}x + lx = -15$

16. $\frac{3}{4}y - \frac{1}{2} = 2y + \frac{1}{2}$

17. $\frac{1}{2}x + \frac{3}{5} = 2x + \frac{-9}{10}$

18. $\frac{3}{5}y = 2y - 7$

C

19. $3(x - 5) = -2x + 5$

20. $\frac{1}{3}(5x - 6) = x + 2$

21. $-t - 9 = \frac{3}{4}\left(2t + \frac{4}{3}\right)$

22. $\frac{1}{2}(-4y - 5) = 7\left(y - \frac{1}{2}\right)$

# EXTRA! Using Equations

Suppose you are asked to find two consecutive integers whose sum is 15. You can use an equation to solve this problem. Start by letting $n$ be the smaller integer. Then $n + 1$ is the larger integer, and the sum of the two integers is $n + n + 1$, or $2n + 1$.

$$2n + 1 = 15$$
$$2n + 1 + (-1) = 15 + (-1)$$
$$2n = 14$$
$$n = 7 \quad \text{and} \quad n + 1 = 8$$

The numbers are 7 and 8.

Find the numbers described by writing and solving an equation.

1. The sum of two consecutive integers is $-7$.
2. The sum of three consecutive integers is 39.
3. One number is 4 less than another number. The sum of the numbers is 22.

# 7-8 Solving Inequalities by Transformations

**Objective** To solve an inequality by transforming it into one which can be solved by inspection.

You can solve an inequality just as you did an equation, by transforming it into an inequality with the same solutions (an **equivalent inequality**). The transformations are similar to the ones used with equations, with two important exceptions. Notice the effect on the inequality signs in **b** and **f.**

---

**a.** Simplify numerical expressions in either member.

$$x - 4 > -1 + 3 \text{ is equivalent to } x - 4 > 2.$$

**b.** Exchange members, *thereby changing the direction of the inequality.*

$$6 < x + 5 \text{ is equivalent to } x + 5 > 6.$$

**c.** Use the properties of addition and multiplication.

$$4(x - 1) \geq 8 \text{ is equivalent to } 4x - 4 \geq 8.$$

**d.** Add the same number to both members.

$$2x - 3 < 7 \text{ is equivalent to } 2x - 3 + 3 < 7 + 3.$$

**e.** Multiply or divide both members by the same *positive* number.

$$3x > 6 \text{ is equivalent to } \frac{3x}{3} > \frac{6}{3}.$$

**f.** Multiply or divide both members by the same *negative* number, *thereby changing the direction of the inequality.*

$$-\frac{x}{2} > 5 \text{ is equivalent to } -2\left(-\frac{x}{2}\right) < -2(5)$$

*Example*   Solve $16 \geq 4(3 - x)$.  The replacement set for $x$ is {the integers}.  Tell which transformations you use.

                                                  Transformation used

*Solution*                  $16 \geq 4(3 - x)$

                 $4(3 - x) \leq 16$                          **b**

                 $12 - 4x \leq 16$                           **c**

          $12 - 4x - 12 \leq 16 - 12$                        **d**

                   $-4x \leq 4$                              **a**

                 $\dfrac{-4x}{-4} \geq \dfrac{4}{-4}$        **f**

                   $x \geq -1$                               **a**

The solution set is the set of integers that are greater than or equal to $-1$, that is, $\{-1, 0, 1, 2, 3, \ldots\}$.

## Class Exercises

Tell which graph represents the solution set of each inequality.  The replacement set for $x$ is $\{-2, -1, 0, 1, 2\}$.

**1.** $x \leq 0$

**2.** $x > -2$

**3.** $x < 0$

**4.** $x \leq 2$

Tell which transformation is used to obtain the second inequality from the first.

**5.** $y - 4 \geq 7; y \geq 11$          **6.** $2(t - 6) > 0; 2t - 12 > 0$

**7.** $t \leq -3 - 9; t \leq -12$         **8.** $-3x < 18; x > -6$

**9.** $5t > 35; t > 7$              **10.** $-4 < z + 9; z + 9 > -4$

## Exercises

Graph the solution set.  The replacement set for $x$ is $\{-3, -2, -1, 0, 1, 2\}$.

**A**   **1.** $x \leq 1$                   **2.** $x + 1 \geq -2$

      **3.** $2x < 1$                 **4.** $x - 4 \geq -3$

Solve. The replacement set for each variable is {the integers}.

**5.** $-3 > z$

**6.** $x + 1 \leq 0$

**7.** $x + (-9) > -2$

**8.** $4 + (-12) \leq x$

**9.** $\frac{2}{3}x < -3$

**10.** $-\frac{1}{2}y \leq 8$

**11.** $\frac{3}{5}y < -6$

**12.** $-y > \frac{1}{2}$

**13.** $t + (-9) \leq -3$

**14.** $y - 3 > 2$

**B** **15.** $3 - t > -2$

**16.** $4y + 1 \geq 13$

**17.** $4(y - 2) \leq 10$

**18.** $5x - 5 < 45$

**19.** $11 - z > 0$

**20.** $\frac{2}{3}x + 4 \geq 0$

**C** **21.** $-\frac{3}{4}(z + 1) \leq -z - 3$

**22.** $-3x + \frac{1}{2} \leq \frac{1}{2}(x - 20)$

## Self-Test

Words to remember:
addition property of equality (p. 231)
equivalent equations (p. 234)

multiplication property of equality (p. 231)
equivalent inequalities (p. 237)

Use one of the properties of equality to form a true sentence.

**1.** If $y = 8$, then $y + 4 = $ __?__  **2.** If $z = 17$, then $z - 9 = $ __?__  [7-6]

**3.** If $x = -6$, then $9x = $ __?__  **4.** If $t = 5$, then $-7t = $ __?__

Solve each equation and check your solution.

**5.** $x + 4 = 1$

**6.** $y - 13 = 9$  [7-7]

**7.** $-5z = -40$

**8.** $t + 5t = -36$

Solve. The replacement set for $x$ is {the integers}.

**9.** $x - 1 > -3$

**10.** $x + 2 \leq -8$  [7-8]

**11.** $-30 < 5x$

**12.** $-8x \geq -24$

Self-Test answers and Extra Practice are at the back of the book.

## Chapter Review

Write the letter that labels the correct answer.

1. The word phrase "twice the sum of $x$ and $y$" may be translated
   into the numerical phrase __?__ .    **[7-1]**
   **A.** $2x + y$    **B.** $2 + xy$    **C.** $2(x + y)$    **D.** $2xy$

2. The numerical expression $1 + 3b$ may be translated into the
   word phrase __?__ .
   **A.** The sum of one and the product of three and $b$.
   **B.** The product of $b$ and the sum of one and three.
   **C.** The sum of one and three and $b$.
   **D.** The product of one and the sum of three and $b$.

What is the value of the expression if $x = -3$?    **[7-2]**

3. $x + 14$
   **A.** 17    **B.** $-17$    **C.** 11    **D.** $-11$

4. $3x - 5$
   **A.** 4    **B.** $-14$    **C.** $-4$    **D.** 1

5. The word sentence "The product of seven and the sum of $t$ and
   three is greater than nine" may be translated into the number    **[7-3]**
   sentence __?__ .
   **A.** $7t + 3 > 9$    **B.** $7(t + 3) > 9$
   **C.** $7t + 3 < 9$    **D.** $7(t + 3) < 9$

6. The number sentence $\frac{1}{2}x + 7 > 5$ may be translated into the
   word sentence __?__ .
   **A.** One half the sum of $x$ and seven is greater than five.
   **B.** The sum of one half $x$ and seven is less than five.
   **C.** The product of one half $x$ and seven is greater than five.
   **D.** The sum of one half $x$ and seven is greater than five.

Which number is a solution of the open sentence?    **[7-4]**

7. $z - 8 = -3$
   **A.** $-5$    **B.** 11    **C.** $-11$    **D.** 5

8. $5x > -30$
   **A.** 0    **B.** $-6$    **C.** $-7$    **D.** $-10$

Which graph represents the solution set? The replacement set for [7-5]
$x$ is $\{-2, -1, 0, 1, 2\}$.

9. $x + 2 = 1$

A. (number line) $-2\ -1\ \ 0\ \ 1\ \ 2$

B. (number line) $-2\ -1\ \ 0\ \ 1\ \ 2$

C. (number line) $-2\ -1\ \ 0\ \ 1\ \ 2$

D. (number line) $-2\ -1\ \ 0\ \ 1\ \ 2$

10. $x + 3 \le 2$

A. (number line) $-2\ -1\ \ 0\ \ 1\ \ 2$

B. (number line) $-2\ -1\ \ 0\ \ 1\ \ 2$

C. (number line) $-2\ -1\ \ 0\ \ 1\ \ 2$

D. (number line) $-2\ -1\ \ 0\ \ 1\ \ 2$

Use the properties of equality to complete the sentence. [7-6]

11. If $t = -8$, then $t + 3 = \underline{\ ?\ }$ .
    A. $-24$　　　　B. $-11$　　　　C. $-5$　　　　D. $24$

12. If $t = -14$, then $-2t = \underline{\ ?\ }$ .
    A. $-16$　　　　B. $28$　　　　C. $-12$　　　　D. $-28$

Which number is the solution of the equation? [7-7]

13. $x - 7 = -20$
    A. $-27$　　　　B. $13$　　　　C. $27$　　　　D. $-13$

14. $4x = -13 - 15$
    A. $-7$　　　　B. $-28$　　　　C. $7$　　　　D. $-6$

Which set is the solution set of the inequality? The replacement set [7-8]
for $x$ is $\{$the integers$\}$.

15. $x - 13 \le 4$
    A. $\{17, 18, 19, \ldots\}$　　　　　　　B. $\{\ldots, 9, 10, 11\}$
    C. $\{\ldots, 15, 16, 17\}$　　　　　　D. $\{\ldots, 14, 15, 16\}$

16. $-4x \le -16$
    A. $\{\ldots, 2, 3, 4\}$　　　　　　　　B. $\{4, 5, 6, \ldots\}$
    C. $\{\ldots, -6, -5, -4\}$　　　　　D. $\{5, 6, 7, \ldots\}$

# Secret Codes

Over the centuries, many methods have been devised for writing secret messages. For example, Julius Caesar used a method in which each letter of a message was replaced by the letter three places to the right in the alphabet. Thus, using our alphabet, the word RED would appear in code as UHG.

Another method of encoding a secret message is by changing the order of the letters in the message. One way of doing this is shown below.

Let's say we want to encode the message:

SPACE   SHIP   ULTRA   MAKES   GALAXY   TOUR

First, we write the message in the spaces of a rectangle as shown at the right. In this case, we have used a rectangle with 8 columns and 4 rows.

Next, we form a key by scrambling the numbers from 1–8 and writing them at the heads of the columns. We are using the key 5-7-2-4-1-6-3-8.

| 5 | 7 | 2 | 4 | 1 | 6 | 3 | 8 |
|---|---|---|---|---|---|---|---|
| S | P | A | C | E | S | H | I |
| P | U | L | T | R | A | M | A |
| K | E | S | G | A | L | A | X |
| Y | T | O | U | R |   |   |   |

To write the message in code, we start with Column 1 and write the letters in order from top to bottom. Then we continue with Columns 2, 3, and so on. It is customary to write the coded message in blocks of 5 letters. Thus, when written in code our message is: ERARA LSOHM ACTGU SPKYS ALPUE TIAX

To *decode* the message, we first need to figure out the number of columns and rows in the rectangle. We can tell directly from the key, 5-7-2-4-1-6-3-8, that there are 8 columns.

To find the number of rows, we count the number of letters in the message, in this case it is 29. We divide 29 by 8 (the number of columns). From this we see that there are 3 rows in the rectangle completely filled with letters and that the remaining 5 letters partially fill the 4th row.

$$\begin{array}{r} 3 \\ 8\overline{)29} \\ 24 \\ \hline 5 \end{array}$$

Now we draw a rectangle as shown at the right and write the message we received starting from top to bottom of Column 1, then going on to Column 2, and so on. When we finish, the original message will be reconstructed.

| 5 | 7 | 2 | 4 | 1 | 6 | 3 | 8 |
|---|---|---|---|---|---|---|---|
|   |   | A |   | E |   | H |   |
|   |   | L |   | R |   | M |   |
|   |   | S |   | A |   |   |   |
|   |   | O |   | R |   |   |   |

1. The following encoded message was obtained by replacing each letter of the original message with the letter three places to the left in the alphabet. Decode the message.

PHXQBYLXOABOP    EXSB    JLOB    CRK

2. Secret agent Dora Dynamic was posing as an accountant in Liverpool, England, while awaiting news of a secret shipment to arrive from Canada. Twenty-four hours after receiving the coded message shown below, she left for Quebec. What did the message say? The key is 8-6-3-1-2-5-9-4-7.

SKLEN HTAET ENOMO ICLEA IHTTR HUCTM SHOIL TSOSN PEEME

3. After five years as a lone rancher in Colorado, Dan Devine received the following encoded message and gave a shout of joy that was heard as far away as Nevada. What did the message say? The key is 1-4-7-6-3-5-2.

IYPRG OTOOA DEPLR VAOOM ERPRF IECRA ROCUS ALA

4. Write a message in code and exchange it with one written by a friend. Can you decode each other's message?

**Research Activity**  The science of secret codes is known as *cryptography*. Go to the library and find other ways to encode messages.

## Chapter Test

1. Write a numerical expression for the word phrase "twelve less than negative two." **[7-1]**

2. Write a word phrase for the numerical expression $\frac{x+1}{8}$.

Evaluate each expression if $x = -1$.

3. $\frac{x-3}{2}$　　　　　　　　　4. $4x + 3$　　　　　　　　**[7-2]**

5. Translate into a number sentence: "The difference when $z$ is subtracted from eleven is greater than zero." **[7-3]**

6. Write a word sentence for the number sentence $5t - 4 \geq -3$.

Tell whether or not the given number is a solution of the given open sentence.

7. $x - 8 = -11$; 3　　　　　　8. $3t \leq 2$; $\frac{1}{2}$　　　　　　**[7-4]**

Graph the solution set. The replacement set for $x$ is $\{1, 2, 3, 4, 5\}$.

9. $x - 3 = 0$　　　　　　　　10. $x + 2 \leq 5$　　　　　　**[7-5]**

Use one of the properties of equality to form a true sentence.

11. If $t = -3$, then $t + 2 = \underline{\ ?\ }$　　12. If $y = 8$, then $-5y = \underline{\ ?\ }$　　**[7-6]**

Solve each equation and check your solution.

13. $x - 8 = 4$　　　　　　　　14. $3x + 2x = -20$　　　　　**[7-7]**

Solve. The replacement set for $x$ is $\{$the integers$\}$.

15. $9x \geq 81$　　　　　　　　16. $x - 13 < 5$　　　　　　　**[7-8]**

# Skill Review

Add or subtract.

**1.** $17 + 3$  **2.** $18 - 5$  **3.** $-16 + 6$  **4.** $-28 - 17$

**5.** $23 - 51$  **6.** $6 + 3$  **7.** $19 - 12$  **8.** $-33 + 11$

**9.** $15 - 26$  **10.** $27 + 6$  **11.** $11 - 33$  **12.** $6 + (-17)$

**13.** $11 + 26$  **14.** $15 - 17$  **15.** $23 - 42$  **16.** $16 + (-12)$

**17.** $55 + (-13)$  **18.** $73 + 26$  **19.** $59 + 12$  **20.** $69 + (-3)$

**21.** $10 + (-27)$  **22.** $16 - 3$  **23.** $17 + 19$  **24.** $19 - (-6)$

**25.** $7 + 4 - 3 + 16$  **26.** $17 + 2 + (-6 - 21)$

**27.** $53 + 111 - 27 + (-26)$  **28.** $19 + 13 - 17 - 6$

Multiply or divide.

**29.** $7 \times 3$  **30.** $4 \times 6$  **31.** $-5 \times 12$  **32.** $2 \times 17$

**33.** $17 \times (-2)$  **34.** $6 \times (-6)$  **35.** $2 \div 2$  **36.** $14 \div (-7)$

**37.** $-64 \div 8$  **38.** $18 \times (-3)$  **39.** $6 \times 7$  **40.** $9 \times 6$

**41.** $-8 \times 7$  **42.** $33 \div 11$  **43.** $60 \div (-5)$  **44.** $120 \div 10$

**45.** $16 \div 8$  **46.** $27 \div (-3)$  **47.** $18 \div 6$  **48.** $3 \times 11$

**49.** $-5 \times (-12)$  **50.** $56 \div 7$  **51.** $24 \div 8$  **52.** $6 \times 12$

**53.** $12 \times 12$  **54.** $16 \div 2$  **55.** $6 \times 11$  **56.** $12 \times (-12)$

**57.** $14 \div 2$  **58.** $28 \div (-2)$  **59.** $7 \times (-7)$  **60.** $6 \times 8$

Perform the indicated operations.

**61.** $10 - 4 \times (-2)$  **62.** $13 + (-12) \div 12$

**63.** $-1 \times (-3) + 5$  **64.** $-68 \div 17 - 14$

**65.** $2 \times (-18) - 3 \times (-10)$  **66.** $60 \div (-5) + (-9) \times (-1)$

**67.** $3 + 5 \times (-11) - 8 \div (-2)$  **68.** $-16 \div (-4) - 2 \times (-5) + (-18)$

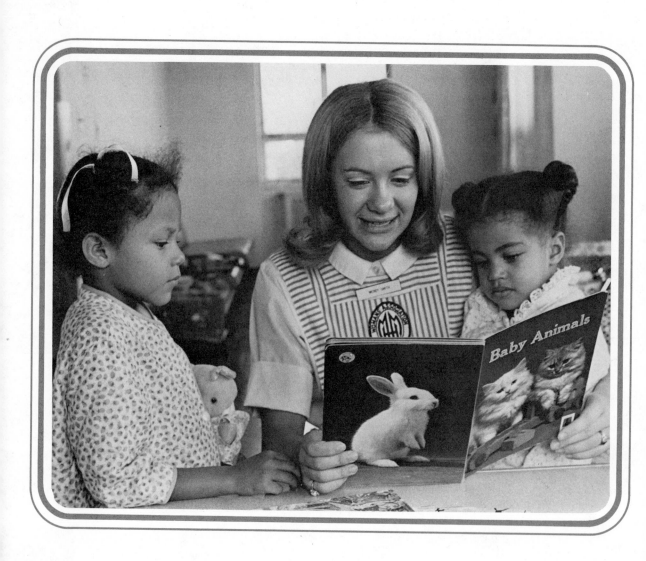

# 8
# Problem Solving

## 8-1 Equations into Word Problems

**Objective** To interpret equations as word problems.

When you are asked to solve an equation such as

$$15x = 75$$

do you ever wonder where it came from and why one might need to solve it? The equation could represent many real-life problems. Consider these:

> Shirley Trench has to bicycle for $x$ hours at the rate of 15 km/h to cover 75 km per day on a long-distance bicycle trip.

> If Les Callen can interview 15 job applicants per day, he will need $x$ days to interview the 75 applicants for one job.

**247**

## Class Exercises

State two practical problems that are expressed by the given equation. For the first problem, use a simple, direct question.

| | |
|---|---|
| *Example* | **24 − x = 8** |
| *Solution* | **1. What number subtracted from 24 gives 8?** |
| | **2. Meg Laramie has a 24-month loan which can be renewed anytime during the last 8 months. How many months must she pay on the loan before she can renew it?** |

**1.** $x + 10 = 50$      **2.** $x - 6 = 24$      **3.** $4x = 28$

**4.** $52x = 260$      **5.** $\frac{x}{30} = 7$      **6.** $\frac{x}{4} = 15$

## Exercises

Write two practical problems that are expressed by the given equation. For the first problem, use a simple, direct question.

**A**
  **1.** $24 + x = 80$          **2.** $12 + x = 48$

  **3.** $x - 10 = 35$        **4.** $24 - x = 18$

  **5.** $12x = 36$           **6.** $8x = 56$

  **7.** $\frac{x}{36} = 50$          **8.** $\frac{x}{12} = 1000$

  **9.** $\frac{1}{4}x = 20$         **10.** $\frac{3}{5}x = 30$

 **11.** $x + 3x = 16$       **12.** $x + (x + 2) = 8$

**B**
 **13.** $2x + 2(x + 4) = 28$      **14.** $x + 2(x - 1) = 10$

For the equation $3x + 5 = 60$, write a problem which could apply to each of the following persons.

**C**
 **15.** A carpenter             **16.** An astronaut

 **17.** A veterinarian         **18.** A scuba diver

 **19.** A football coach       **20.** A farmer

# 8-2 Word Problems into Equations

**Objective** To write an equation that expresses the numerical relationships in a given word problem.

A word problem generally states some numerical relationships and asks a question. We use the given information to write an equation which we can solve to find the answer. We can usually begin by considering the following questions.

| |
|---|
| **1.** What is asked for? |
| **2.** What variable expressions can be used to describe what is asked for? (It is sometimes helpful to choose a letter which suggests what is asked for, such as $w$ for width, or $n$ for number.) |
| **3.** Will a sketch help to make the problem clearer? |
| **4.** What other information is given? How can we use it to write an equation? |

The example shows how to apply these suggestions.

*Example* │ Write an equation which expresses the following problem.

The length of a rectangle is 3 cm greater than the width. If the perimeter of the rectangle is 26 cm, what are the dimensions of the rectangle?

*Solution*

**1.** What is asked for?  The dimensions, that is, the length and width of a rectangle.

**2.** What variable expressions can be used?  Let $w$ = width in centimeters. Then $w + 3$ = length in centimeters.

**3.** Will a sketch help?

**4.** What other information is given? How can we use it to write an equation?  The perimeter is 26 cm. This means the sum of the lengths of the sides is 26 cm. Then we can write the equation $w + w + (w + 3) + (w + 3) = 26.$

## Class Exercises

1. One number is 10 greater than another number. If $x$ represents the lesser number, how can we represent the greater number? If $x$ represents the greater number, how can we represent the lesser number?

2. One number is twice another number. If $x$ represents the first number, how can we represent the second number? If $x$ represents the greater number, how can we represent the lesser number?

3. The product of two numbers is 24. If $x$ represents one of the numbers, how can we represent the other number?

4. How can we represent the number of cents in $x$ nickels? $x$ dimes? $x$ dollars?

5. The two equal sides of an isosceles triangle are each 3 cm longer than the third side. If $x$ represents the length of the short side, how can we represent the perimeter of the triangle?

State an equation which could be used to solve the problem.

6. The sum of two numbers is 23, and one of the numbers is 8 greater than the other number. Find the lesser number.

7. The sum of two numbers is 18 and one number is twice the other number. Find the numbers.

8. The sum of two consecutive integers is 23. Find the numbers.

## Exercises

Write an equation which can be used to solve the problem. Use the suggestions listed on page 249.

| *Example* | One number is 5 more than 3 times another number. The sum of the two numbers is 25. Find the lesser number. |
|---|---|
| Solution | We are asked to find the lesser number. Let's let $x$ represent the lesser number. Then $3x + 5$ represents the greater number. (A sketch will not help make the problem clearer.) The sum of the numbers is 25, so we can use the equation $x + (3x + 5) = 25$. |

**A**

1. The sum of 23 and some number is 40. Find the number.

2. When 5 is subtracted from some number, the difference is 18. Find the number.

3. When 21 is added to some number, the sum is 33. Find the number.

4. When a certain number is subtracted from 31, the difference is 11. Find the number.

5. The sum of two numbers is 19, and one number is 8 greater than the other. Find the numbers.

6. Find two consecutive integers whose sum is 43.

7. Find two consecutive integers whose sum is 101.

8. Find two consecutive even numbers whose sum is 26.

9. A 120 m long highway sound barrier is constructed in two pieces. One piece is 45 m longer than the other. Find the length of each piece.

10. The perimeter of a square is 24 m. Find the length of each side.

11. The perimeter of an equilateral triangle is 45 cm. Find the length of each side.

**B** 12. The length of a rectangle is 5 cm greater than the width. The perimeter is 70 cm. Find the length and width.

13. The two equal sides of an isosceles triangle are each 11 cm longer than the third side. The perimeter of the triangle is 58 cm. Find the length of each side.

14. The perimeter of a rectangle is 40 m. The length of the rectangle is 10 m greater than the width. Find the length and the width.

**C** 15. An average bath uses 136 L of water. With that much water, you could take two brief showers and wash a load of laundry. Washing a load of laundry requires 40 L more than a brief shower. How many liters of water does each activity require?

16. Terry France fell asleep with the television on and a light burning. By the time she awoke she had wasted 2.48 kW·h of electricity. The television wasted 30 times as much energy as the light bulb. How many kilowatt-hours did each appliance waste?

17. Mike has some dimes and nickels with a total value of $3.55. The number of dimes he has is 3 more than twice the number of nickels. How many nickels does he have?

18. The sum of the ages of Juan and Rosa is 36 years. In 6 years Juan will be 3 times as old as Rosa will be then. How old is Juan now?

# 8-3 Solving and Checking Word Problems

**Objective** To solve and check a word problem.

Once we have set up an equation that expresses a word problem, we can solve the equation to answer the problem. We always check the answer to see that it satisfies the original problem as well as the equation, to be sure we used the right equation.

*Example* | Joyce Curtis and Cy Gruver formed a partnership to open a restaurant. Joyce invested $6000 more than Cy. Together they invested $20,000 and raised $30,000 from three other partners. How much did Cy invest?

*Solution* |

**1. What is asked for?**

The number of dollars Cy invested.

**2. What variable expressions can be used?**

Let $d$ = the number of dollars Cy invested. Then $d + 6000$ = the number of dollars Joyce invested.

**3. Will a sketch help?**

No

**4. What other information is given, and how can we use it to write an equation?**

Together they invested 20,000 dollars. Therefore, $d + d + 6000 = 20,000$. The other information given is unnecessary.

Solve the equation.

$$d + d + 6000 = 20,000$$
$$2d + 6000 = 20,000$$
$$2d = 14,000$$
$$d = 7000$$

Does the solution of the equation satisfy the original problem?

Yes. Joyce invested 6000 dollars more than Cy, so she invested 13,000 dollars. Then together they invested $13,000 + 7000$ or 20,000 dollars.

Cy Gruver invested $7,000.

Notice that in the example, not all the given information was necessary for solving the problem. The information concerning the $30,000 invested by three other partners was not needed. Some of the exercises that follow may also contain information that is not needed and which should be ignored.

## Problems

**A** **1–14.** Solve Exercises 1–14 on pages 250–251.

**B** **15.** David Cho paid $65 for 6 tickets to a basketball championship game. As a season ticket holder, he was entitled to buy 2 tickets at the regular season price, which is $3.50 less than the championship-game price. How much does each kind of ticket cost?

**16.** A town offered plots of land on which residents could plant gardens. One piece of land was divided into 15 identical plots. The length of each plot was 1 m greater than the width. The perimeter of each plot was 14 m. Find the dimensions of each plot.

**17.** Lenore Buranich tutors 3 students for a total of 6 hours per week. She charges the second student $2 more per week than the first, and she charges the third student half again as much per week as the second. She earns a total of $47 per week. How much does each student pay?

**C** **18.** One angle of a triangle is 70° less than twice a second angle, and the second angle is 25° more than half the third angle. The perimeter of the triangle is 24 cm. Find the measure of each angle. (Recall that the sum of the angles of a triangle is 180°.)

**19.** Bill Barbieri needed $90 to have his car repaired. His brother lent him some money, and his sister lent him twice as much. Together the loans amounted to half as much as Bill had set aside to pay for car repairs, and he was just able to pay the bill. How much did he borrow, and how much did he have saved?

**20.** A board 49 cm long is cut so that the length of the longer piece is 7 cm greater than twice the length of the shorter. How long is the shorter piece of board?

**21.** The sum of the ages of Greta and George is 11. In 5 years Greta will be twice as old as George is then. How old is Greta now?

**22.** Jack and Jill hiked from home to a bird sanctuary at the rate of 5 km/h and then returned home by the same route at a rate of 7 km/h. If the round trip took them 7 h, how far is it from their home to the bird sanctuary?

**23.** The sum of a number and its reciprocal is $\frac{5}{2}$. What are the numbers?

## Self-Test

Write two practical problems that are expressed by the given equation.
For the first problem, use a simple direct question.

1. $20 + x = 39$  [8-1]

2. $12x = 84$

3. $x - 7 = 23$

4. $\frac{1}{3}x = 9$

Write an equation that could be used to solve the problem.

5. The sum of 18 and some number is 51. Find the number.  [8-2]

6. When 13 is subtracted from some number, the difference is 44. Find the number.

7. The sum of two numbers is 71, and one of the numbers is 16 greater than the other number. Find the numbers.

8. The length of a rectangle is 20 cm greater than the width. The perimeter of the rectangle is 120 cm. Find the dimensions of the rectangle.

Write an equation and use it to solve the problem.

9. The sum of two numbers is 50, and one number is 12 greater than the other number. Find the lesser number.  [8-3]

10. The difference when 19 is subtracted from a number is 12. Find the number.

11. Find two consecutive integers whose sum is 39.

12. The sum of two numbers is 51, and one number is 27 greater than the other. One number is odd and is 3 more than 3 times the other number, which is even. Find the numbers.

Self-Test answers and Extra Practice are given at the back of the book.

# 8-4 Scale Drawings

**Objective** To interpret and use scale drawings.

In Chapter 6, we learned about similar figures. We can use similar figures to solve problems involving *scale drawings*. In a **scale drawing,** we represent an object by means of a similar figure. The **scale** of the drawing is the ratio of a unit of distance measured on the drawing to the corresponding actual distance.

For example, an architect may draw a rough floor plan for a house on the scale 1 cm $\longrightarrow$ 3 m (read "one centimeter represents three meters").

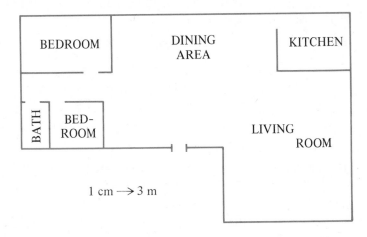

1 cm $\longrightarrow$ 3 m

Since 3 m = 300 cm, the ratio of distances in the floor plan to actual distances is 1 to 300, or 1:300.

| *Example* | If a map is drawn to the scale 1 cm $\longrightarrow$ 190 km and the distance between Montreal and Chicago measures 6 cm on the map, what is the approximate actual distance between the two cities? |

| *Solution* | We have the proportion |

$$\frac{x}{6} = \frac{190}{1}$$

$$6\left(\frac{x}{6}\right) = 6\left(\frac{190}{1}\right)$$

$$x = 1140$$

So the distance is approximately 1140 km.

## Problems

**A**  **1.** A scale drawing of a tree house has the scale 1 cm $\longrightarrow$ 1.5 m. The width of the tree house in the drawing is 1.5 cm. What actual length does this represent?

**2.** A drawing showing the anatomy of the human eye has the scale 5 cm $\longrightarrow$ 1 cm. The diameter of the eye measures 12.5 cm in the drawing. What length does this represent?

**3.** A map of Denver, Colorado has scale 1 cm $\longrightarrow$ 0.5 km. What map distance corresponds to an actual distance of 9 km?

**4.** Look at the house floor plan in this section. Measure to determine the actual dimensions of the two bedrooms.

**5.** Make a scale drawing of a rectangular table top measuring 1.5 m by 2.25 m, using the scale 1 cm = 0.25 m.

**6.** Make a scale drawing of a rectangular room 5 m by 7.5 m using the scale 2 cm = 1 m.

**B**  **7.** Make a scale drawing showing three cities, A, B, and C, where A lies 75 km due west of B, and C lies 50 km due south of B. Use 1 cm = 10 km, and determine how far it is from A to C.

**8.** On an aerial photograph of his farm, Rusty Cronholm measures the distance from the farmhouse to the pond as 1.5 cm. He knows the actual distance to be 3.75 km. How far is it from the farmhouse to the west wheat field if this distance measures 3.5 cm on the photograph?

The diagram shows three cities.

**9.** What is the scale of the drawing?

**10.** Find the actual distance between Weston and Northburg.

**11.** What is the actual distance between Northburg and Eastville?

**C**  **12.** Two lookout stations A and B are 10 km apart and get a fix on a ship at sea. Station A observes an angle of 70° between the ship and station B, while station B observes an angle of 75° between the ship and station A. Use a scale drawing to determine the distance of the ship from station A.

**13.** Two ranger-lookout stations A and B are 15 km apart. Station A sights a fire at an angle of 40° from station B, and station B observes the same fire at an angle of 55° from station A. How far is the fire from station A?

# A Physicist

Maria Goeppert-Mayer (1906–1972) was a joint winner (with Johannes H. D. Jensen and Eugene P. Wigner) of the 1963 Nobel Prize for Physics. The prize was awarded for their explanation of properties of atomic nuclei in terms of a structure of shells, or orbits, in which protons and neutrons are allowed to move.

Goeppert-Mayer received a Ph.D. degree from the University of Göttingen (now in West Germany). In 1930, she came to the United States to do research at Johns Hopkins University. Later she continued her career at Columbia University, the Institute for Nuclear Studies at the University of Chicago, and the University of California.

In 1947, the observation was made that some particular nuclei are more stable and abundant in nature than most. All of these have a particular number of neutrons (such as 50, 82, or 126). In 1949, Goeppert-Mayer explained these numbers, now called magic numbers, in terms of the nuclear shell theory.

**Career Activity** Find out what some of the different branches of physics are and what training is required for them.

# 8-5 Interest Problems

**Objective** To solve word problems involving simple and compound interest.

A person who borrows money pays the lender interest. Interest is money paid for the use of money. The interest paid depends on the amount of money borrowed, called the principal, the rate of interest, and the length of time, usually given in years, for which the money is used. The relationship is given by the following formula:

> ## formula
>
> $$\text{Interest} = \text{Principal} \times \text{rate} \times \text{time}$$
> $$\text{or}$$
> $$I = Prt$$

Interest paid only on the original principal is called simple interest.

**Example 1** | The Wasileskis have been offered an opportunity to invest $1000 at an annual interest rate which will allow them to double their investment in $12\frac{1}{2}$ years. What is the interest rate?

**Solution** | Interest = $Prt$.
$I = 1000$, $P = 1000$, and $t = 12.5$

$$1000 = 1000 \times r \times 12.5$$
$$1000 = 12,500r$$
$$\frac{1000}{12,500} = r$$
$$0.08 = r$$

The Wasileskis' investment will earn 8% annual interest.

Institutions such as banks and savings-and-loan companies usually pay compound interest to depositors. This means that the interest is periodically added to the principal and interest is then paid on the new principal. The interest may be compounded semiannually, quarterly, monthly, or even daily, and is usually figured from tables or by computers.

*Example 2*  The Lindstroms deposited $300 in a savings account at 6.5% compounded semiannually. They made no withdrawals in the first eighteen months. How much money was in the account at the end of that time?

*Solution*  For the first six months (or one-half year),
$P = 300$, $r = 0.065$, and $t = 0.5$.
$I = Prt = 300 \times 0.065 \times 0.5$
$\qquad = 9.75$

Then for the second six months,
$P = 300 + 9.75 = 309.75$
$I = 309.75 \times 0.065 \times 0.5$
$\quad = 10.07$ (rounded to the nearest cent)

Then for the third six months,
$P = 309.75 + 10.07 = 319.82$
$I = 319.82 \times 0.065 \times 0.5$
$\quad = 10.39$

$319.82 + 10.39 = 330.21$

After 18 months the Lindstroms had $330.21 in their account.

## Problems

Solve.

In problems 1–5, find the simple interest earned.

A   1. $150 at 7% for 3 years.

2. $500 at 8.5% for 10 years.

3. $6000 at 5.75% for 6 years.

4. $750 at 6% for 12 years.

5. $12,000 at 8% for 9 years.

6. You receive simple interest of $30 at the end of one year for money in a savings account. The interest rate is 6%. How much money was in your account?

7. If you invest $3000 for one year at 7%, how much would you have at the end of one year?

8. Mrs. Goodson owns 6 bonds, each worth $1000. She receives 7.5% simple interest each year on each bond. What is her yearly income from her bonds?

9. The Stonehill State Bank loaned $15,000 to a businessman at 8% annual interest for a 3-month period. How much money was due to be paid back at the end of the 3 months?

10. An investment of $36,000 produces $2700 of interest income each year. What is the rate of interest on this investment?

**B** 11. Ace Savings and Loan pays 5% compounded semiannually on its savings accounts. How much will be in an account after 2 years if $600 is deposited originally?

12. Adam Tillman has $3000 invested at 6% annual interest. How much more must he invest at 8% annual interest if his annual income from both investments must total $600?

13. A person offers to lend a friend money on the following basis: 5% interest for the first year, 7% interest for the second year, 9% interest for the third, and so on. No interest is due until the end of the loan period. If $1000 is borrowed for 3 years, how much must be paid back at the end of the loan period? Would you borrow from this person? What would be the interest rate for the fifth year? The sixth year?

14. Alice Andrews has an annual income of $930 from three investments. If she has $3000 invested at 6%, and $5000 invested at 7%, how much does she have invested at 8%?

**C** 15. Sheila Semenza plans to buy 1000 shares of stock selling at $16 per share. She can buy the stock under either of two plans.

Plan 1. Buy the shares with a cash payment of $16,000 of her own money.

Plan 2. Buy the shares with a cash payment of $8,000 of her own money together with $8,000 borrowed at 8% annual interest, and repay the loan when she sells the shares.

Assuming that she holds the stock for one year and then sells it at $20 per share, which plan yields the greater rate of return on her own money? Why?

16. During the course of a year a merchant's retail sales totaled $540,000. Included in that total was a sum covering an 8% sales tax. How much did the merchant owe the sales-tax collector at the end of that year?

17. Jerrold Mann borrowed $5000 for one year at 9% interest. Payment is made monthly and each month's interest is computed on the unpaid balance of the loan. How much interest did he pay in the first four months?

# 8-6 Environmental Problems

**Objective** To solve simple word problems dealing with the environment.

Mathematics can be an important aid in analyzing and solving many of the problems concerning our environment. These problems involve overpopulation, air and water pollution, noise pollution, deterioration of cities, the need for public transportation, and many other facets of everyday life.

*Example*  A recent study showed that of the 215,000,000 people in the United States, an estimated 16,000,000 suffer some degree of hearing loss directly related to noise. To the nearest percent, what percent of the population is that?

*Solution*  Let $n$ represent the percent of the population suffering hearing loss related to noise. Then:

$$16,000,000 = \frac{n}{100} \times 215,000,000$$

$$\frac{n}{100} = \frac{16,000,000}{215,000,000}$$

$$\frac{n}{100} \approx 0.074$$

$$n \approx 7.4$$

To the nearest percent, 7% of the population suffer some degree of hearing loss directly related to noise.

## Problems

Solve.

**A**  1. In Millsville, an air-pollution alert is called when smoke particles in the air reach a level of 315 parts per million (ppm). If an analysis showed that smoke particles made up 0.03% of the air, would an alert be sounded?

2. Temperatures in a deep mine increase, on the average, about 1°C for each 55 m of depth. If the surface ground temperature is 20°C, at what depth would the temperature in a mine reach 35°C?

3. In the year 1600 A.D., there were 8684 species of birds. Of these, about 1.09% have disappeared. How many species of birds have disappeared?

**B** 4. The cost of operating an electric appliance is given by

$$\frac{\text{wattage of appliance} \times \text{hours of operation}}{1000} \times \text{Cost per kW·h} = \text{operating cost}$$

What is the annual cost of operating a 300 W color television if it is used an average of 4 h per day and the electric rate is 6.2¢ per kW·h?

5. An iceberg can be melted to produce 200,000 m³ of water per day. If one person uses about 0.16 m³ of water per day, how many persons will it supply?

6. Safety records for a factory showed 1.2 injuries requiring medical treatment for each 100,000 h spent on the job. If the factory employs 700 people who each work an average of 1700 h per year, how many such injuries should be expected at the factory in one year?

**C** 7. Solar energy strikes the panels of a communications satellite with an intensity of 1.38 kW/m². If a rectangular panel with an area of 0.1 m² converts 16% of this energy into electric power, how many watts of electric power does it supply?

8. For each kg of mass transported, a bicycle rider expends about 730 J of energy per km. If a 75 kg rider pedals a 12 kg bicycle 20 km, how many joules are used?

9. The number of years it takes for a population to double in size can be estimated by dividing the annual number of additional persons per 1000 population into the number 693. If the world population continues to increase at the annual rate of 20 persons per 1000 population, how long will it take for the population to double?

10. Los Angeles uses approximately 1,800,000 kL of water each day. About 15% of it comes through the 480 km Colorado Aqueduct, 21% from local wells, and 64% from the Owens Valley. If the Colorado Aqueduct is out of service for 2 weeks, about how much more water would have to be supplied from the other sources?

# Application

## Commuting Costs

Stacy commutes by train between Troy and Dover, a distance of 38 km. She works a 5-day week. This year, the month of August begins on a Tuesday and ends on a Thursday. What is her cheapest plan for commuting if she (1) works the entire month? (2) takes vacation the 2nd week of August? (3) takes vacation the 2nd and 3rd weeks of August?

Commuting by car costs 8¢ per km and $2.50 per day for parking. Compare the costs of commuting by car and by train.

| Train fares Dover–Troy | |
| --- | --- |
| One-way: | $2 |
| 12 rides: | $20 |
| Monthly: | $52 |

## Self-Test

Words to remember:
scale drawing [p. 255]         interest [p. 258]         principal [p. 258]
scale [p. 255]                 interest rate [p. 258]

Solve.

1. The scale on a map of Boston is 1 cm ⟶ 0.25 km. The distance on the map from Larz Anderson Bridge to the Harvard Bridge is 6.5 cm. What actual distance does this represent?  [8-4]

2. On a scale drawing of a school gymnasium the scale is 1 cm ⟶ 5 m. The gymnasium measures 30 m by 37.5 m. What size is the drawing?

3. Ellis Throckmorton deposited $500 at 5.5% interest for 3 years. What was the simple interest earned?  [8-5]

4. Angela Ciccarelli invested $3000 at 6% annual interest. How much must she invest at 7.5% annual interest for her annual income from both investments to total $600?

5. The oceans cover about 71% of the 507,000,000 km² of the earth's surface. What area is this?  [8-6]

6. The Trans-Alaska pipeline system is about 1300 km long and about 1 m in diameter. The pipeline cost $3 billion to complete. What is the cost per kilometer?

Self-Test answers and Extra Practice are given at the back of the book.

# Chapter Review

Write the letter that names the correct answer.

1. A problem expressed by $17 + x = 34$ is __?__ .　　　　　　　　[8-1]
   A. A number added to 34 is 17. Find the number.
   B. Twice a number is 34. Find the number.
   C. 17 added to a number is 34. Find the number.
   D. 34 added to a number is 17. Find the number.

2. The perimeter of an isosceles triangle is 40 cm. The two equal　　[8-2]
   legs each measure 5 cm more than the third leg. An equation
   which can be used to find the lengths of the sides is __?__ .
   A. $x + (x + 5) + (x + 5) = 40$
   B. $x + (x - 5) + (x - 5) = 40$
   C. $2x + (5 + x) = 40$
   D. $40 - x - (x + 5) = x$

3. Two consecutive integers whose sum is 47 are __?__ .　　　　　　[8-3]
   A. 17 and 30　B. 23 and 24　C. 18 and 19　D. 28 and 29

4. In order to earn the money to buy a pair of jogging shoes, Gabriel
   Marquez worked Saturday gardening and three afternoons during the week helping out in his uncle's store. The $12 he earned
   gardening was one half what he earned working in the store during the week, and the total was just enough to buy the shoes.
   The shoes cost __?__ .
   A. $8　　　　　B. $18　　　　C. $36　　　　D. $28

5. Joan O'Brien spent twice as long mowing her lawn as she did
   raking. The total time was 2 h and 15 min. She spent __?__
   mowing her lawn.
   A. 45 min　　B. 1 h 15 min　C. 1 h 30 min　D. 1 h

6. The distance between Washington, D.C. and Richmond, Virginia, on a map is 12 cm. The scale of the map is 1 cm ⟶ 12 km. The approximate actual distance is __?__.
   **A.** 100 km    **B.** 12 km    **C.** 144 km    **D.** 81 km

[8-4]

7. Dennis finds a scale drawing of the floor plan of his house and decides that the shortest path from the television set to the cookie jar in the kitchen is one that measures 11 cm on the floor plan. If the scale is 1 cm ⟶ 0.5 m, this distance is __?__.
   **A.** 5.5 m    **B.** 55 m    **C.** 5 m    **D.** 11.5 m

8. The interest for one year on $400 deposited in a savings account at 6.75%, compounded semi-annually, is __?__.
   **A.** $13.50    **B.** $13.96    **C.** $427.46    **D.** $27.46

[8-5]

9. Alice invested $200 at 6% annual interest and $350 at 5.75% annual interest, both compounded annually. If she makes no withdrawals, how much will she have after two years?
   **A.** $224.72    **B.** $616.13    **C.** $582.13    **D.** $66.13

10. Central School collected 40% more scrap aluminum than West School, which, in turn, collected 25% more than Southern. If the total weight of scrap aluminum collected in the clean-up campaign was 560 kg, how much did Central School collect?
    **A.** 140 kg    **B.** 245 kg    **C.** 175 kg    **D.** 70 kg

[8-6]

11. In a certain city, 20% of the factories one year violated air-pollution control laws, and each of these factories was fined $1000. On the other hand, 28% of the factories far exceeded air-pollution control standards and each received an incentive award of $500 from the city. The net income for the city from these transactions was $7500. How many factories are in the city?
    **A.** 200    **B.** 140    **C.** 125    **D.** 132

# Mathematics A Century Ago

If you had been in a mathematics class one hundred years ago, you might have been asked to solve a problem such as the following:

A hare is 7 of his own leaps before a hound, and takes 5 leaps while the hound takes 3, but 4 of the hound's leaps are equal to 7 of the hare's. How many leaps must the hound take to gain on the hare the length of one of the hare's leaps? How many leaps must the hound take to catch the hare?

*Solution* Since 1 of the hound's leaps is $\frac{7}{4}$ of a leap of the hare, 3 of the hound's leaps are equal to $\frac{21}{4}$, or $5\frac{1}{4}$, of the hare's leaps; hence, in taking 3 leaps the hound gains $\frac{1}{4}$ of one leap of the hare, and therefore he must take 4 times 3 leaps, or 12 leaps, to gain 1 leap of the hare; and to gain 7 leaps, he must take 7 times 12 leaps, or 84 leaps.

Mathematics texts from that period included many exercises and very little text. Sections of problems like the one above alternated with drill sections like the following:

1. 3 times 8 are how many times 4?
2. 12 times 3 are how many times 9?
3. 6 times 4 are how many times 8?
4. 3 times 10 are how many times 6?

You might enjoy using the methods you have learned in this chapter to solve some problems from long ago.

1. A fox is 80 rods before a greyhound, and is running at the rate of 27 rods in a minute. The greyhound is following at the rate of 31 rods in a minute. In how many minutes will the greyhound overtake the fox?

**2.** If it takes 1 yard and 1 fourth of a yard of cloth to make a pair of pantaloons, how many yards would it take to make 8 pairs?

**3.** A boy having $\frac{4}{5}$ of a watermelon, wished to divide his part equally between his sister, his brother, and himself, but was at a loss to know how to do it; but his sister advised him to cut each of the fifths into 3 equal parts. How many pieces did each have? What part of the whole melon was each piece?

**4.** A fish's head weighs 5 pounds, his tail weighs as much as his head added to half the weight of his body, and his body weighs as much as his head and tail together. What is the weight of the fish?

**5.** A woman driving her geese to market, was met by a man, who said, Good-morrow, madam, with your hundred geese; says she, I have not a hundred; but if I had half as many more as I now have, and two geese and a half, I should have a hundred; how many had she?

**6.** A boy being asked his age, answered that if $\frac{1}{2}$ and $\frac{1}{4}$ of his age, and 20 more, were added to his age, the sum would be 3 times his age. What was his age?

**7.** An ignorant fop wanting to purchase an elegant house, a facetious gentleman told him he had one which he would sell him on these moderate terms, namely, that he should give him a penny for the first door, 2 pennies for the second door, 4 pennies for the third door, and so on, doubling at every door which were 36 in all. Pray, what would the house have cost him?

## Chapter Test

Write two practical problems that are expressed by the given equation. For the first, use a simple, direct question.

**1.** $18 - x = 52$  **2.** $\frac{1}{2}x = 21.5$  [8-1]

Write an equation which can be used to solve the problem.

**3.** The perimeter of a rectangle is 28. The length is twice the width. What are the dimensions?  [8-2]

**4.** The sum of two numbers is 36. One of them is 8 greater than the other. What are the numbers?

Solve.

**5.** The difference between two numbers is 3, and 5 subtracted from the larger is one half the smaller. What are the two numbers?  [8-3]

**6.** Each of the two equal sides of an isosceles triangle is 3 m longer than one half the third side. The perimeter is 54 m. What are the lengths of the sides?

**7.** A map has the scale 1 cm ⟶ 10 km. What is the actual distance between two towns which are 6.5 cm apart on the map?  [8-4]

**8.** A scale drawing of an insect has scale 2 cm ⟶ 0.25 cm. What length on the drawing represents an actual wingspan of 1 cm?

**9.** If you invest $5000 for one year at 6%, how much would you have at the end of the year?  [8-5]

**10.** Diane Tetreaut invests $500 at an annual simple interest rate that will allow her to triple her investment in 15 years. What is the rate?

**11.** A sleeping bag 4 cm thick provides protection at temperatures down to 5°C. At −50°C, a sleeping bag must be 2 cm more than twice that thickness. How thick is that?  [8-6]

**12.** A city one year had a population density of 3100 persons/km². The next year the population density fell 10%. If the city's area is 95.5 km², what was the new total population?

# Skill Review

Add or subtract.

1. $8.6 + 3.2$
2. $5.7 + 6.3$
3. $4.03 - 2.8$
4. $8.79 - 3.5$
5. $8.7 - 9.3$
6. $28.2 - 7.43$
7. $3.3 + (-8.8)$
8. $9.86 - (-9.6)$
9. $4.40 - 1.50$
10. $2.718 - 2.18$
11. $0.423 + 3.10$
12. $-8.2 - 5.1$
13. $10.3 - (-8.39)$
14. $9.38 + (-10.83)$
15. $-9.42 - (-7.77)$
16. $1.772 - 4.538$
17. $5.171 - (-5.717)$
18. $-1.284 - 0.25$
19. $8.105 + 8.007$
20. $16.548 - 23.219$
21. $-9.48 - 8.92$
22. $42.98 - 16.88$
23. $8.244 - (-9.88)$
24. $-2.9 + 7.352$

Multiply or divide.

25. $2.1 \times 6.7$
26. $6.9 \times 8.9$
27. $3.1 \times 1.3$
28. $1.159 \div 2$
29. $76.89 \div 1.5$
30. $-4.6 \times 2.1$
31. $-112.86 \div 2.2$
32. $7.77 \div (-11)$
33. $-3.40 \times 0.06$
34. $39.3 \div (-0.3)$
35. $-28.7 \div (-3.5)$
36. $18.00 \times 0.3$
37. $-26.11 \div 0.02$
38. $0.22 \div (-5.5)$
39. $-12.2 \times 14.0$
40. $27.5 \div (-90)$
41. $58.6 \times 17$
42. $-99.1 \div 98$

Perform the indicated operations.

43. $3.19 - 5 \times 0.17$
44. $-3.1 \times (-2.4) + 18.26$
45. $92.4 \div 8.4 - (-2.13)$
46. $-5.21 + 9.18 \div (0.027)$
47. $-3.12 \times 8.5 - 2.41 \times (-15.6)$
48. $-8.68 \div (0.031) + (-2.9) \times (-3.1)$
49. $3.019 \times (-2.3) + (-9.243) \div (-0.09)$
50. $(-2.31) \times (-1.1) + 3.2 \times (-5.7) - 6.82$

270

# 9

# Areas and Volumes

## 9-1 Areas of Rectangles and Parallelograms

**Objective** To find the areas of rectangles and parallelograms.

The **area** of a geometric figure is the amount of its interior surface. The parallelogram on the left below is a rectangle, and its area is the product of its length and width. However, the parallelogram on the right is *not* a rectangle, and its area is *not* the product of its two dimensions.

Rectangle

5 cm

Area = (5 × 3) cm²

Parallelogram, but not rectangle

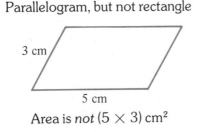

5 cm

Area is *not* (5 × 3) cm²

In order to find the area of a parallelogram, it is first helpful to discuss what is meant by its *base* and its *height*. Any side of a parallelogram can be considered as its **base**. The perpendicular distance between the base and the opposite side is the **height** of the parallelogram.

**271**

## formula

**Area of a parallelogram = base × height**
$$A = bh$$

The formula $A = bh$ can be used for any kind of parallelogram. For a square, however, most people prefer to use the simpler formula $A = s^2$, where $s$ represents the length of a side.

Area is frequently measured in square meters ($m^2$) or square centimeters ($cm^2$). Other measures used for area are square kilometers ($km^2$) and square millimeters ($mm^2$). Sometimes we choose to think about an unspecified unit of length. Then the unit of area is simply called a square unit. If a specific unit is not stated, we assume that *units* and *square units* are implied.

Since $1 \, cm = 10 \, mm$, $1 \, cm^2 = 100 \, mm^2$.
Since $1 \, km = 1000 \, m$, $1 \, km^2 = 1{,}000{,}000 \, m^2$.

| Parallelogram | Rhombus | Rectangle | Square |
|---|---|---|---|
| $A = bh$ | $A = bh$ | $A = bh$ | $A = s^2$ |
| $= 8 \times 4$ | $= 5 \times 4$ | $= 6 \times 4$ | $= 4^2$ |
| $= 32 \, (cm^2)$ | $= 20$ | $= 24$ | $= 16$ |

## Class Exercises

1. Is area measured in centimeters or square centimeters?

2. Is perimeter measured in centimeters or square centimeters?

Complete.

**3.** $1 \, m^2 = \underline{\phantom{?}} \, cm^2$

**4.** $3 \, m^2 = \underline{\phantom{?}} \, mm^2$

**5.** $0.01 \, km^2 = \underline{\phantom{?}} \, m^2$

For each parallelogram below, give its base, height, and area.

**6.**

**7.**

**8.**

**9.**

**10.**

**11.**

**12.**

**13.** Give the perimeters of the parallelograms shown in Exercises 10–12.

**14.** A square has perimeter 12 cm. What is its area?

**15.** A rectangle has perimeter 44 and area 72. Can you *guess* what its dimensions are?

## Exercises

For each parallelogram, give its base, height, and area.

**A 1.**

**2.**

**3.**

**4.**

**5.**

**6.**

Find the area and perimeter of each parallelogram below. Record your answers in a table like that shown.

|  | 7. | 8. | 9. | 10. | 11. | 12. |
|---|---|---|---|---|---|---|
| area |  |  |  |  |  |  |
| perimeter |  |  |  |  |  |  |

**13.** Study your answers for Exercises 7–9. They show that parallelograms can have different __?__ but the same __?__ .

**14.** Exercises 10–12 show that parallelograms can have different __?__ but the same __?__ .

## Problems

Solve.

**B** 1. The perimeter of a square is 20 cm. What is its area?

2. A rectangle has length 8 and perimeter 28. What is its area?

3. The area of a parallelogram is 120 cm². Its base is 16 cm. What is its height?

4. The area of a parallelogram is 350 cm². Its height is 14 cm. What is its base?

5. A square has area 81 m². What is its perimeter?

6. If you double the side of a square, do you double its perimeter? Do you double its area?

7. If you triple the length and width of a rectangle, do you triple its perimeter? Do you triple its area?

# 9-2 Areas of Triangles and Trapezoids

**Objective** To find the areas of triangles and trapezoids.

Any side of a triangle can be called its **base.** The perpendicular distance from the opposite vertex to the base line is the **height** of the triangle. The area of a triangle is one half the product of its base and height.

```
┌─ formula ──────────────┐
│                        │
│  Area = ½ × base × height │
│                        │
│  A = ½bh               │
│                        │
└────────────────────────┘
```

$A = \frac{1}{2} \times 5 \times 4$

$= 10$

$A = \frac{1}{2} \times 7 \times 3$

$= 10.5$

The parallel sides of a trapezoid are called its **bases.** The perpendicular distance between the bases is called the **height** of the trapezoid. The area of a trapezoid is one half the product of the height and the sum of the bases.

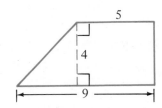

```
┌─ formula ──────────────────────────┐
│                                    │
│  Area = ½ × (sum of bases) × (height) │
│                                    │
│  A = ½(a + b)h                     │
│                                    │
└────────────────────────────────────┘
```

$A = \frac{1}{2} \times (5 + 9) \times 4$

$= 28$

## Class Exercises

For each triangle below, the base *b* is indicated. State the height.

**1.**

*b*

**2.**

*b*

**3.**

*b*

**4.**

*b*

**5–8.** Find the area of each triangle above.

**9.** David and Debby calculated the area of △*ABC* in different ways. Who was correct?

David: Area $= \frac{1}{2}(15 \times 8)$          Debby: Area $= \frac{1}{2}(10 \times 12)$

For each trapezoid below, give the lengths of its two bases and also give its height. Then give its area.

**10.**

**11.**

**12.**

**13.** Carol made a congruent copy of a triangle, turned it upside down, and slid the two triangles together to form a parallelogram as shown.
   **a.** What is the area of this parallelogram?
   **b.** If you did not know the formula for the area of a triangle, explain how you could figure it out.

## Exercises

**A**   In each of Exercises 1–10, find the area.

**1.**

**2.**

**3.**

**4.**

**5.**

**6.**

**7.**

**8.**

**9.**

**10.**

Find the area and perimeter of each triangle below.

**11.**

14 cm

11.2 cm

13 cm

15 cm

**12.**

17 m

8 m

10 m

21 m

**13.**

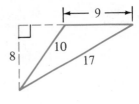

9

8

10

17

Find the area of each trapezoid below.

**14.**

8

12

20

**15.**

14

10

8

8

**16.**

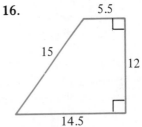

5.5

15

12

14.5

17. Draw an acute triangle, a right triangle, and an obtuse triangle, each having a base 5 cm and height 2 cm. Find the area of each triangle.

**B**

18. One of the equal sides of an isosceles right triangle is 4 cm long. What is the area of the triangle?

19. The area of a triangle is 50 m². The base is 10 m. What is the height?

20. *ABCD* is a trapezoid. By measuring, find *AB, DC,* and the height of the trapezoid in centimeters. Then calculate its area.

21. Find the area of trapezoid *ABCD* by subtracting the area of three right triangles from the area of rectangle *APQR*.

22. Draw a figure like the one shown with the lengths given:
$AP = 8$ cm, $PB = 6$ cm, $BQ = 3$ cm,
$QC = CR = 4$ cm, $RD = 3$ cm,
$DA = 6$ cm, $AB = 10$ cm, $BC = 5$ cm,
$CD = 5$ cm
**a.** Measure the height of the trapezoid and calculate its area.
**b.** Find the area of the trapezoid as described in Exercise 21.

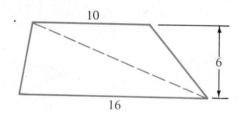

23. Find the area of the trapezoid by two different methods.

   *Method 1*   Add the areas of two triangles.

   *Method 2*   Use the formula

$$A = \tfrac{1}{2}(a + b)h.$$

**C**

24. **a.** What is the area of triangle I?
   **b.** What is the area of triangle II?
   **c.** Add the areas of triangles I and II and show that the sum can be written as $\tfrac{1}{2}(a + b)h$.

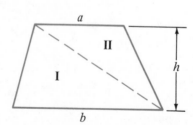

# 9-3 Areas of Circles

**Objective** To find areas of circles and of regions involving circles.

Recall that there are two different formulas for the circumference of a circle. If $C$ represents the circumference of the circle, $d$ represents its diameter, and $r$ represents its radius, then:

$$C = \pi d \quad \text{or} \quad C = 2\pi r$$

Two approximate values of $\pi$ are 3.14 and $\frac{22}{7}$.

The formula for the area of a circle is given below.

**formula**

**Area of circle $= \pi \times$ (radius)$^2$**
$$A = \pi r^2$$

*Example* | **Find the area of a circle with diameter 5 m.**

*Solution* | $A = \pi r^2$
$\approx 3.14 \times (2.5)^2 = 3.14 \times 6.25$
$\approx 19.625 \ (m^2)$

## Class Exercises

Use $\pi \approx 3.14$ for Exercises 1–3 and $\pi \approx \frac{22}{7}$ for Exercises 4–6.

|  | 1. | 2. | 3. | 4. | 5. | 6. |
|---|---|---|---|---|---|---|
| diameter | 4 cm | 0.6 mm | ? | $\frac{3}{11}$ | 28 | ? |
| area | ? | ? | ? | ? | ? | $\frac{7}{22}$ |
| circumference | ? | ? | 7.85 m | ? | ? | ? |

## Exercises

Find the area of the circle described. Use $\pi \approx 3.14$.

**A**  1. radius = 4 km

2. diameter = 1 m

3. radius = 0.6 cm

4. diameter = 2000 km

5. radius = 16 cm

6. diameter = 3 mm

Find the area of the circle described. Use $\pi \approx \frac{22}{7}$.

**7.** radius = 1

**8.** diameter = 1

**9.** radius = $2\frac{4}{5}$

**10.** radius = $5\frac{1}{4}$

**11.** diameter = $\frac{7}{22}$

**12.** diameter = 70

If the radius of a circle is multiplied by 2, the circumference is also multiplied by 2 but the area is multiplied by 4. (Try it and see!) This fact is recorded in the table below. Copy and complete this table.

|  | Example | **13.** | **14.** | **15.** | **16.** |
|---|---|---|---|---|---|
| Radius is multiplied by | 2 | 3 | 4 | 5 | ? |
| Circumference is multiplied by | 2 | ? | ? | ? | ? |
| Area is multiplied by | 4 | ? | ? | ? | 100 |

Find the area of each shaded portion. Leave your answer in terms of $\pi$.

**B** **17.**

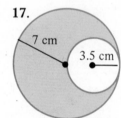
7 cm
3.5 cm

**18.**

9 m
18 m

**19.**

24 cm
12 cm

**20.** If a circle has area 50.24 cm², what is its radius, approximately?

**21.** If a circle has area $9\frac{5}{8}$ square units, what is its radius, approximately?

**22.** If a circle has area 314 km², what is its diameter, approximately?

Find the area and perimeter of each shaded portion. Leave your answers in terms of $\pi$.

**C** **23.**

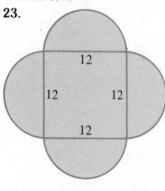
12
12
12
12

**24.**

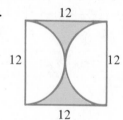
12
12
12
12

**25.**

8
8

**26.**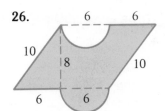

**27.**

**28.**

## Self-Test

Words to remember:

area [p. 271]                    base [p. 271]                    height [p. 271]

**1.** A square has side 6 cm. What is its area?                    [9-1]

**2.** A parallelogram has base 2 m and height 6 cm. What is its area?

**3.** A rectangle has area 72 cm² and height 6 cm. What is its base?

**4.** A square has area 64 cm². What is its perimeter?

**5.** The base of a triangle is 26 mm long and its height is 34 mm.    [9-2]
What is its area?

**6.** A trapezoid has bases of 2 m and 3 m, and height 4.3 m. What is its area?

**7.** The legs of a right triangle are 8 cm and 3 cm. What is its area?

**8.** The area of a triangle is 25 m². The base is 5 m. What is the height?

Find the area of the circle described.

**9.** radius = $1\frac{3}{4}$ units (Use $\pi \approx \frac{22}{7}$.)                    [9-3]

**10.** diameter = 10 cm (Use $\pi \approx 3.14$.)

**11.** circumference = $30\pi$
(Leave answer in terms of $\pi$.)

**12.** Find the area of the shaded part of the figure. (Leave answer in terms of $\pi$.)

Self-Test answers and Extra Practice are at the end of the book.

# 9-4 Volumes of Prisms and Cylinders

**Objective** To find the volumes of prisms and cylinders.

The figures below are **prisms.** The shaded regions of each are the **bases** of the prism. The perpendicular distance between the bases is called the **height** of the prism. The shape of the polygonal base determines the name of the prism.

**Triangular Prism**

**Square Prism**

**Rectangular Prism or Rectangular Solid**

A **cylinder** is like a prism except that its bases are circles instead of polygons. The amount of space occupied by any solid is called its **volume.** The same formula can be used to find the volumes of both prisms and cylinders. The *base area* is the area of *one* base.

**Prism**

**Cylinder**

**formula**

**Volume = Base area × height**
$$V = Bh$$

**formula**

**Volume = Base area × height**
$$V = Bh, \quad \text{or} \quad V = \pi r^2 h$$

*Example* | Find the volumes.

**a.**

5 cm

6 cm

10 cm

**b.**

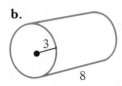

3

8

*Solution* | **a.** $B = 10 \times 6 = 60 \ (\text{cm}^2)$

$V = Bh$

$= 60 \ \text{cm}^2 \times 5 \ \text{cm} = 300 \ \text{cm}^3$

**b.** $B = \pi \times 3^2 = 9\pi$

$V = Bh$

$= 9\pi \times 8 = 72\pi$ (cubic units)

## Class Exercises

1. In the formula $V = Bh$, what do the letters $V$, $B$, and $h$ stand for?

2. For the rectangular solid shown, find the values of $B$, $h$, and $V$.

3. Suppose that the right-hand side of the solid is considered as its base. Then

$$B = 5 \times 6 = 30.$$

   **a.** What is the height to this base?
   **b.** Using this height and base, calculate $V$.

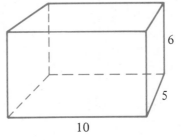

4. $1 \ \text{cm}^3 = \underline{\ ?\ } \ \text{mm}^3$

5. $1 \ \text{m}^3 = \underline{\ ?\ } \ \text{cm}^3$

6. $1 \ \text{km}^3 = \underline{\ ?\ } \ \text{m}^3$

Find the volumes of the solids below. (Give answers to Exercises 8 and 9 in terms of $\pi$.)

7.

8.

9.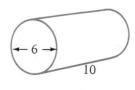

## Exercises

Find the volumes of the prisms shown below.

**A** 1.

2.

3.

Find the volumes of the prisms shown below.

**4.**

**5.**

**6.**

Find the volumes of the cylinders below. Leave answers in terms of $\pi$.

**7.**

8 cm

10 cm

**8.**

←12 cm→

15 cm

**9.**

2 m

10 cm

Make a drawing of each of the following solids. Then calculate its volume.

**10.** A soup can with height 10 cm and radius 3 cm.

**11.** A quarter with height 2 mm and diameter 23 mm.

**12.** A rectangular solid with length 12 cm, width 9 cm, and height 4 cm.

**B**  **13.** A triangular prism with height 10 and with a right triangular base with sides 5, 12, and 13.

**14.** Cement blocks are used for constructing walls of many buildings. Find the volume of the cement block shown.

10 cm

10 cm

20 cm

20 cm

30 cm

**15.** A copper pipe is 10 m long. Its inner radius is 2.4 cm and its outer radius is 2.6 cm. Find the volume of the metal in the pipe. Use $\pi \approx 3.14$.

2.6 cm

2.4 cm

10 m

**C**  **16.** If you double *each* of the three dimensions of a rectangular solid, does the volume of the solid also double?

**17.** If you triple both the radius and the height of a cylinder, does the volume also triple?

# 9-5 Volumes of Pyramids and Cones

**Objective** To find the volumes of pyramids and cones.

The figures below are all **pyramids.** The shaded region of each is called the **base** of the pyramid. The shape of the polygonal base determines the name of the pyramid.

**Triangular Pyramid**

**Square Pyramid**

**Hexagonal Pyramid**

The triangular side faces of each pyramid are called **lateral faces.** These lateral faces meet at the **lateral edges,** which in turn meet at the **vertex** of the pyramid. The perpendicular distance from the vertex to the base is called the **height** of the pyramid.

The formula for the volume of a pyramid is closely related to the volume formula for a prism.

**Prism**

$$V = Bh$$

**Pyramid**

┌─ **formula** ─────────┐

$$V = \frac{1}{3}Bh$$

└───────────────────────┘

A **cone** is like a pyramid except that its base is a circle instead of a polygon. Even the volume formulas for a pyramid and cone are alike. And the formula for the volume of a cone is closely related to the volume formula for a cylinder.

height

radius

**Cylinder**

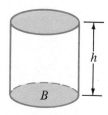

$h$

$B$

$$V = Bh$$
$$= \pi r^2 h$$

**Cone**

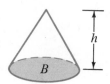

$h$

$B$

**formula**

$$V = \frac{1}{3}Bh$$
$$= \frac{1}{3}\pi r^2 h$$

*Example 1* | Find the volume of the square pyramid shown.

*Solution* | The base area $B = 10^2 = 100$

The volume $V = \frac{1}{3}Bh$

$$= \frac{1}{3} \times 100 \times 12 = 400$$

*Example 2* | Find the volume of the cone shown.

*Solution 1* | Use two formulas: $B = \pi r^2$ and $V = \frac{1}{3}Bh$

$B = \pi r^2 \approx 3.14 \times 10^2$

$$\approx 314$$

$V = \frac{1}{3}Bh \approx \frac{1}{3} \times 314 \times 15 \approx 1570$

*Solution 2* | Use one formula: $V = \frac{1}{3}\pi r^2 h$

$V = \frac{1}{3}\pi r^2 h \approx \frac{1}{3} \times 3.14 \times 10^2 \times 15$

$$\approx 3.14 \times 100 \times 5 \approx 1570$$

## Class Exercises

Classify each of the figures below.  For example, the two figures in Examples
1 and 2 on page 286 are classified as a square pyramid and a cone.

**1.**

**2.**

**3.**

**4.**

**5.** Give the formula you would use to find the volume of each figure in
Exercises 1–4.

**6.** For the figure in Exercise 2, name:
    **a.** the vertex         **b.** the lateral edges         **c.** the lateral faces

**7.** For the figure in Exercise 4:
    **a.** name two radii         **b.** $\angle VOY = $ __?__
    **c.** $\angle VOX = $ __?__       **d.** $VO$ is called the __?__

**8.** Draw a cone with radius 3 cm and height 6 cm.  Then find its volume.

## Exercises

The figure shows an upside-down square pyramid.

**A**

**1.** Name its vertex.

**2.** Name its four lateral edges.

**3.** Name its four lateral faces.

**4.** Its base area $B = $ __?__

**5.** Its height $= $ __?__

**6.** Its volume $= $ __?__

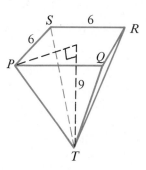

A cylinder and a cone have equal radii and equal
heights.

**7.** If the volume of the cylinder is 60 cm³, find
the volume of the cone.

**8.** If the volume of the cone is 45 cm³, find the
volume of the cylinder.

Find the volumes of the figures.

9. A cylinder with radius 6 cm and height 10 cm. Use $\pi \approx 3.14$.

10. A cone with radius 6 cm and height 10 cm. Use $\pi \approx 3.14$.

Find the volumes of the figures.

11.

A rectangular pyramid

12. Base area = 24

A triangular pyramid

13.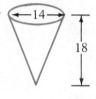

A cone (Use $\pi \approx \frac{22}{7}$.)

**B** 14. Find the volume of the bottle shown. Assume that the top of the bottle is a cone.

15. Find the capacity of the bottle in liters. (1 L = 1000 cm³)

16. *O* is the center point of a cube with edges 30 cm. Find the volume of the pyramid with vertex *O* and base *ABCD*.

17. Find the ratio of the volume of the pyramid to the volume of the cube.

18. Find the volume of the rectangular solid.

19. Find the volume of the pyramid with vertex *G* and base *BCD*.

20. Find the ratio of the volume of the pyramid to the volume of the rectangular solid.

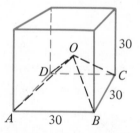

**C** 21. A cylinder has volume 616 cubic units and radius 7 units. What is its height? (Use $\pi \approx \frac{22}{7}$.)

22. A cone has volume 33 cubic units and height $\frac{7}{2}$ units. What is its radius? (Use $\pi \approx \frac{22}{7}$.)

# Application Comparing Volumes

An experiment can help explain the "$\frac{1}{3}$" in the formula $V = \frac{1}{3}Bh$ for the volume of a cone.

   You will need paper, a pencil, ruler, compass, protractor, scissors, paste, and a cup of sand. Our object is to construct a cylinder and a cone with the same base and the same height. You will use the fact that a triangle with sides 3 cm, 4 cm, and 5 cm long is a right triangle. The circumference of a circle with radius 3 cm is $6\pi$ cm, or approximately 18.8 cm.

We want the base of the cone to have circumference $6\pi$. The circumference of a circle with radius 5 cm is $10\pi$. To find the portion of a circle with radius 5 cm which will form the desired cone, we set up a proportion:

$$\frac{6\pi}{10\pi} = \frac{x}{360°}, \quad \text{or} \quad x = 216°$$

1. Draw the patterns above using the dimensions given.
2. Cut along the solid black lines and fold on the dashed lines.
3. Paste the tabs and fasten together. Let dry.
4. Fill the cone with sand, leveling it with the edge of a ruler.
5. Dump the sand from the cone to the cylinder.
6. *Estimate* how many times Steps 4 and 5 must be performed before the cylinder is level full.
7. Repeat Steps 4 and 5 until the cylinder is level full.
8. Compare your estimate in Step 6 with the actual result in Step 7.
9. Tell how the result of the experiment is related to the formula for the volume of a cylinder and the formula for the volume of a cone.

## 9-6 Surface Areas of Prisms and Cylinders

**Objective** To find the lateral areas and total surface areas of prisms and cylinders.

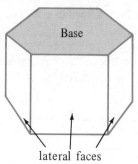

The hexagonal prism shown has eight faces. In addition to its two hexagonal bases, it has six **lateral faces,** each a rectangle. The total area of these lateral faces is called the **lateral area** of the prism. If the area of the two bases is added to the lateral area, we get the **total surface area** of the prism.

Base

lateral faces

**Example 1** | The base of the triangular prism shown has area 84 cm².

Find:

**a.** the lateral area

**b.** the total surface area

13 cm
84 cm²
10 cm
15 cm
14 cm
10 cm
10 cm

*Solution*

**a.** Left face area = $13 \times 10 = 130$

Right face area = $14 \times 10 = 140$

Back face area = $15 \times 10 = 150$

Lateral area = $130 + 140 + 150$

$= 420$ (cm²)

**b.** Total surface area = lateral area + (2 × base area)

$= 420 + (2 \times 84)$

$= 588$ (cm²)

Refer to the Example above and notice the following:

Lateral area $= (13 \times 10) + (14 \times 10) + (15 \times 10)$

Lateral area $= (13 + 14 + 15) \times 10$

**formula**

**Lateral area = (perimeter of base) × height**

The lateral area of a cylinder is calculated by a similar formula.

**formula**

> Lateral area = (circumference of base) × height
> = **2πrh**

If we add the area of the top ($\pi r^2$) and the bottom ($\pi r^2$), we get:

**formula**

> Total surface area = **Lateral area + (2 × base area)**
> = **2πrh + 2πr²**

*Example 2* | For the cylinder shown, find:
| **a.** the lateral area
| **b.** the total surface area

*Solution* | **a.** Lateral area = **2πrh**
| = **2π × 3 × 5 = 30π**
| **b.** Total surface area = lateral area + (2 × base area)
| = **30π + (2 × π × 3²)**
| = **30π + 18π = 48π**

## Class Exercises

**1.** How many lateral faces does a pentagonal prism have?

**2.** What is the total number of faces of a pentagonal prism?

Find the lateral area and the total surface area of each solid below. (Leave the answer to Exercise 5 in terms of π.)

**3.**

**4.**

**5.**

## Exercises

Find (a) the lateral area and (b) the total surface area of each solid shown.
(Leave the answers for Exercises 5 and 6 in terms of $\pi$.)

**A  1.**

**2.**

**3.**

**4.**

**5.**

**6.**

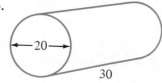

## Problems

Solve.

**B  1.** The base of a prism is a triangle with sides 4, 5, and 6. The height of the prism is 8. Find its lateral area.

**2.** The base of a prism is a right triangle with sides 3, 4, and 5. The height of the prism is 6. Find its total area.

**3.** Each edge of a cube is 5 cm. Find (a) its total surface area and (b) its volume.

**4.** The total surface area of a cube is 600 cm². Find the length of each edge.

**C  5.** The volume of a cube is 27 cm³. What is its total surface area?

**6.** A piece of cardboard is folded on the dotted lines to make a box. Find:
**a.** the height of the box
**b.** its total surface area
**c.** its volume

# 9-7 Mass and Liquid Capacity

**Objective** To find the liquid capacity or mass of an object and to convert from one unit to another.

One of the advantages of the metric system is that it is easy to convert from units of volume, such as cubic centimeters, to units of **mass,** such as grams (g) or kilograms (kg).

> **1 cm³ of water has a mass of 1 g under standard conditions. (Standard conditions are 4°C at sea-level pressure.) 1000 cm³ of water has a mass of 1000 g, or 1 kg.**

The table shows that the mass of 1 cm³ of steel is 7.7 g. In other words, steel is 7.7 times heavier than water. The table also shows that gold is 19.3 times heavier than water, so that 1000 cm³ of gold would have a mass of

$$(19.3 \times 1000) \text{ g} = 19{,}300 \text{ g, or } 19.3 \text{ kg.}$$

Volumes of liquids and gases are often given in liters (L) and milliliters (mL) instead of cubic centimeters.

$$1 \text{ L} = 1000 \text{ cm}^3$$
$$1 \text{ mL} = 1 \text{ cm}^3$$

| Material | Mass of 1 cm³ |
|----------|---------------|
| pine | 0.5 g |
| ice | 0.9 g |
| water | 1.0 g |
| aluminum | 2.7 g |
| steel | 7.7 g |
| copper | 8.9 g |
| silver | 10.5 g |
| gold | 19.3 g |

If you fill a cubical container 10 cm on a side with water, then its **capacity** would be

$$10 \times 10 \times 10 = 1000 \text{ cm}^3, \quad \text{or} \quad 1 \text{ L.}$$

The mass of 1 L of water is 1 kg. This is explained below.

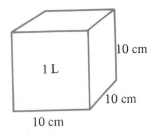

Volume of 1 L of water = 1000 cm³ of water
Mass of 1 L of water = 1000 g
= 1 kg

Volume = $10 \times 10 \times 10$
= 1000 (cm³)
= 1 L

The table gives the masses of 1 L of other liquids and gases under standard conditions.

| Liquid or Gas | Mass of 1 L |
|---|---|
| helium | 0.000179 kg |
| air | 0.00129 kg |
| oxygen | 0.00143 kg |
| gasoline | 0.66 kg |
| fresh water | 1.00 kg |
| ocean water | 1.025 kg |
| milk | 1.03 kg |
| mercury | 13.6 kg |

*Example 1*   A can is filled with **12 L** of gasoline. Find the mass of this gasoline.

*Solution*   **Mass of 12 L** $= 12 \times 0.66$

$= 7.92$ **(kg)**

*Example 2*   Find the mass of ocean water in a tank **10 m** by **8 m** by **8 m**.

*Solution*   **Volume** $= 10 \text{ m} \times 8 \text{ m} \times 8 \text{ m} = 640 \text{ m}^3$

$= 640{,}000{,}000 \text{ cm}^3 = 640{,}000 \text{ L}$

**Mass** $= 640{,}000 \times 1.025 = 656{,}000$ **(kg)**

## Class Exercises

Tell whether each of the following is a unit of solid volume, liquid volume, mass, or more than one of these.

**1.** g   **2.** L   **3.** $cm^3$   **4.** kg

**5.** $m^3$   **6.** mL   **7.** $mm^3$   **8.** metric ton (1000 kg)

Complete the following.

**9.** $1 \text{ L} = \underline{\ ?\ } \text{ cm}^3$   **10.** $3.1 \text{ L} = \underline{\ ?\ } \text{ cm}^3$   **11.** $\underline{\ ?\ } \text{ L} = 500 \text{ cm}^3$

**12.** $650 \text{ mL} = \underline{\ ?\ } \text{ L}$   **13.** $1300 \text{ mL} = \underline{\ ?\ } \text{ L}$   **14.** $340 \text{ mL} = \underline{\ ?\ } \text{ cm}^3$

**15.** $1 \text{ kg} = \underline{\ ?\ } \text{ g}$   **16.** $3.5 \text{ kg} = \underline{\ ?\ } \text{ g}$   **17.** $\underline{\ ?\ } \text{ kg} = 400 \text{ g}$

Give the mass of each of the following. (Use the table above and the one on page 293.)

**18.** 2 L of fresh water   **19.** 2 L of ocean water

**20.** 3 $cm^3$ of ice   **21.** 1000 $cm^3$ of pine

# Exercises

Complete the following.

**A**  **1.** 1 kg = __?__ g

**4.** 1 L = __?__ cm³

**7.** 2 L = __?__ mL

**2.** 2.1 kg = __?__ g

**5.** 3.89 L = __?__ cm³

**8.** 1.48 L = __?__ mL

**3.** __?__ kg = 1200 g

**6.** __?__ L = 512 cm³

**9.** 0.7 L = __?__ mL

Give the mass of each either in grams or kilograms.

**10.** 3 L of fresh water

**12.** 2 L of ocean water

**14.** 5 mL of milk

**16.** 50 cm³ of ice

**18.** 1 cm³ of gold

**11.** 4.5 L of fresh water

**13.** 500 L of oxygen

**15.** 250 mL of mercury

**17.** 3000 cm³ of aluminum

**19.** 8 cm³ of silver

**B**  **20.** 1 m³ of helium

**21.** 1 m³ of oxygen

**22.** A bar of gold measuring 25 cm by 15 cm by 10 cm.

**23.** A pine board measuring 2 m by 20 cm by 4 cm.

**24.** Milk filling a container 10 cm by 10 cm by 16 cm.

# Problems

Solve.

**B**  **1.** King Midas is unsure whether his bar of gold is pure gold. The bar measures 22 cm by 18 cm by 6 cm and has mass 32.8 kg. Advise the king on whether or not it is pure.

**2.** Find the volume and the mass of the air in your classroom. (Assume the air is under standard conditions.)

**3.** If the mass of 1 cm³ of gray tin is 5.75 g and the mass of 1 cm³ of white tin is 7.31 g, how much greater is the mass of 500 cm³ of white tin than 500 cm³ of gray tin?

**4.** The mass of 1 cm³ of a gem diamond is 3.5 g. The mass of 1 cm³ of a ruby or sapphire is 4.0 g and the mass of 1 cm³ of an emerald is 2.7 g. Compare the masses of 20 mm³ of an emerald, a gem diamond, and a ruby.

**C**  **5.** A copper wire and an aluminum wire have the same length and the same mass. About how many times larger is the radius of the aluminum wire than the radius of the copper wire?

# 9-8 Spheres

**Objective** To find the surface areas and volumes of spheres.

The diagram shows a **sphere** with **center** $C$ and **radius** 5 cm. It consists of all points in space that are 5 cm from point $C$. When we refer to the volume of a sphere, we mean the amount of space it contains.

The formulas for the surface area and volume of a sphere are given below.

---

## formulas

$$\text{Area} = 4 \times \pi \times (\text{radius})^2$$
$$A = 4\pi r^2$$

$$\text{Volume} = \frac{4}{3} \times \pi \times (\text{radius})^3$$
$$V = \frac{4}{3}\pi r^3$$

---

**Example** | A sphere has radius 6. Find (a) its area and (b) its volume. Leave answers in terms of $\pi$.

*Solution* | **a.** Area $= 4\pi r^2 = 4 \times \pi \times 6^2 = 4 \times \pi \times 36 = 144\pi$ (square units)

**b.** Volume $= \frac{4}{3}\pi r^3 = \frac{4}{3} \times \pi \times 6^3 = \frac{4}{3} \times \pi \times \overset{72}{\underset{1}{216}} = 288\pi$ (cubic units)

## Class Exercises

1. Explain why a basketball more nearly satisfies the definition of a sphere than a baseball does.

Complete the following analogies with choice a, b, c, or d.

2. Sphere:Circle = Cube: ?
   **a.** Pyramid          **b.** Prism          c. Square          **d.** Cylinder

3. Cone:Pyramid = Cylinder: ?
   **a.** Sphere          **b.** Prism          c. Circle          **d.** Triangle

4. Find the area and the volume of a sphere with radius 1.

5. Find the area and the volume of a sphere with radius 2.

6. If the radius of a sphere is doubled, is the area doubled? Is the volume doubled?

# Exercises

Copy and complete the table below. Leave answers in terms of $\pi$.

**A**

|                  | 1. | 2. | 3. | 4. |
|------------------|----|----|----|----|
| radius of sphere | 3  | 5  | 9  | 10 |
| surface area     | ?  | ?  | ?  | ?  |
| volume           | ?  | ?  | ?  | ?  |

**B**  5. A sphere fits snugly inside a cube. Find the volume of the space between the cube and the sphere. Use $\pi \approx 3.14$.

6. A sphere fits snugly inside a cylinder. Which is greater, the lateral area of the cylinder or the area of the sphere?

**C**  7. Which has the greater mass, an aluminum ball with radius 2 cm or a gold ball with radius 1 cm? (The mass of 1 cm³ of aluminum is 2.7 g, and the mass of 1 cm³ of gold is 19.3 g.)

8. A sphere has area $100\pi$. What is its radius?

9. A scoop of ice cream has the shape of a sphere with radius 3 cm. The scoop sits on top of an ice cream cone with radius 3 cm and height 10 cm. Is the cone big enough to hold all the ice cream if it should melt?

10. Half a sphere is called a **hemisphere**. One astronomical observatory consists of a hemispheric dome on a cylindrical base. The radius of the base of the cylinder is 40 m and the height of the cylinder is 30 m.
    a. Draw a figure representing the observatory.
    b. What is the volume of the observatory?
    c. What is the total surface area of the observatory?

# *EXTRA!* Spheres and Cylinders

1. If the sphere fits snugly inside the cylinder, it is said to be inscribed in the cylinder. What is the volume of the sphere? (Leave the answer in terms of $\pi$.)

2. What is the volume of the cylinder? (Leave the answer in terms of $\pi$.)

3. What is the ratio of the volume of the sphere to the volume of the cylinder?

4. If a sphere is inscribed in a cylinder with radius 10, find the ratio of the volume of the sphere to the volume of the cylinder.

5. Do you get the same ratio for any sphere inscribed in a cylinder?

|← 8 →|

# A Mathematician

Archimedes (287?–212 B.C.), considered by many to be one of the three greatest mathematicians of all history, was a Greek citizen who lived in Syracuse, Sicily. He discovered the use of levers and said, "Give me a place to stand on and I will move the earth." While bathing he discovered that a floating body loses in weight an amount equal to that of the liquid displaced. Although he was a physicist and engineer as well as a mathematician, he was most proud of his proof that the ratio of the volume of a sphere inscribed in a cylinder to the volume of the cylinder is 2:3. At his request, a cylinder and its inscribed sphere and this ratio was engraved on his tombstone.

**Research Activity** Find out more about Archimedes and his many famous discoveries.

## Self-Test

Words to remember:
prism [p. 282]       base [p. 282]       height [p. 282]
cylinder [p. 282]    pyramid [p. 285]    lateral face [p. 285]
cone [p. 286]        lateral area [p. 290]   total surface area [p. 290]
mass [p. 293]        capacity [p. 293]   sphere [p. 296]

Find the volume. (Use $\pi \approx 3.14$.)

1. A cylinder with base diameter 10 and height 6.                    [9-4]

2. A pentagonal prism with base area 60 and height 9.

3. A cube with edge 15 mm.

4. A rectangular prism which measures 12 cm by 8 cm by 11 cm.

5. A square pyramid with base area 16 and height 5.                 [9-5]

6. A hexagonal pyramid with base area 60 cm² and height 7 cm.

7. A cone whose base has radius 4 and height 7.

8. A cone whose base has diameter 20 cm and height 25 cm.

9. The base of a prism is a triangle with sides 3, 5, and 7. The    [9-6]
   height of the prism is 9. Find its lateral area.

Find the lateral area and the total surface area of each solid below.

10.     11.     12.

13. $5.5 \text{ L} = \underline{\ ?\ } \text{ cm}^3$          14. $400 \text{ g} = \underline{\ ?\ } \text{ kg}$       [9-7]

15. If the mass of 1 cm³ of silver is 10.5 g and of 1 cm³ of gold is
    19.3 g, what is the difference in mass of 50 cm³ of each?

16. If the mass of 1 cm³ of hydrogen is 0.0000899 g, what is the
    mass of 1 L of hydrogen?

17. Find the area and the volume of a sphere with radius 1.         [9-8]

18. What is the area of a sphere with radius 10 cm?

19. What is the volume of a sphere with radius $\frac{3}{2}$?

20. If the area of a sphere is $16\pi$, what is its volume in terms of $\pi$?

Self-Test answers and Extra Practice are given at the back of the book.

# Chapter Review

Write the letter that labels the best answer.

1. $1 \text{ km}^2 =$ __?__ $\text{m}^2$ [9-1]
   A. 100      B. 1000      C. 10,000      D. 1,000,000

2. A square has perimeter 32 mm. Its area is __?__.
   A. $32 \text{ mm}^2$    B. $64 \text{ cm}^2$    C. $16 \text{ mm}^2$    D. $64 \text{ mm}^2$

3. The area of a parallelogram is $100 \text{ cm}^2$ and its base is 8 cm. Its height is __?__.
   A. 16 cm      B. 25 cm      C. 12.5 cm      D. 10 cm

4. The area of a trapezoid with bases 4 m and 6 m and height 8 m is __?__. [9-2]
   A. $80 \text{ m}^2$      B. $192 \text{ m}^2$      C. $40 \text{ m}^2$      D. $48 \text{ m}^2$

5. The area of a triangle is $100 \text{ cm}^2$ and its base is 10 cm. Its height is __?__.
   A. 10 cm      B. 5 cm      C. 20 cm      D. $500 \text{ cm}^2$

6. The area of a triangle with base 16 cm and height 5 cm is __?__.
   A. 80 cm      B. $80 \text{ cm}^2$      C. $40 \text{ cm}^2$      D. 40 cm

7. The area of a circle with radius 7 is __?__. (Use $\pi \approx \frac{22}{7}$.) [9-3]
   A. 154      B. 1078      C. 343      D. 3388

8. If the number of units in the circumference of a circle is the same as the number of square units in its area, the diameter of the circle is __?__.
   A. 1      B. 2      C. 4      D. $2\pi$

9. The area of a circle with radius 10 cm is __?__. (Use $\pi \approx 3.14$.)
   A. 314 cm    B. $314 \text{ cm}^2$    C. $31.4 \text{ cm}^2$    D. $628 \text{ cm}^2$

10. The volume of a cylinder with diameter 5 and height 10 is __?__. [9-4]
    A. $62.5\pi$      B. $250\pi$      C. $50\pi$      D. 250

11. The volume of a rectangular solid 10 cm by 8 cm by 5 cm is __?__.
    A. $400 \text{ cm}^2$    B. $400\pi \text{ cm}^2$    C. $400 \text{ cm}^3$    D. 400 cm

12. $1 \text{ cm}^3 =$ __?__ $\text{mm}^3$
    A. 10      B. 1000      C. 100      D. 10,000

**13.** A square pyramid has __?__ triangular faces.  [9-5]
   **A.** two      **B.** three      **C.** four      **D.** five

**14.** The volume of a pyramid with base area 15 cm² and height 12 cm is __?__ .
   **A.** 180 cm³    **B.** 60 cm³    **C.** 180$\pi$ cm²    **D.** 60$\pi$ cm²

**15.** The volume of a cone whose base has diameter 5 m and height 6 m is __?__ .
   **A.** 50 m³    **B.** 50$\pi$ m³    **C.** 12.5 m³    **D.** 12.5$\pi$ m³

**16.** The base of a prism is a rhombus with side 8 cm. If the height  [9-6]
   of the prism is 10, its lateral area is __?__ .
   **A.** 640 cm²    **B.** 320 cm²    **C.** 80 cm²    **D.** 160 cm²

**17.** The total surface area of a rectangular solid 10 cm by 8 cm by 6 cm is __?__ .
   **A.** 480 cm³    **B.** 96 cm²    **C.** 376 cm²    **D.** 188 cm²

**18.** The total surface area of a cylinder with diameter 20 m and height 50 m is __?__ .
   **A.** 1200$\pi$ m²    **B.** 1000 m²    **C.** 1000$\pi$ m²    **D.** 1100$\pi$ m²

**19.** 10 L = __?__ cm³  [9-7]
   **A.** 1000    **B.** 10,000    **C.** 100,000    **D.** 1,000,000

**20.** Since the mass of 1 L of milk is 1.03 kg, the mass of 1 cm³ is __?__ .
   **A.** 1.03 g    **B.** 103 g    **C.** 1.03 kg    **D.** 0.103 g

**21.** The unit which is *not* a unit of volume is __?__ .
   **A.** cm³    **B.** L    **C.** mm³    **D.** kg

**22.** The area of a sphere with radius 6 is __?__ .  [9-8]
   **A.** 144$\pi$    **B.** 288$\pi$    **C.** 36$\pi$    **D.** 216$\pi$

**23.** The volume of a sphere with radius 9 is __?__ .
   **A.** 324$\pi$    **B.** 3888$\pi$    **C.** 81$\pi$    **D.** 972$\pi$

**24.** If the number of square units in the area of a sphere is the same as the number of cubic units in its volume, the radius of the sphere is __?__ .
   **A.** 3    **B.** $\frac{1}{3}$    **C.** $\pi$    **D.** $\frac{3}{4}$

# Accuracy of Measurement; Significant Digits

The diagram below shows several equivalent ways of reporting the length of $\overline{XY}$.

$XY = 52$ mm to the nearest mm
$51.5$ mm $\leq XY < 52.5$ mm
$XY = (52 \pm 0.5)$ mm          $\longleftarrow$ $\pm$ is read *plus or minus*

The measurement $XY = 52$ mm is given to *two significant* digits. The measurement might be given more accurately to three significant digits; for example, as $XY = 52.3$ mm.

The measurements $XY = 52$ mm and $XY = 5.2$ cm are considered equally accurate. Both are given to two significant figures. Likewise, the measurements 384 mm and 0.384 m are considered equally accurate. Both are given to three significant digits. On the other hand, the measurements $PQ = 40$ mm and $PQ = 4$ cm are not considered equally accurate.

| 40 mm | two significant digits | $39.5$ mm $\leq PQ < 40.5$ mm |
|-------|------------------------|-------------------------------|
| 4 cm  | one significant digit  | $3.5$ cm $\leq PQ < 4.5$ cm    |

Suppose the dimensions of a rectangle are 40 mm and 30 mm measured to the nearest millimeter. The calculations below show that its area could be between $1165.25$ mm² and $1235.25$ mm².

30 mm ☐ 40 mm

**Smallest Possible Dimensions**

Length $= 39.5$ mm
Width $= 29.5$ mm
Area $= 1165.25$ mm²

**Given Dimensions**

Length $= 40$ mm
Width $= 30$ mm
Area $= 1200$ mm²

**Greatest Possible Dimensions**

Length $= 40.5$ mm
Width $= 30.5$ mm
Area $= 1235.25$ mm²

## Exercises

1. If the length of $\overline{AB}$ is 8 cm measured to the nearest centimeter, then the exact length is between __?__ and __?__ .

2. If the length of $\overline{XY}$ to the nearest millimeter is 183, then the exact length is between __?__ and __?__ .

3. If a certain length is given as $(21 \pm 0.5)$ cm, then the exact length is between __?__ and __?__ .

4. If a length is given as $(21 \pm 0.1)$ cm, then the exact length is between __?__ cm and __?__ cm.

Give the number of significant digits in each measurement.

5. 35 cm          6. 143 mm          7. 1.503 m          8. 40.0 cm

9. 0.117 kg       10. 7 g            11. 3.4 km          12. 0.29 mg

In Exercises 13–16, tell which measurement is more accurate.

13. 5 cm or 50 mm                    14. 300 cm or 3 m

15. 2 km or 2000 m                   16. 2300 g or 2.3 kg

The length and width of a rectangle measure 8 and 2 to the nearest centimeter.

17. The greatest possible length and width are __?__ cm and __?__ cm.

18. The greatest possible perimeter is __?__ cm.

19. The greatest possible area is __?__ cm².

20. The least possible length and width are __?__ cm and __?__ cm.

21. The least possible perimeter is __?__ cm.

22. The least possible area is __?__ cm².

**Calculator Activity** The dimensions of a rectangular solid are 67 mm, 45 mm, and 20 mm measured to the nearest millimeter. Find the least and greatest possible volumes of the solid.

**Research Activity** Find out how significant digits are used in scientific notation.

## Chapter Test

For each parallelogram, give the base, height, and area.

1.

2.

[9-1]

3. What is the area of a triangle with base 15 mm and height 1 cm?  [9-2]

4. The area of a trapezoid is 68 cm². If its height is 8 cm and one base is 10 cm long, how long is the other base?

5. What is the area of a circle with diameter 7? (Use $\pi \approx \frac{22}{7}$.)  [9-3]

6. If a circle has area 28.26 m², what is its radius? (Use $\pi \approx 3.14$.)

7. 5 cm³ = __?__ mm³  [9-4]

8. If the volume of a cylinder is 2355 cm³ and the radius of the base is 10 cm, what is the height of the cylinder? (Use $\pi \approx 3.14$.)

9. Find the volume of a cone with height 10 cm and base radius 2 cm. (Use $\pi \approx 3.14$.)  [9-5]

10. Is it possible for a triangular pyramid, a square pyramid, and a hexagonal pyramid to have the same volume?

11. If the base of a prism is a right triangle with sides 3 cm, 4 cm, and 5 cm, and the height of the prism is 10 cm, what is the total surface area of the prism?  [9-6]

12. Find the total surface area (in terms of $\pi$) of a cylinder with height 5 m and radius 1.2 m.

13. The mass of 1 cm³ of butter is 0.87 g. What is the mass of 100 cm³ of butter?  [9-7]

14. The mass of 1 cm³ of olive oil is 0.918 g. What is the mass of 1 L of olive oil?

15. Find the volume (in terms of $\pi$) of a sphere with radius $1\frac{1}{2}$.  [9-8]

16. Find the area (in terms of $\pi$) of a sphere with diameter 3.

## Cumulative Review

Convert into a number sentence or numerical expression. [Ch. 7]

**1.** The sum of 2 and the product of 2 and $x$.

**2.** The product of seven and the sum of $x$ and three is greater than four.

Write a word sentence or word phrase.

**3.** $3x + 7 \leq 22$

**4.** $4(x - 3)$

Evaluate when the value of $x$ is $-1$.

**5.** $x^2 - x + 2$

**6.** $\dfrac{x - 7}{x + 3}$

Solve. In Exs. 9 and 10, the replacement set for $x$ is {the integers}.

**7.** $x + 7 = -x - 3$

**8.** $4y + 7 = 31$

**9.** $3x \leq 12 - 9$

**10.** $-4x + 2 > 10$

Write an equation and use it to solve the problem. [Ch. 8]

**11.** Alison earned $57.50 last week at an hourly wage of $2.50. How many hours did she work?

**12.** If Paco wants to earn $50 interest next year, how much should he invest at 8% annual interest?

**13.** Marcia is making a scale drawing of her room. If she uses the scale 1 cm ⟶ 0.5 m, how long should she draw her model railroad, which measures 2.5 m?

**14.** What is the area of a triangle with base 1 cm and height 5 cm? [Ch. 9]

**15.** What is the area of a rhombus with base 5 cm and height 1 cm?

**16.** A trapezoid has area 15 and bases 3 and 2. What is its height?

**17.** What is the area of a circle with circumference $16\pi$?

**18.** What is the volume and total surface area of a square prism with base area 36 and height 8?

**19.** A cone with height 5 and radius 2 has what volume?

**20.** A sphere has volume $\dfrac{32\pi}{3}$. What is its radius?

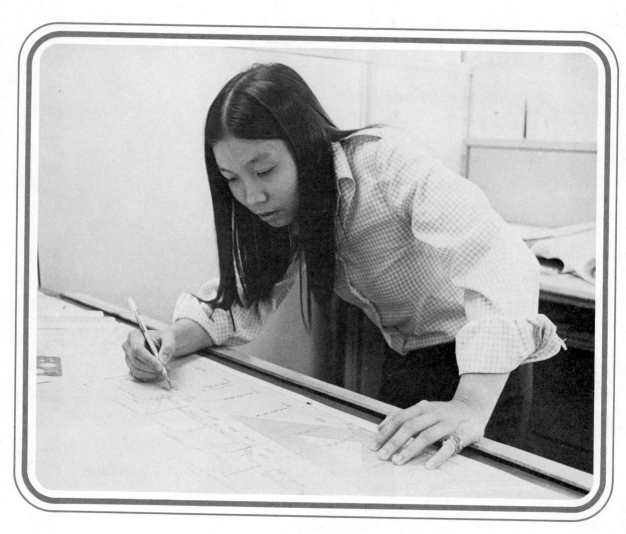

A draftsperson preparing a set of plans for a new building.

# 10 Probability

## 10-1 Experiments with Equally Likely Outcomes

**Objective** To determine the probability of an outcome when the outcomes are equally likely.

When you toss a fair coin, there are exactly two possible *outcomes:* the coin will land either heads up or tails up. These two outcomes are equally likely to occur. Therefore the *probability,* or *chance,* that the coin lands heads up is $\frac{1}{2}$.

When an experiment is conducted in such a way that the outcomes are strictly a matter of chance, we say that the outcomes occur **at random,** or **randomly.** The experiments described in this chapter are generally understood to be random experiments.

**Example**  You randomly draw a slip of paper from a box containing 4 slips: a red slip, a black slip, a white slip, and a pink slip.
  **a.** What are the possible outcomes?
  **b.** What is the probability of each outcome?

**Solution**  **a.** There are 4 possible outcomes:

  **b.** Since each slip is equally likely to be drawn, the probability of each outcome is $\frac{1}{4}$.

307

This example suggests that when an experiment can result in *n* different outcomes that are equally likely, the probability that any one of these will occur is $\frac{1}{n}$.

## Class Exercises

Is the experiment random? Explain.

1. Choose an ice cream flavor from the 8 flavors available at a shop.

2. Roll an ordinary *die* (the singular of dice) and observe the number of dots on top.

3. Vote for 1 candidate out of the 3 who are running for office.

4. Choose 1 of the 4 exits after shopping in a department store.

The pointer is spun and stops at random. Assume that the pointer will not stop on a division line.

5. Name the possible outcomes.

6. How many possible outcomes are there?

7. Are the outcomes equally likely?

8. What is the probability of each outcome?

## Exercises

An ordinary die is rolled.

A

1. What are the possible outcomes?   2. How many outcomes are there?

3. What is the probability that 3 dots land on top?

4. What is the probability of each outcome?

Assume that in each experiment the outcomes occur randomly. State the number of possible outcomes and the probability of each outcome.

5. One card is drawn from a standard deck of 52 cards.

6. One marble is chosen from a bag with 10 differently colored marbles.

7. One team is selected from 20 teams.

8. The pointer on a spinner stops at one of the numbers 1, 2, or 3.

9. A quarter and a nickel are tossed.   10. Two dice are rolled.

**B** **11.** One winner is to be selected from among 10 persons. Describe a way in which the selection can be made randomly.

**12.** A die is rolled. Do you think it is equally likely that the outcome will be 4 or will be an odd number? Explain.

**13.** A card is drawn from a standard deck of 52 cards. Do you think it is equally likely that the card drawn is a red card or a black card? Explain.

**14.** A card is drawn from a standard deck of 52 cards. Do you think it is equally likely that the card drawn is a club or is a red card? Explain.

**15.** Two coins are tossed. Do you think it is equally likely that the outcome will be two heads or will be two tails? Explain.

**16.** Two coins are tossed. Do you think it is equally likely that the outcome will be two heads or will not be two heads? Explain.

# *EXTRA!* Matching Birthdays

What are the chances that two people in your class have the same birthday? The answer depends on how many people are in the class. The results are presented in the tables below.

| Class size | 20 | 21 | 22 | 23 | 24 | 25 |
|---|---|---|---|---|---|---|
| Probability | 0.41 | 0.46 | 0.49 | 0.50 | 0.54 | 0.57 |

| Class size | 26 | 27 | 28 | 29 | 30 |
|---|---|---|---|---|---|
| Probability | 0.60 | 0.63 | 0.65 | 0.68 | 0.71 |

Here is a slightly different problem. What are the chances that someone else in your class has the same birthday as you? The following tables show the probability that this happens.

| Class size | 20 | 21 | 22 | 23 | 24 | 25 |
|---|---|---|---|---|---|---|
| Probability | 0.050 | 0.053 | 0.056 | 0.059 | 0.061 | 0.064 |

| Class size | 26 | 27 | 28 | 29 | 30 |
|---|---|---|---|---|---|
| Probability | 0.066 | 0.067 | 0.071 | 0.074 | 0.077 |

You can see from the tables that the probabilities in the second situation are always less than the probabilities in the first situation. Can you explain why?

# 10-2 The Probability of an Event

**Objective** To determine the probability of an event when the outcomes are equally likely.

In experiments involving chance, we are often interested in not just one particular outcome but rather in a group of favorable outcomes, called an **event**. For example, consider the experiment of drawing a card from a well-shuffled standard deck of 52 cards. What is the probability that the event "an ace is drawn" will occur? Of the 52 cards, 4 are aces. Thus there are

4 chances in 52

that the event will occur. We can represent the probability, $p$, that an ace will be drawn by writing:

$$p(\text{ace}) = \frac{4}{52} = \frac{1}{13}$$

In general, if an experiment can result in $n$ different equally likely outcomes, and an event consists of $f$ favorable outcomes, then the probability that the event will occur is the ratio $\frac{f}{n}$.

---
**formula**

$$p = \frac{\text{number of favorable outcomes}}{\text{number of possible outcomes}}$$

$$p = \frac{f}{n}$$

---

*Example*  Six slips of paper are labeled with the letters of *potato*. The slips are shuffled in a hat and you randomly draw one slip. What is the probability that you draw:

**a.** the letter *t*?

**b.** either the letter *o* or the letter *a*?

**c.** the letter *z*?

**d.** one of the letters *p, o, t,* or *a*?

Solution | **a.** $p(t) = \frac{f}{n} = \frac{2}{6} = \frac{1}{3}$

**b.** $p(o \text{ or } a) = \frac{3}{6} = \frac{1}{2}$

**c.** $p(z) = \frac{f}{n} = \frac{0}{6} = 0$

**d.** $p(p, o, t, \text{ or } a) = \frac{f}{n} = \frac{6}{6} = 1$

Parts **(c)** and **(d)** illustrate the following:

## rules

**The probability of an *impossible* event is 0.**
**The probability of a *certain* event is 1.**
**All other probabilities are between 0 and 1.**

## Class Exercises

Each of the cards pictured at the right has a
letter and a color. Each card is equally likely
to be drawn. Find each probability.

| a | b | c | a | b |
|---|---|---|---|---|
| c | d | e | f | a |

**1.** $p(\text{pink})$

**2.** $p(\text{gray})$

**3.** $p(a)$

**4.** $p(b)$

**5.** $p(e)$

**6.** $p(g)$

**7.** $p(\text{vowel})$

**8.** $p(\text{consonant})$

**9.** $p(\text{pink } a)$

**10.** $p(\text{gray } a)$

**11.** $p(a, b, c, d, e, \text{ or } f)$

**12.** $p(\text{pink } e)$

**13.** $p(a \text{ or } b)$

**14.** $p(\text{pink or gray})$

**15.** $p(c \text{ or } d)$

**16.** $p(a, b, c, \text{ or } d)$

**17.** What is the probability of an *event* that is certain to occur?

**18.** What is the probability of an *event* that cannot occur?

## Exercises

Consider drawing a card from a well-shuffled standard deck of 52 cards. Find each probability.

A  **1.** $p(6)$                    **2.** $p(\text{jack})$

   **3.** $p(\text{club})$          **4.** $p(\text{black})$

   **5.** $p(\text{red})$           **6.** $p(\text{spade})$

   **7.** $p(\text{king or ace})$   **8.** $p(\text{4 of diamonds})$

   **9.** $p(\text{queen of hearts})$   **10.** $p(\text{red 3})$

   **11.** $p(\text{even number})$   **12.** $p(\text{red or black})$

   **13.** $p(\text{black 7, 8, or 9})$   **14.** $p(\text{multiple of 3})$

An ordinary die is rolled. Find each probability.

**15.** $p(5)$                        **16.** $p(8)$

**17.** $p(5 \text{ or } 6)$          **18.** $p(1, 2, \text{ or } 3)$

**19.** $p(7)$                        **20.** $p(\text{even number})$

**21.** $p(1, 2, 3, 4, 5, \text{ or } 6)$   **22.** $p(\text{number greater than 2})$

A jar contains 2 orange, 5 blue, 3 red, and 4 yellow marbles. A marble is drawn at random from the jar. Find each probability.

**23.** $p(\text{orange})$            **24.** $p(\text{blue})$

**25.** $p(\text{red})$               **26.** $p(\text{green})$

**27.** $p(\text{orange or red})$     **28.** $p(\text{blue or yellow})$

**29.** $p(\text{orange or blue})$    **30.** $p(\text{orange or yellow})$

**31.** $p(\text{orange, blue or red})$   **32.** $p(\text{blue, red, or yellow})$

**33.** $p(\text{orange, blue, red, or yellow})$

A counting number less than 30 is chosen at random. What is the probability that the number chosen:

B  **34.** is a multiple of 4?    **35.** is a square?    **36.** is a prime?

C  **37.** A piggy bank contains one penny, one nickel, one dime, and one quarter. It is shaken until two coins fall out at random. What is the probability that at least 30¢ falls out?

   **38.** Amy removes an ace from a standard deck of 52 playing cards. Then Bill chooses a card at random from the remaining cards. What is the probability that he picks an ace? That he picks a jack?

# 10-3 Odds

**Objective** To determine the odds in favor of an event and the odds against an event.

*Example 1* | You toss an ordinary die. What is the probability that:
  **a.** the top face shows exactly one dot?
  **b.** the top face does not show exactly one dot?

*Solution* | **a.** $p = \dfrac{f}{n} = \dfrac{1}{6}$     **b.** $p = \dfrac{f}{n} = \dfrac{5}{6}$

Notice that it is certain that the top face either will show exactly one dot or will not show exactly one dot. You can see, then, why

$$\underbrace{p(\text{the event occurs})}_{\dfrac{1}{6}} + \underbrace{p(\text{the event does not occur})}_{\dfrac{5}{6}} = 1$$

In general:

> **— rule —**
>
> If the probability that an event occurs is $p$, then the probability that the event does not occur is $1 - p$.

If an event does not have probability 1, then the **odds in favor of the event** are given by the following:

> **— formula —**
>
> **odds in favor** $= \dfrac{\text{probability that the event occurs}}{\text{probability that the event does not occur}}$

If an event has nonzero probability, then the **odds against the event** are given by the following:

> **— formula —**
>
> **odds against** $= \dfrac{\text{probability that the event does not occur}}{\text{probability that the event occurs}}$

*Example 2* | A bag contains 3 red marbles, 4 green marbles, and 2 white marbles.

**a.** What are the odds in favor of drawing a red marble?

**b.** What are the odds against drawing a green marble?

*Solution*

**a.** $p(\text{red}) = \dfrac{f}{n} = \dfrac{3}{9} = \dfrac{1}{3}$

$p(\text{not red}) = 1 - \dfrac{1}{3} = \dfrac{2}{3}$

Odds in favor $= \dfrac{1}{3} \div \dfrac{2}{3} = \dfrac{1}{3} \times \dfrac{3}{2} = \dfrac{1}{2}$

The odds in favor of drawing a red marble are 1 to 2.

**b.** $p(\text{green}) = \dfrac{f}{n} = \dfrac{4}{9}$

$p(\text{not green}) = 1 - \dfrac{4}{9} = \dfrac{5}{9}$

Odds against $= \dfrac{5}{9} \div \dfrac{4}{9} = \dfrac{5}{9} \times \dfrac{9}{4} = \dfrac{5}{4}$

The odds against drawing a green marble are 5 to 4.

## Class Exercises

1. If the probability of snow is $\frac{1}{2}$, what is the probability that it will not snow?

2. If the probability that the team will not win the basketball game is $\frac{2}{5}$, what is the probability that the team will win?

Exercises 3–10 refer to the experiment of tossing a quarter and a dime.

3. What are the possible outcomes?

4. How many outcomes are there?

For each event, state:
**a.** the probability that the event will occur;
**b.** the probability that the event will not occur;
**c.** the odds in favor of the event.

5. Both coins land heads up.

6. Both coins land tails up.

7. Exactly one coin lands heads up.  8. At least one coin lands tails up.

9. The dime lands heads up.  10. The quarter does not land heads up.

## Exercises

A card is drawn at random from a standard deck of 52 cards. What are the odds in favor of drawing:

**A**
1. a queen?
2. a club?
3. a red card?

4. a black 6?
5. a 2 or 3?
6. a red 7 or 8?

7. the 4 of hearts?
8. a red card with an even number?

9. the ace or king of clubs?
10. the 8, 9, or 10 of spades?

11. a card other than a diamond?
12. a card other than a jack?

Exercises 13–32 refer to the experiment of tossing a white die and a yellow die together.

**B**
13. Make a list of the outcomes.

14. How many different outcomes are there?

Find:
a. the probability of the event.
b. the odds *against* the event.

15. Both dice show the same number.
16. Both dice show an even number.

17. One die shows a 3. The other shows a 4.
18. Both dice show a 5 or a 6.

19. Both dice show a number less than 5.

20. Both dice show a number greater than 1.

21. The white die shows a 2. The yellow die shows a number greater than 3.

22. The white die shows an even number. The yellow die shows an odd number.

23. Exactly one die shows a 6.

24. Exactly one die shows a multiple of 3.

25. At least one die shows an odd number.

26. At least one die shows a number greater than 4.

27. The sum of the numbers is 6.

28. The sum of the numbers is 10.

29. The number on the white die is 5 less than the number on the yellow die.

30. The number on one die is 2 greater than the number on the other.

31. The product of the numbers is 12.

32. The number on one die is twice the number on the other die.

# EXTRA! Independent Events

Suppose we toss a coin and then roll a die. What is the probability that the coin will show heads *and* the die will show 5 dots? Tossing the coin has no effect on rolling the die and we can list all the pairs of events that can occur, as is shown in the table at the right.

$$p(\text{heads}) = \frac{1}{2} \qquad p(\text{5 dots}) = \frac{1}{6}$$

| | |
|---|---|
| H-1 | T-1 |
| H-2 | T-2 |
| H-3 | T-3 |
| H-4 | T-4 |
| H-5 | T-5 |
| H-6 | T-6 |

Notice that there are 12 possible pairs of events in all, and that the pair of events, the coin shows heads *and* the die shows 5, occurs just once. Thus the probability that both events occur together is $\frac{1}{12}$. That is,

$$p(\text{H and 5}) = \frac{1}{12}$$

Notice also that

$$p(\text{H}) = \frac{1}{2} \quad \text{and} \quad p(5) = \frac{1}{6}$$

and that

$$p(\text{H}) \times p(5) = \frac{1}{2} \times \frac{1}{6} = \frac{1}{12}$$

In this particular case, we see that $p(\text{H and 5}) = p(\text{H}) \times p(5)$.

Events which have no effect on each other, such as tossing a coin and rolling a die, are called **independent** events.

As the example above suggests, the probability that a pair of independent events will occur is equal to the product of the probabilities of each individual event.

> ## rule
>
> If *A* and *B* are independent events, then
> $$p(A \text{ and } B) = p(A) \times p(B)$$

State whether or not the following pairs of events are independent. If they are, find the probability that they both occur.

1. A bag contains a red marble, a blue marble, and a yellow marble. You draw a marble, replace it, and draw again. $A$ = event of drawing a red marble on the first draw, $B$ = event of drawing a red marble on the second draw.

2. Same as problem 1, except you do not replace the first marble.

3. You randomly decide to walk or ride a bicycle, then randomly decide to head north, south, east, or west. $A$ = the event you walk, $B$ = the event you head south.

4. You throw a die. $A$ = the event that the number of dots which come up is odd. $B$ = the event that the number of dots which come up is a prime number.

## Self-Test

Symbols and words to remember:

$p(\text{ace})$ [p. 310]                                           $p = \frac{f}{n}$ [p. 310]

random experiment [p. 307]          probability of an outcome [p. 307]
event [p. 310]                                      probability of an event [p. 310]
odds in favor of an event [p. 313]      odds against an event [p. 313]

Is the experiment random?

  **1.** You choose a penny, a quarter, or a dollar bill from a hat.                    [10-1]
  **2.** You roll a fair die.

Write the number of possible outcomes and the probability of each outcome.
  **3.** A letter is randomly chosen from $a, b, c, d, e$.
  **4.** A marble is drawn at random from a bag containing a red, an orange, a yellow, and a green marble.

Each of 7 cards is marked with a letter of the word *referee*. If a card is drawn at random, what is the probability of drawing:

  **5.** an $e$?    **6.** an $s$?    **7.** an $f$?    **8.** an $r$, an $e$, or an $f$?   [10-2]

Tony has 6 tape cassettes in his car. One cassette stars the Melodies, 2 star Jake Jamison, and 3 star Carol and the Cliches. Tony selects a cassette at random. What are the odds:

  **9.** in favor of selecting a cassette by Jake?                               [10-3]
**10.** against selecting a cassette by Jake?
**11.** in favor of selecting a cassette by the Melodies?
**12.** against selecting a cassette by Carol and the Cliches?

Self-Test answers and Extra Practice are at the back of the book.

# 10-4 Estimating Probabilities

**Objective** To estimate the probability of an event on the basis of results obtained from repeated observations.

In the experiments discussed earlier in this chapter, each outcome had an equal chance of occurring. Thus we could assign the same probability to each one.

In most actual situations, however, we can only *infer* or estimate the probability of a given outcome on the basis of repeated observations. For example, the batting average of a baseball player is the ratio of the number of safe hits the player has made to the number of times the player has been officially at bat for some period of time in the past. If a player has an average of 0.300, then we could give $\frac{3}{10}$ as an estimate of the probability that the player will get a hit the next time at bat. Of course, this does not mean that the player will actually get a hit 3 out of every 10 times at bat, but the *experimental probability* $\frac{3}{10}$ can help us predict the future performance of the player.

## Class Exercises

1. Alice sank 16 free throws out of 25 attempts. What is the experimental probability that she will make a basket on the next free throw?

2. In a recent season, the Montreal Expos had a club batting average of 0.260. For a randomly selected time at bat, what is the experimental probability that the team scores a hit?

3. Suppose you knew that in the past 50 years it snowed in Denver on New Year's Day 12 out of the 50 years. What would you estimate to be the probability that it will snow in Denver next New Year's Day?

4. A quarterback has completed 8 out of 15 passes in one game. What is the experimental probability that he will not complete his next pass?

5. Suppose you toss a fair coin 8 times and get heads each time. Estimate the probability that you will get heads on your ninth toss.

6. Jeffrey was a competitor in 8 diving meets. He won 5 of them. Is it reasonable to predict that the probability that he wins his next meet is $\frac{5}{8}$? Explain.

7. A sports announcer correctly predicted the winning soccer team each of the last five times. Is the announcer's next prediction certain to be correct?

# Exercises

An experiment consists of drawing a marble from a jar. Assume that you know nothing about the number or color of the marbles in the jar. The results of the first 30 draws are shown in the table at the right. What is the experimental probability that the next draw will be:

| Red | ЖЖ | IIII |
|---|---|---|
| Yellow | IIII | |
| Blue | ЖЖ | ЖЖ |
| Green | ЖЖ | II |

**A**

1. a green marble?

2. a blue marble?

3. a red marble?

4. a yellow marble?

5. a red or a green marble?

6. a yellow or a blue marble?

7. an orange marble?

8. a marble that is not blue?

Refer to the experiment above. What would you estimate the odds to be in favor of the next draw:

9. a blue marble?

10. a red marble?

11. a green or a yellow marble?

12. a red or a blue marble?

13. a marble that is not red?

14. a marble that is not yellow?

A traffic engineer observed 200 cars traveling south-bound on Main Street, approaching the intersection of Main Street and Elm Avenue. She found that of the 200 cars, 16 turned right onto Elm, 45 turned left onto Elm, and the rest continued along Main Street. What is the experimental probability that the next car along:

15. will turn right?

16. will turn left?

17. will continue straight?

18. will turn right or left?

19. will not turn left?

20. will not turn right?

# 10-5 Estimating from a Sample

**Objective** To decide whether or not a sample is random, and to draw conclusions based on random samples.

In real-life situations it is often impractical or impossible to obtain exact data. For example, suppose a group of scientists wanted to determine the level of smog in the air. They could make a judgment about the quality of the air by analyzing a *few* *samples*. The samples must be randomly selected so the information obtained from them will be reliable.

Have you ever received a telephone call in which you were asked to rate and compare several different brands of a product? Marketing surveys of this type, opinion polls, and television ratings are familiar situations in which statistical methods have an influence on decision-making.

*Example*

Suppose you make a survey of 50 students in your school to see which musical instrument is the most popular one to listen to.

**a.** Would the sample be random if you include in the survey all the members of the school band?

**b.** Would the sample be random if you ask every tenth student passing through an auditorium door on the way to an assembly?

**c.** If the sample were random and 35 students named the guitar as their preference, how many students out of the 590 in the school would you estimate to prefer the guitar?

*Solution*

**a.** No, because band members would probably have a greater preference for brass and percussion instruments than other students.

**b.** Yes, if the students are entering in a random order, and if all students must attend the assembly.

**c.** $\frac{35}{50}$, or 0.7 of the students in the sample prefer the guitar. Therefore, you would estimate that about

$$0.7 \times 590 = 413$$

of the students in the school prefer the guitar.

## Class Exercises

Will the experiment produce a random sample? If not, describe a method for selecting a random sample.

1. Choose 4 members of your class by calling for volunteers.

2. Toss a coin to decide which of two teams will kick off first.

3. Choose 6 cans of orange juice from ten 6-can packages by choosing one package at random.

4. A newspaper predicts the outcome of an election by tallying readers' responses to a poll printed in the newspaper.

5. A telephone poll is conducted by calling the fifth name on every twentieth page of the telephone book.

6. A quality-control engineer in a light-bulb factory selects the first five bulbs manufactured each working day.

## Exercises

**A**

1. The Alpha Motor Company is testing the reliability of the wheel alignment on its cars. When 500 randomly chosen cars are tested, 8 are found to have faulty alignment. What is the probability that a random purchaser will receive a car with faulty wheel alignment?

2. From a consignment of 100,000 bolts, 400 were chosen at random. Of these, 8 were found to be defective. About how many defective bolts could be expected in the entire consignment?

3. A survey was taken of 150 households selected at random in Elmview, a city of 15,000 households. In 87 of the 150 households, at least one person was watching television. About what percent of the Elmview households would you predict were not watching television at the time the survey was taken?

4. Dwyer's Department Store polled 120 customers who were randomly chosen. They found that 81 of the 120 had Dwyer's charge cards. Dwyer's has about 5400 charge accounts. About how many charge accounts would Dwyer's have if every customer in the sample had had a charge card?

5. You choose 60 orange trees at random in a citrus grove containing 1960 trees. You find that the oranges on 39 trees are ripe enough to be picked. About how many trees in the grove would you expect to have oranges that are ready to be picked?

6. A manager in a factory will allow no more than 0.5% defective parts. When 500 parts were randomly selected from a shipment, 3 were found to be defective. Did the shipment meet the manager's requirements?

**B**

7. A survey was taken of 200 people who were chosen at random. Of these people, 132 exercised regularly. Among the 132, 25% go swimming every week. What is the probability that a randomly selected person swims every week?

Passage of a certain bond issue requires a 60% favorable vote. In a random sample of 250 voters from a population of 12,000 it was found that 156 favored passage, 85 were opposed, and the rest were undecided.

8. About how many people in all would you estimate favor passage?

9. About how many people in all would you estimate oppose passage?

10. About how many people in all would you estimate are undecided?

11. On the basis of the sample, would you estimate that the bond issue will pass or not? Explain.

# Application

## Estimating Animal Populations

How can we estimate the number of fish in a lake? Naturally, it is impractical to count the fish one by one. However, we can use our knowledge of probability to estimate the fish population.

Suppose that on Monday we catch some fish, say 60, and put tags on their fins. Then we release the fish back into the lake. A few days later we take another random sample of fish from the lake and observe how many have tags on their fins. Let us say that of 40 fish caught, 5 had tags. Now it is possible, but *very* unlikely, that there are just 95 fish in the lake. That is, there could be 60 fish with tags and 35 without tags. Each of these 95 fish would then have been caught exactly once in the two hauls. It is more realistic to assume that the proportion of tagged fish in the lake is equal to the proportion of tagged fish in the second catch:

$$\frac{1}{8} = \frac{60}{x}; \quad x = 480$$

A likely estimate for the total number of fish is 480.

**Research Activity** Find out how animal populations of endangered species are estimated.

# 10-6 Random Variables and Expected Value

**Objective** To recognize a random variable and compute its expected value.

Suppose we toss a die, and let $X$ be the number of dots which come up. A variable such as $X$, whose value is determined by a random experiment, is called a **random variable.** The possible values of $X$ and their probabilities of occurrence are listed below.

$X = 3$

| Possible values of $X$ | 1 | 2 | 3 | 4 | 5 | 6 |
|---|---|---|---|---|---|---|
| Probability of occurrence | $\frac{1}{6}$ | $\frac{1}{6}$ | $\frac{1}{6}$ | $\frac{1}{6}$ | $\frac{1}{6}$ | $\frac{1}{6}$ |

Of course, there is no way to know in advance what the value of a random variable will be in a single trial. But frequently in applications we only need to know the *average* value of a random variable, such as the *average* number of phone calls per day received at a switchboard, or the *average* time it takes to commute to work. Fortunately, there is a way to closely predict the average value of a random variable over a large number of trials.

To see how this can be done, let us consider an actual experiment in which a die was tossed 150 times. The number of times each score occurred was counted, and the results are as shown below.

| Value of $X$ | Frequency |
|---|---|
| 1 | 23 |
| 2 | 28 |
| 3 | 30 |
| 4 | 21 |
| 5 | 23 |
| 6 | 25 |
| Total | 150 |

The average value of $X$ in this experiment is

$$\frac{\text{sum of observed values}}{\text{no. of trials}} = \frac{1 \times 23 + 2 \times 28 + 3 \times 30 + 4 \times 21 + 5 \times 23 + 6 \times 25}{150}$$

$$= \frac{518}{150} \approx 3.45 \textbf{ (observed average)}$$

To see how this result could have been estimated beforehand, let us re-examine the computation. We had

$$\frac{1 \times \text{(frequency of 1)} + 2 \times \text{(frequency of 2)} + \cdots + 6 \times \text{(frequency of 6)}}{\text{no. of trials}}$$

This can be rewritten as

$$1 \times \frac{\text{frequency of 1}}{\text{no. of trials}} + 2 \times \frac{\text{frequency of 2}}{\text{no. of trials}} + \cdots + 6 \times \frac{\text{frequency of 6}}{\text{no. of trials}}$$

But $\dfrac{\text{frequency of an event}}{\text{no. of trials}} \approx p(\text{event})$ for a large number of trials, so our average should be close to

$$1 \times p(1) + 2 \times p(2) + \cdots + 6 \times p(6)$$
$$= 1 \times \tfrac{1}{6} + 2 \times \tfrac{1}{6} + 3 \times \tfrac{1}{6} + 4 \times \tfrac{1}{6} + 5 \times \tfrac{1}{6} + 6 \times \tfrac{1}{6}$$
$$= \tfrac{21}{6} = 3.5 \text{ (\textbf{predicted average})}$$

This predicted average is called the **expected value** of the random variable.

## rule

**To find the expected value of a random variable, multiply each possible value by its probability and add the results.**

*Example* | At a county fair, Jacqueline has won a prize which she is to select at random from a grab bag containing 6 \$2 prizes, 3 \$5 prizes, and 1 \$10 prize. If $V =$ the dollar value of her prize, what is the expected value of $V$?

*Solution* | **Step 1.** List all the possible values of $V$, together with their probabilities.

| Possible values of $V$ | 2 | 5 | 10 |
|---|---|---|---|
| Probability of occurrence | $\frac{6}{10}$ | $\frac{3}{10}$ | $\frac{1}{10}$ |

**Step 2.** Multiply each possible value by its probability and add.

$$2 \times \tfrac{6}{10} + 5 \times \tfrac{3}{10} + 10 \times \tfrac{1}{10} = \tfrac{37}{10} = 3.70$$

The expected value of $V$ is \$3.70.

## Class Exercises

In the preceding example:

1. can Jacqueline win a prize worth $3.70?

2. what is the significance of the $3.70 amount?

Find the expected value of the random variable.

3.

| Possible values of $B$ | 2 | 5 | 7 |
|---|---|---|---|
| Probability of occurrence | 0.2 | 0.5 | 0.3 |

4.

| Possible values of $C$ | $-3$ | $-1$ | 0 | 2 |
|---|---|---|---|---|
| Probability of occurrence | $\frac{1}{4}$ | $\frac{3}{8}$ | $\frac{1}{8}$ | $\frac{1}{4}$ |

## Exercises

**A**  1. Joel finds that when he takes the elevator down from his fifth-floor apartment, it takes 2 min 20% of the time, 3 min 50% of the time, and 4 min the rest of the time. If it takes him 3 min to walk down the stairs, which way is faster on the average?

2. The solid shown at the right has 2 triangular faces and 3 rectangular faces. If $N$ = the number of sides of a face chosen at random, what is the expected value of $N$?

3. In a bag of apples, the frequencies of the masses of individual apples, to the nearest 10 g, are shown below. If $M$ = the mass of an apple selected at random, find the expected value of $M$ to the nearest gram.

**B**  **4.** A nickel, a dime, and a quarter are tossed together. If $B =$ the total number of heads which come up, what is the expected value of $B$?

**5.** A player tosses a die. If it comes up an odd number, the player receives that number of points. If it comes up an even number, the player loses that number of points. Is the player likely to have a positive score after many trials? Explain.

# A Mathematician

You are familiar with equations of one or even two variables, but did you ever think of solving equations with four variables?

Shih-Chieh Chu (1280–1303) has been described as one of the greatest mathematicians of all time. He traveled extensively throughout China, where students flocked to study under his guidance. Chu wrote two books of major importance. The first, called *Introduction to Mathematical Studies,* was used as a textbook for students beginning their study of mathematics. The second contained Chu's "method of the four elements." The method, based on the "method of the celestial elements," contained a way of working with four unknown quantities in the same algebraic equation. The celestial elements were *t'ien* (heaven), *ti* (earth), *jen* (man), and *wu* (things or matter) and were represented by the variables *u*, *v*, *w*, and *x*, respectively. With this mathematical system discovered by Chu, the development of algebra in China reached a peak.

**Research Activity** Look up Emmy Noether and François Vieta in an encyclopedia, and note their contributions to the field of algebra.

**Career Activity** To do research, you must have a good understanding of the particular field you choose to study. What do you think you need to know to do research in mathematics? Here are just a few of the many fields of mathematics which researchers study. Find a description of each field in an encyclopedia or mathematics dictionary.

Calculus  Geometry  Set Theory  Complex Variables  Trigonometry

## Self-Test

[10-4]

1. A weather bureau correctly predicted the weather 28 times out of the past 30 days. What is the probability that the bureau will be correct today?

2. The school bus arrived early 3 out of the past 5 days. What is the probability that it will not be early tomorrow?

3. You toss a fair die 6 times and get an odd number each time. What is the probability of rolling an odd number on the next toss?

4. A baseball pitcher has won 8 of his last 12 games. What is the probability that he will win his next game?

An inspector on an assembly line chose 400 fuses at random out of 6000 fuses. She found that 3 of the 400 fuses were defective.

[10-5]

5. What is the probability that a consumer will get a defective fuse?

6. What is the probability that a consumer will not get a defective fuse?

7. About how many defective fuses could be expected in the 6000 fuses?

8. If you randomly choose a fuse, what are the odds against your getting a defective fuse?

9. A record of Ellen's archery scores showing the percent of arrows which hit each score on the target is shown at the right. If $S$ = Ellen's score on one shot, what is the expected value of $S$?

[10-6]

10. A coin is taken at random from a purse which contains 1 penny, 2 nickels, 4 dimes, and 3 quarters. If $X$ = the value of the coin in cents, find the expected value of $X$.

11. The pyramid-shaped die at the right has 4 congruent triangular faces which are marked with 1, 2, 3, and 4 dots, respectively. If $Y$ = the number of dots on the bottom face on a single toss, what is the expected value of $Y$?

12. A student guesses at random on a quiz consisting of 2 true-false questions, the first worth 4 points and the second worth 6 points. If $S$ = the student's quiz score, what is the expected value of $S$?

Self-Test answers and Extra Practice are at the back of the book.

# Chapter Review

Write the letter that labels the correct answer.

1. The probability that one of $n$ equally likely outcomes will occur is ___?___.     [10-1]

   **A.** 0          **B.** 1          **C.** $n$          **D.** $\frac{1}{n}$

2. An ordinary die is rolled. The probability that 5 dots show up is ___?___.

   **A.** 5          **B.** $\frac{1}{5}$          **C.** $\frac{1}{6}$          **D.** $\frac{5}{6}$

3. What is the probability of an impossible event?     [10-2]
   **A.** 1                          **B.** 0
   **C.** $\frac{1}{2}$                          **D.** depends on the experiment

4. The probability that an ordinary die will turn up with a prime number of dots is ___?___.

   **A.** $\frac{1}{2}$          **B.** $\frac{1}{3}$          **C.** 0          **D.** $\frac{1}{6}$

5. A box contains 2 red, 3 yellow, and 2 green marbles. The probability that a marble chosen at random is not yellow is ___?___.

   **A.** $\frac{2}{7}$          **B.** $\frac{3}{7}$          **C.** $\frac{5}{7}$          **D.** $\frac{4}{7}$

6. If the probability of rain today is 0.3, then the probability that it will not rain today is ___?___.     [10-3]

   **A.** $\frac{2}{3}$          **B.** $\frac{1}{3}$          **C.** 0.7          **D.** 0.3

7. A card is drawn at random from a standard deck of 52 cards. The odds against drawing the queen of hearts are ___?___.

   **A.** 52 to 1     **B.** 51 to 1     **C.** $\frac{51}{52}$     **D.** $\frac{1}{52}$

8. A red die and a white die are thrown together. The odds in favor of the red die showing more dots than the white die are ___?___.
   **A.** 15 to 36     **B.** 21 to 36     **C.** 5 to 7     **D.** 1 to 1

9. If the odds in favor of an event are 3 to 2 then the probability of the event is ___?___.

   **A.** $\frac{3}{5}$          **B.** $\frac{2}{5}$          **C.** $\frac{2}{3}$          **D.** $\frac{3}{2}$

10. An insurance company sent out 50,000 mail advertisements for    [10-4]
    an insurance policy. As a result, they sold 2100 policies. Esti-
    mate the probability that a single advertising letter will result in
    a sale.
    A. 0.21        B. $\frac{21}{50}$         C. 4.2%          D. 42%

11. In Exercise 10, what are the odds against a single letter resulting
    in a sale?
    A. 479 to 21    B. 21 to 479    C. 500 to 21    D. 21 to 500

12. A random sample of 150 machine parts contained 3 defective    [10-5]
    parts. Estimate the probability that a part chosen at random is
    good.
    A. $\frac{1}{50}$        B. $\frac{49}{50}$        C. $\frac{147}{153}$        D. $\frac{3}{147}$

13. In Bayview High School, 96 out of 120 students chosen at ran-
    dom planned to continue their education after graduation. If
    the school has 2500 students, about how many would you esti-
    mate plan to continue their education after graduation?
    A. 2000        B. 500        C. 2400        D. 1904

14. If each value of a random variable is doubled, its expected value    [10-6]
    __?__.
    A. doubles              B. stays the same
    C. increases by 2       D. is divided by 2

| Possible values of X | −2 | 1 | 3 | 5 |
| --- | --- | --- | --- | --- |
| Probability of occurrence | 0.1 | 0.2 | 0.3 | 0.4 |

15. In the table above, the expected value of X is __?__.
    A. 1.75        B. 2.75        C. 2.9        D. 3.3

16. After many trials, the average value of a random variable will
    probably __?__.
    A. equal the expected value
    B. be less than the expected value
    C. be greater than the expected value
    D. be close to the expected value

# Random Experiments

You have learned some important ideas in probability. But how well do they work? The real test of usefulness is actually to perform some random experiment many times, and compare the results with what your knowledge of probability would lead you to expect. A computer can help us do this because it can simulate a random experiment and repeat it many times at high speed. It can also tell us things we would like to know about the results.

The program on the next page, written in BASIC, simulates the experiment of throwing a pair of dice. It will repeat this experiment 300 times, record the sum of dots on each trial, and print a histogram of the frequency of each possible sum. (*Note:* Check your computer handbook on the use of the RND function.)

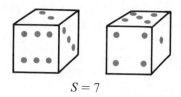

$S = 7$

Let $S$ stand for the sum of the dots on the top faces of a pair of dice. The table below shows the sum $S$ for each of the 36 equally likely ways the pair of dice can turn up.

| 1st die \ 2nd die | 1 | 2 | 3 | 4 | 5 | 6 |
|---|---|---|---|---|---|---|
| 1 | 2 | 3 | 4 | 5 | 6 | 7 |
| 2 | 3 | 4 | 5 | 6 | 7 | 8 |
| 3 | 4 | 5 | 6 | 7 | 8 | 9 |
| 4 | 5 | 6 | 7 | 8 | 9 | 10 |
| 5 | 6 | 7 | 8 | 9 | 10 | 11 |
| 6 | 7 | 8 | 9 | 10 | 11 | 12 |

Sum $S$ for a pair of dice

**1.** What is the probability of each possible value of $S$?

**2.** What is the expected value of $S$?

Run the computer program two times.

**3.** What similarity do you see in the shape of the two histograms?

**4.** Use the first histogram to calculate the average value of S. Is it close to the expected value of S?

```
10  PRINT TAB(30);"SUM OF DICE"
15  PRINT
20  FOR Z=1 TO 300
25  LET S=INT(6*RND(0))+INT(6*RND(0))+2
30  PRINT S;
35  GOTO S-1 OF 40,50,60,70,80,90,100,110,120,130,140
40  LET A=A+1
45  GOTO 145
50  LET B=B+1
55  GOTO 145
60  LET C=C+1
65  GOTO 145
70  LET D=D+1
75  GOTO 145
80  LET E=E+1
85  GOTO 145
90  LET F=F+1
95  GOTO 145
100 LET G=G+1
105 GOTO 145
110 LET H=H+1
115 GOTO 145
120 LET I=I+1
125 GOTO 145
130 LET J=J+1
135 GOTO 145
140 LET K=K+1
145 NEXT Z
150 PRINT
152 PRINT
155 PRINT TAB(30);"HISTOGRAM"
160 PRINT
165 LET L=A
170 GOSUB 280
175 LET L=B
180 GOSUB 280
185 LET L=C
190 GOSUB 280
195 LET L=D
200 GOSUB 280
205 LET L=E
210 GOSUB 280
215 LET L=F
220 GOSUB 280
225 LET L=G
230 GOSUB 280
235 LET L=H
240 GOSUB 280
245 LET L=I
250 GOSUB 280
255 LET L=J
260 GOSUB 280
265 LET L=K
270 GOSUB 280
275 STOP
280 LET M=M+1
285 PRINT M+1;
290 FOR N=1 TO L
295 PRINT TAB(4);"*";
300 NEXT N
305 PRINT
310 RETURN
315 END
```

## Chapter Test

1. In an experiment with 7 equally likely outcomes, each outcome has probability ___?___ .  [10-1]

2. If the outcomes of an experiment are a matter of chance, the outcomes occur ___?___ .

3. A ___?___ event has probability 1.  [10-2]

4. A card is drawn randomly from a standard deck. The probability that it is a club is ___?___ .

5. The probability that an ordinary die will turn up with more than 4 dots is ___?___ .

6. If you choose a pair of socks at random from a drawer containing 1 blue sock and 2 brown socks, the probability of getting a matching pair is ___?___ .

7. If the probability of an event is $\frac{2}{7}$, the odds in favor of it are ___?___ .  [10-3]

8. If you toss an ordinary die, the odds in favor of its showing a number of dots which is a multiple of 3 are ___?___ .

9. In playing chess against Ivan, John has won 9 games, drawn 3, and lost 7. The probability that John will not win his next game against Ivan is ___?___ .  [10-4]

10. A tennis player has successfully returned 9 out of 14 first serves by the opponent. The probability that the player will not return the next first serve is ___?___ .

11. A random sample of 200 households in Glenville contained 93 households with school-age children. Of 2200 households in Glenville about ___?___ have school-age children.  [10-5]

12. In a random sample of 25 residents of Willowdale, population 1250, 9 indicated they would attend a town meeting. About ___?___ people planned to attend the meeting.

13. A hand of 5 cards contains 3 sevens and 2 tens. If $V =$ the face value of a card randomly chosen from this hand, then the expected value of $V$ is ___?___ .  [10-6]

14. One face of a cube is marked with 1 dot, 2 other faces are each marked with 2 dots, and the remaining 3 faces are each marked with 3 dots. If this die is thrown, the expected value of the score is ___?___ .

# Skill Review

Add or subtract.

**1.** $1\frac{1}{2} + 2\frac{1}{4}$

**2.** $5 + 2\frac{1}{6}$

**3.** $3\frac{1}{3} + 3\frac{1}{3}$

**4.** $-16\frac{3}{4} + 5\frac{1}{3}$

**5.** $-\frac{15}{2} + 4\frac{1}{2}$

**6.** $\frac{32}{3} - 6\frac{3}{4}$

**7.** $15\frac{1}{2} - \frac{21}{5}$

**8.** $\frac{7}{3} + \frac{1}{3}$

**9.** $-2\frac{5}{8} - \frac{16}{3}$

**10.** $22\frac{1}{2} - (-6)$

**11.** $17 - \left(-16\frac{11}{21}\right)$

**12.** $5\frac{3}{8} + 15\frac{1}{4}$

**13.** $37\frac{1}{3} - \left(-7\frac{1}{3}\right)$

**14.** $11\frac{12}{25} - 12\frac{13}{25}$

**15.** $5\frac{1}{8} + 6\frac{1}{4}$

**16.** $\left(-\frac{3}{2} - \frac{3}{2}\right)$

**17.** $-14\frac{2}{7} - 2\frac{2}{3}$

**18.** $13\frac{5}{8} - 3\frac{5}{8}$

**19.** $-\frac{11}{3} - \frac{3}{11}$

**20.** $\frac{6}{7} + \left(-\frac{22}{7}\right)$

**21.** $\frac{17}{3} + \frac{2}{3}$

**22.** $5\frac{1}{4} + 6\frac{3}{4}$

**23.** $\frac{23}{3} - \frac{3}{23}$

**24.** $16\frac{5}{7} - 23\frac{1}{5}$

Multiply or divide.

**25.** $\frac{1}{4} \times \frac{1}{2}$

**26.** $\frac{3}{2} \times \frac{2}{3}$

**27.** $1\frac{1}{2} \times 2\frac{1}{4}$

**28.** $13 \div 1\frac{1}{3}$

**29.** $\frac{15}{2} \div \frac{2}{3}$

**30.** $-\frac{3}{5} \times \frac{6}{7}$

**31.** $-5\frac{1}{2} \div \frac{1}{2}$

**32.** $\frac{13}{6} \times \frac{3}{2}$

**33.** $-5 \times \left(-\frac{3}{5}\right)$

**34.** $-\frac{17}{5} \div \frac{5}{17}$

**35.** $-\frac{11}{21} \times \frac{3}{7}$

**36.** $6\frac{1}{4} \div \left(-1\frac{1}{2}\right)$

**37.** $-\frac{2}{3} \times \frac{6}{17}$

**38.** $\frac{27}{121} \times \frac{11}{3}$

**39.** $4\frac{1}{6} \times \left(-1\frac{2}{3}\right)$

**40.** $-3 \times \frac{33}{27}$

**41.** $1\frac{1}{5} \times \frac{35}{48}$

**42.** $\frac{15}{32} \div \left(-\frac{16}{5}\right)$

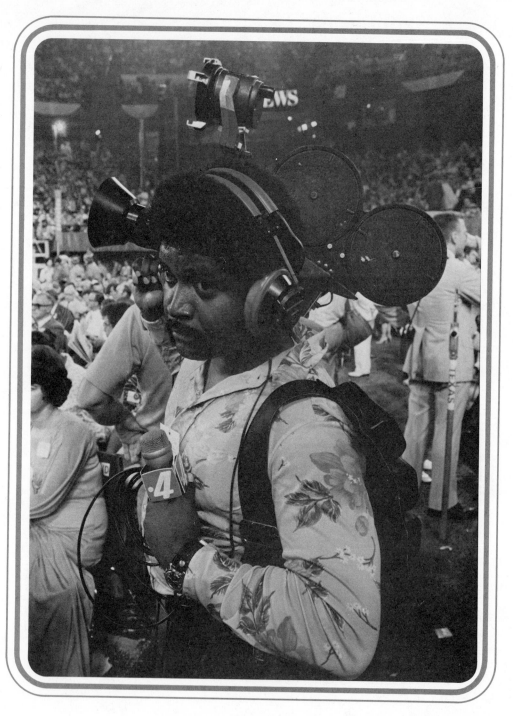

A television cameraperson filming a political convention.

# 11

# The Number Plane

## 11-1 Graphing an Ordered Pair of Numbers

**Objective** To graph an ordered pair of numbers in the plane.

We have learned how to set up a coordinate system on a line, associating each number with exactly one point on the line.

By drawing two perpendicular number lines that intersect at the origin of each, we can set up a **rectangular coordinate system in the plane.** Using this system, we can then associate an *ordered pair of numbers* with each point in the plane. An **ordered pair of numbers** is simply a pair of numbers (called *components* of the ordered pair) whose order is important. We associate one number, the *first component,* with the horizontal number line (called the *x*-axis), and the other number, the *second component,* with the vertical number line (called the *y*-axis). Note that the positive direction is to the right on the horizontal axis and is upward on the vertical axis.

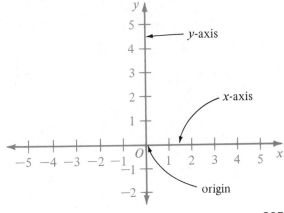

**335**

To find the point associated with an ordered pair of numbers, say $(-2,4)$, we proceed as follows:

1. Draw a line $l$ perpendicular to the $x$-axis, passing through the point on it labeled $-2$.
2. Next draw a line $m$ perpendicular to the $y$-axis, passing through the point labeled 4 on that axis.
3. The point where $l$ and $m$ intersect is the graph of $(-2,4)$. Special graph paper with a printed grid is helpful for locating points in this way.

*Example* | Graph $(3,2)$, $(-3,2)$, $(-3,-2)$, and $(3,-2)$.

*Solution*

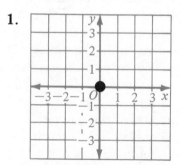

Another way to think of finding the graph of an ordered pair is in terms of sliding a checker. For example, to locate the graph of $(-3,2)$ you can:

1. Start at the origin.

1.

**2.** Move 3 units to the left along the x-axis.

**2.**

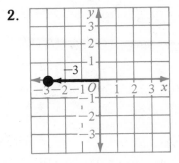

**3.** Move 2 units up parallel to the y-axis.

**4.** The checker is now at the point paired with $(-3,2)$.

**3.**

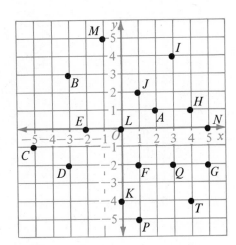

## Class Exercises

Name the graph of each ordered pair.

*Example* | **(1,2)**
*Solution* | **J**

**1.** (4,1)

**2.** (1,−2)

**3.** (−3,−2)

**4.** (3,4)

**5.** (0,−4)

**6.** (−3,3)

**7.** (−2,0)

**8.** (4,−4)

**9.** (0,0)

**10.** (2,1)

**11.** (5,0)

**12.** (3,−2)

**13.** (−5,−1)

**14.** (1,−5)

**15.** (5,−2)

**16.** (−1,5)

## Exercises

Name the graph of each ordered pair.

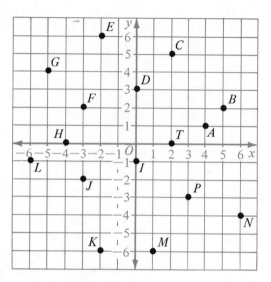

**A**

1. $(-4,0)$    2. $(2,5)$

3. $(5,2)$    4. $(6,-4)$

5. $(-3,-2)$    6. $(-5,4)$

7. $(2,0)$    8. $(4,1)$

9. $(0,3)$    10. $(3,-3)$

11. $(-2,-6)$    12. $(-3,2)$

13. $(0,-1)$    14. $(1,-6)$

15. $(-2,6)$    16. $(-6,-1)$

In Exercises 17–22, graph the specified points on the plane. Connect them in the order listed. Use a separate set of axes for each exercise.

*Example* | $(3,2), (0,-1), (3,-4), (6,-1), (3,2)$

*Solution*

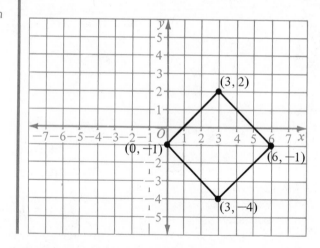

17. $(-1,0), (3,2), (-2,3), (2,5), (-1,0)$

18. $(-2,3), (1,1), (-2,-1), (1,-3), (-2,-5), (-2,3)$

19. $(-6,-5), (-1,-3), (-1,-1), (4,1), (-6,-5)$

20. $(-1,-1), (4,-1), (4,1), (-1,1), (0,0), (-1,-1)$

21. $(0,1), (2,1), (0,3), (2,5), (0,5), (-2,3), (0,1)$

22. $(-1,2), (1,1), (1,-2), (4,2), (0,6), (-1,2)$

In Exercises 23–28, the vertexes of a polygon are specified.

**a.** Locate the graphs of the given ordered pairs and sketch the polygon on a coordinate plane.

**b.** Find the area of the polygon.

*Example* $(-2,1), (1,4), (4,1)$

*Solution*

**a.** Sketch the polygon, a triangle.

**b.** Count the units in the base (6) and the height (3). Use $A = \frac{1}{2}bh$.

$$A = \frac{1}{2}(6)(3) = 9$$

The area is 9 square units.

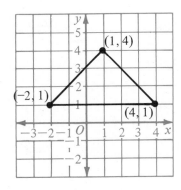

**B** **23.** $(1,3), (-5,3), (-2,-2)$

**24.** $(4,0), (4,7), (0,5)$

**25.** $(5,1), (5,-5), (-1,1), (-1,-5)$

**26.** $(1,2), (1,8), (5,2), (5,8)$

**27.** $(-3,-1), (0,3), (7,3), (4,-1)$

**28.** $(0,-3), (2,1), (7,1), (8,-3)$

# Application  Using A Map

Here is a part of the map of Spaceville.

All the avenues running north and south, except Main Avenue, are named by letters. The streets running east and west, except Broadway, are named by numbers. The Spaceville City Hall is located at the intersection of Broadway and Main Avenue. If you were standing in front of City Hall and were asked by someone how to get to the corner of B Avenue and 1st Street, you could tell the person to go 2 blocks west and 4 blocks south.

What set of directions would you provide if you were asked how to get to the intersection of

**1.** D Ave. and 5th St.?

**2.** F Ave. and 8th St.?

**3.** Main Ave. and 2nd St.?  **4.** F Ave. and Broadway?

**5.** B Ave. and 6th St.?  **6.** F Ave. and 2nd St.?

# 11-2 The Coordinates of a Point in the Plane

**Objective** To assign coordinates to a point in the plane.

We have seen that a point in the plane can be assigned to *every* ordered pair of numbers.

To assign a pair of coordinates to a given point *P* in the plane:

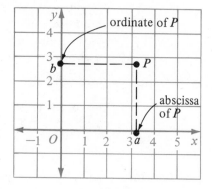

1. Draw a perpendicular from *P* to the *x*-axis, intersecting the axis at a point with coordinate *a*.
2. Draw a perpendicular from *P* to the *y*-axis, intersecting it at a point with coordinate *b*.
3. Then the coordinates of *P* are *(a,b)*, or about $(3\frac{1}{4}, 2\frac{3}{4})$ in this figure. The first number, *a*, is called the **x-coordinate**, or **abscissa**, of *P*. The second number, *b*, is the **y-coordinate**, or **ordinate**, of *P*.

The two axes of a rectangular coordinate system separate the rest of the plane into four regions, called **Quadrants I, II, III,** and **IV.** The location of each quadrant is shown here, along with the range of values for the coordinates of any point in that quadrant.

| | |
|---|---|
| Quadrant II | Quadrant I |
| $x < 0$ | $x > 0$ |
| $y > 0$ | $y > 0$ |
| Quadrant III | Quadrant IV |
| $x < 0$ | $x > 0$ |
| $y < 0$ | $y < 0$ |

*Example* | Give the coordinates of each lettered point in the figure.

*Solution* | $A(0,1)$, $B(3,2)$, $C(1,3)$, $D(-2,2)$, $E(-1,-2)$, $F(2,-1)$, $O(0,0)$

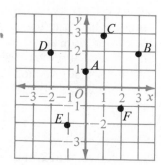

## Class Exercises

Exercises 1–16 refer to the figure at the right. State the coordinates of the given point.

**1.** *A*    **2.** *B*    **3.** *C*    **4.** *D*

**5.** *K*    **6.** *M*    **7.** *F*    **8.** *N*

**9.** Name all points shown in Quadrant I.

**10.** Name all points shown in Quadrant II.

**11.** Name all points shown in Quadrant III.

**12.** Name all points shown in Quadrant IV.

**13.** Name all points that are not in a quadrant.

**14.** Name all points having abscissa −2.

**15.** Name all points having ordinate 2.

**16.** Name all points having ordinate 0.

## Exercises

Exercises 1–30 refer to the figure at the right.

In Exercises 1–16, write the coordinates of the given point.

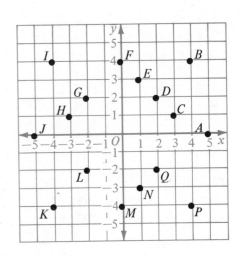

**A**    **1.** *A*    **2.** *K*    **3.** *P*    **4.** *H*

   **5.** *D*    **6.** *L*    **7.** *O*    **8.** *J*

   **9.** *E*    **10.** *M*    **11.** *I*    **12.** *Q*

   **13.** *B*    **14.** *F*    **15.** *N*    **16.** *C*

**17.** Name all points shown in Quadrant I.

**18.** Name all points shown in Quadrant II.

**19.** Name all points shown in Quadrant III.

**20.** Name all points shown in Quadrant IV.

**B**    **21.** Name all points shown whose abscissas are positive.

   **22.** Name all points shown whose abscissas are negative.

**23.** Name all points shown whose ordinates are negative.

**24.** Name all points shown whose ordinates are positive.

**25.** Name all points shown whose ordinates are 0.

**26.** Name all points shown whose ordinates are −4.

**27.** Name all points shown whose abscissas are 0.

**28.** Name all points shown whose abscissas are 2.

C **29.** Name all points shown for which the abscissa is equal to the ordinate.

**30.** Name all points shown for which the sum of the abscissa and ordinate is 4.

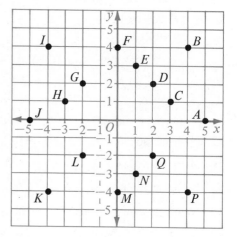

# EXTRA! Pictures in the Plane

Graph each set of ordered pairs below on a coordinate plane. Then join the points in order by drawing line segments. What have you drawn?

| Figure A | Figure B | Figure C | Figure D |
|---|---|---|---|
| **1.** (1,0) | **1.** (6,17) | **1.** (−4,9) | **1.** (0,−6) |
| **2.** (−1,1) | **2.** (8,17) | **2.** (4,9) | **2.** (1,−2) |
| **3.** (−5,−1) | **3.** (6,14) | **3.** (9,11) | **3.** (11,−7) |
| **4.** (−7,1) | **4.** (1,1) | **4.** (0,11) | **4.** (8,0) |
| **5.** (−10,0) | **5.** (3,0) | **5.** (−4,9) | **5.** (11,7) |
| **6.** (−6,6) | **6.** (3,−3) | **6.** (−2,−2) | **6.** (9,12) |
| **7.** (0,8) | **7.** (2,−5) | **7.** (−4,−5) | **7.** (1,3) |
| **8.** (7,6) | **8.** (2,−9) | **8.** (−7,−7) | **8.** (1,5) |
| **9.** (10,0) | **9.** (1,−12) | **9.** (−10,−8) | **9.** (−1,5) |
| **10.** (6,1) | **10.** (−2,−13) | **10.** (−10,−11) | **10.** (−1,3) |
| **11.** (2,−1) | **11.** (−6,−12) | **11.** (−6,−12) | **11.** (−9,12) |
| **12.** (1,0) | **12.** (−7,−10) | **12.** (3,−10) | **12.** (−11,7) |
| **13.** (2,−12) | **13.** (−7,−7) | **13.** (3,−11) | **13.** (−8,0) |
| **14.** (1,−13) | **14.** (−4,−4) | **14.** (8,−10) | **14.** (−11,−7) |
| **15.** (0,−13) | **15.** (−4,−1) | **15.** (8,−4) | **15.** (−1,−2) |
| **16.** (−1,−12) | **16.** (−2,1) | **16.** (9,11) | **16.** (0,−6) |
| | **17.** (0,1) | | |
| | **18.** (6,17) | | |

## Self-Test

Words to remember:
rectangular coordinate system [p. 335]
ordered pair of numbers [p. 335]
x-coordinate [p. 340]          abscissa [p. 340]          y-coordinate [p. 340]
ordinate [p. 340]              quadrant [p. 340]

1. Name the graph of each ordered pair:
   **a.** $(0,-3)$  **b.** $(1,-1)$   **c.** $(-3,0)$
   **d.** $(-2,1)$  **e.** $(-2,-2)$  **f.** $(1,2)$

[11-1]

On a coordinate plane, **a.** sketch the polygon whose vertexes are given and **b.** find the area of the polygon.

2. $(1,1), (1,-1), (-1,-1), (-1,1)$

3. $(0,-2), (0,1), (4,1), (4,-2)$

4. $(-2,1), (3,1), (3,4)$

Exercises 5–8 refer to the figure at the right.

5. Write the coordinates of the given points: **a.** $A$   **b.** $F$
   **c.** $K$   **d.** $B$   **e.** $G$
   **f.** $L$

[11-2]

6. Name all points shown in Quadrant III.

7. Name all points shown whose abscissas are negative.

8. Name all points shown whose ordinates are 0.

Self-Test answers and Extra Practice are at the back of the book.

# 11-3 Equations in Two Variables

**Objective** To find solutions for an equation in two variables.

An equation such as

$$4x = 8$$

contains only one variable, $x$, and has only one solution, 2.

The equation

$$4x + y = 8$$

contains two variables, $x$ and $y$. A solution of an equation in two variables consists of two numbers, one for each variable. It can therefore be written as an ordered pair of numbers in the form $(x, y)$. Thus, we can see by inspection that three possible solutions for this equation are

$$(1,4), (2,0), \text{ and } (0,8).$$

| | |
|---|---|
| *Example 1* | **Tell which of the given ordered pairs are solutions of $4x + y = 8$.** |
| | **a. $(-2,0)$    b. $(3,-2)$    c. $(-1,12)$** |
| *Solution* | **a. $4(-2) + 0 \neq 8$, so $(-2,0)$ is not a solution.** |
| | **b. $4(3) - 2 \neq 8$, so $(3,-2)$ is not a solution.** |
| | **c. $4(-1) + 12 = 8$, so $(-1,12)$ is a solution.** |

To find solutions for an equation such as

$$-2x + y = 3$$

we can substitute various numbers for $x$ and then solve for $y$ in each case. It is easier, however, if we first write an equivalent equation expressing $y$ in terms of $x$:

$$-2x + y = 3$$
$$2x - 2x + y = 2x + 3$$
$$y = 2x + 3$$

Now when we replace $x$ with any number, we can find the corresponding value for $y$ by solving a simple equation in one variable. For example:

If $x = 1$, then $y = 2(1) + 3 = 5$.

If $x = -\frac{1}{2}$, then $y = 2\left(-\frac{1}{2}\right) + 3 = 2$.

If $x = -2$, then $y = 2(-2) + 3 = -4 + 3 = -1$.

As always, it is a good idea to check these solutions, $(1,5)$, $(-\frac{1}{2},2)$, $(-2,-1)$ to see whether or not they satisfy the original equation, $-2x + y = 3$.

The number of solutions in this case is infinite, because $x$ can have an infinite number of values.

**Example 2** | Find solutions for $x + 3y = 6$, when $x = 3$ and when $x = -6$.

*Solution* | $x + 3y = 6$

$x + 3y + (-x) = 6 + (-x)$

$3y = 6 - x$

$\frac{1}{3}(3y) = \frac{1}{3}(6 - x)$

$y = 2 - \frac{1}{3}x$

When $x = 3$, $y = 2 - \frac{1}{3}(3) = 2 - 1 = 1$

When $x = -6$, $y = 2 - \frac{1}{3}(-6) = 2 + 2 = 4$

So $(3,1)$ and $(-6,4)$ are the solutions required.

## Class Exercises

State whether or not the given ordered pair is a solution of the given equation.

**1.** $(5,1)$, $x + y = 6$        **2.** $(2,-1)$, $x + y = 3$

**3.** $(7,2)$, $x - y = 9$        **4.** $(5,2)$, $x - y = 3$

**5.** $(-1,2)$, $2x + y = 0$        **6.** $(-1,-2)$, $2x - y = 0$

For each equation, give an equivalent equation for $y$ in terms of $x$.

*Example* | **a.** $x + y = 3$     **b.** $x - y = 5$

*Solution* | **a.** $y = 3 - x$     **b.** $x - 5 = y$   or   $y = x - 5$

**7.** $x + y = 4$        **8.** $2x + y = 3$        **9.** $x - y = 2$

**10.** $x - y = -3$        **11.** $2y = 4x$        **12.** $\frac{1}{2}y = 3x$

If $y = x - 4$, supply the value of $y$ in each ordered pair so that the ordered pair is a solution of the equation.

**13.** $(4,\underline{\ ?\ })$    **14.** $(6,\underline{\ ?\ })$    **15.** $(-2,\underline{\ ?\ })$    **16.** $(0,\underline{\ ?\ })$

If $y = 3x + 1$, supply the value of $y$ in each ordered pair so that the ordered pair is a solution of the equation.

**17.** $(0,\underline{\ ?\ })$    **18.** $(2,\underline{\ ?\ })$    **19.** $(-3,\underline{\ ?\ })$    **20.** $\left(\frac{1}{3},\underline{\ ?\ }\right)$

## Exercises

In Exercises 1–10, tell which of the given ordered pairs are solutions of the given equation.

|   |   | a. | b. | c. |
|---|---|----|----|----|
| A | **1.** $x + 2y = 5$ | $(1,2)$ | $(2,1)$ | $(7,-1)$ |
|   | **2.** $x - y = 5$ | $(7,1)$ | $(6,1)$ | $(5,1)$ |
|   | **3.** $2x + y = 7$ | $(4,3)$ | $(3,1)$ | $(4,-1)$ |
|   | **4.** $2x - y = 3$ | $(3,3)$ | $(2,1)$ | $(1,-1)$ |
|   | **5.** $x - 2y = 6$ | $(6,0)$ | $(0,3)$ | $(10,2)$ |
|   | **6.** $3x + y = 8$ | $(2,2)$ | $(3,-1)$ | $(4,-2)$ |
|   | **7.** $2x + 3y = 10$ | $(2,2)$ | $(3,1)$ | $(8,-2)$ |
|   | **8.** $3x + 2y = 0$ | $(2,-3)$ | $(3,-2)$ | $(1,-1)$ |
|   | **9.** $2y = 8 - 3x$ | $(2,1)$ | $(4,0)$ | $(5,1)$ |
|   | **10.** $4y = 3 + 5x$ | $(1,2)$ | $(2,3)$ | $(5,7)$ |

In Exercises 11–25 **a.** Solve the equation for $y$ in terms of $x$;
**b.** find solutions of the equation which have abscissas of $-5, -1, 0, 1$, and $5$.
Check your results in the original equation.

*Example*  |  $2x + y = 8$

*Solution*  |  **a.**          $2x + y = 8$
$\qquad 2x + y - 2x = 8 - 2x$
$\qquad\qquad\qquad y = 8 - 2x$

**b.** If $x = -5$, $y = 8 - 2(-5) = 8 + 10 = 18$

If $x = -1$, $y = 8 - 2(-1) = 8 + 2 = 10$

If $x = 0$, $y = 8 - 2(0) = 8 - 0 = 8$

If $x = 1$, $y = 8 - 2(1) = 8 - 2 = 6$

If $x = 5$, $y = 8 - 2(5) = 8 - 10 = -2$

*Check*

$2(-5) + 18 \overset{?}{=} 8$   $2(-1) + 10 \overset{?}{=} 8$   $2(0) + 8 \overset{?}{=} 8$

$\quad -10 + 18 = 8$   $\quad -2 + 10 = 8$   $\quad 8 = 8$

$2(1) + 6 \overset{?}{=} 8$   $2(5) + (-2) \overset{?}{=} 8$

$\quad 2 + 6 = 8$   $\quad 10 - 2 = 8$

Therefore, $(-5, 18)$, $(-1, 10)$, $(0, 8)$, $(1, 6)$, and $(5, -2)$ are solutions of $2x + y = 8$.

**11.** $x + y = 7$      **12.** $x + y = 3$      **13.** $-x + y = 2$

**14.** $-x + y = 0$      **15.** $x - y = 6$      **16.** $x - y = -2$

**B**  **17.** $x + 2y = 5$      **18.** $-x + 3y = 6$      **19.** $-x - 2y = 4$

**20.** $x - 3y = 0$      **21.** $4x + 2y = 5$      **22.** $3x + 2y = 4$

**23.** $3x + \frac{1}{2}y = 2$      **24.** $4x - \frac{1}{3}y = 1$      **25.** $x - \frac{5}{6}y = 10$

Find any three ordered pairs that are solutions of the given equation.

**26.** $y - x = -1$      **27.** $x + y = -6$      **28.** $x - y = 0$

**29.** $4x + y = 8$      **30.** $x - 5y = -5$      **31.** $-3x + 2y = 0$

**32.** $5x - 4y = 20$      **33.** $-\frac{1}{3}x + y = 0$      **34.** $-x + \frac{1}{2}y = 3$

# EXTRA! Completing a Table

Rachel had completed a table of values for $x$ and $y$ that showed solutions of the equation

$$2x + y = 6$$

when she was called to the telephone. While she was gone, her dog chewed the paper up leaving the result shown at the right. Make a copy of the table and see if you can complete it for Rachel.

| x | y |
|---|---|
| 1 | 4 |
| 2 |   |
| 3 |   |
|   | -4 |
|   | -6 |
|   | -10 |

# 11-4 The Graph of a Linear Equation

**Objective** To graph an equation in two variables.

We cannot graph separately each solution of the equation

$$y = x + 1$$

because the number of solutions is infinite. Nevertheless, by select-ing a few values for $x$ we may be able to detect a *pattern* in the graph of the corresponding solutions. A table giving the values of $y$ cor-responding to some replacements for $x$ is shown below. The points representing the graphs of these ordered pairs are pictured beside the table.

| $x$ | $y$ |
|-----|-----|
| $-2$ | $-1$ |
| $-1$ | $0$ |
| $-\dfrac{1}{2}$ | $\dfrac{1}{2}$ |
| $0$ | $1$ |
| $\dfrac{1}{2}$ | $1\dfrac{1}{2}$ |
| $2$ | $3$ |

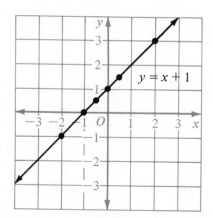

A look at the figure should convince you that these points all lie on the same straight line. This line can in fact be shown to consist of all the points that represent solutions of the equation. It is therefore the **graph of the solution set of the equation,** although we usually call it simply **the graph of the equation.**

In general, any equation that can be written in the form

$$ax + by + c = 0,$$

where $x$ and $y$ are variables and $a$, $b$, and $c$ are numbers (with $a$ and $b$ not both zero), is called a **linear equation in two variables** because its graph is always a straight line in the plane.

Because only two points are needed to determine a unique line, if we are graphing an equation that we know is linear, we need find only two solutions in order to draw its graph.

*Example*  |  Graph $2x + y = 6$.

*Solution*  |  The two easiest solutions to find are those of the form $(0,y)$ and $(x,0)$.

When $x = 0$, we have

$$2(0) + y = 6$$
$$0 + y = 6$$
$$y = 6$$

When $y = 0$, we have

$$2x + 0 = 6$$
$$2x = 6$$
$$x = 3$$

It is usually a good idea to find a third point just to check one's work. If we let $x = 1$, then we have

$$2(1) + y = 6$$
$$2 + y = 6$$
$$y = 4$$

| $x$ | $y$ |
|---|---|
| 0 | 6 |
| 3 | 0 |
| 1 | 4 |

## Class Exercises

In Exercises 1–8, state ordered pairs of the form $(x,0)$ and $(0,y)$ that are solutions of the given equation.

1. $x + y = 4$
2. $x + y = -4$
3. $x - y = 3$
4. $-x + y = 5$
5. $x + 2y = 6$
6. $x + 2y = -4$
7. $-x + 5y = 5$
8. $3x + 2y = 12$

## Exercises

Graph each equation on a coordinate plane. Use a separate set of axes for each equation.

**A**  1–8. Graph each equation in Class Exercises 1–8.

9. $2x + y = 4$
10. $-2x + y = -2$
11. $3x - y = 6$
12. $x - 3y = -3$
13. $2x + 5y = 10$
14. $2x - 3y = 12$

Graph each equation on a coordinate plane. Use a separate set of axes for each equation.

| | |
|---|---|
| *Example* | $y = 4$ |
| *Solution* | Use $y = 0x + 4$. **Find three solutions.**<br>$x = 1, y = 0(1) + 4 = 4$<br>$x = 2, y = 0(2) + 4 = 4$<br>$x = 3, y = 0(3) \doteq 4$<br>**Solutions are (1,4),<br>(2,4), and (3,4). Graph<br>these points and draw the<br>line.** |

**B**   **15.** $y = 2$        **16.** $x = -4$        **17.** $y = 0$

     **18.** $y = -3$        **19.** $x = 6$        **20.** $y = \frac{3}{2}$

# Application

## The Computer and Linear Equations

For a science project, Nina watered 6 identical lima bean gardens by different amounts. The crop yields were as shown below.

| water applied daily in cm | 0.5 | 1.0 | 1.5 | 2.0 | 2.5 | 3.0 |
|---|---|---|---|---|---|---|
| yield of lima beans in kg | 1.6 | 1.8 | 2.0 | 2.4 | 2.6 | 2.8 |

Can Nina use these data to predict crop yields for other amounts of daily watering? If we plot her findings as shown on the graph at the right, we see that the points are very nearly in line.

     The computer program on page 351 gives the equation of the line which best fits the points on the graph. Notice how the coordinates of the points are entered in line 40. The sample run tells us that the equation of the desired line is $y = 0.5x + 1.32$. From its graph, shown beside the sample run, Nina could predict, for example, that about 3.0 kg of lima beans would grow if she applied 3.3 cm of water daily.

yield of lima beans in kilograms

water applied daily in centimeters

Use graph paper and the computer to answer each question.

**1.** The chart below shows the distance a spring stretched when different masses were hung from it.

| Mass in kg | 0.3 | 0.6 | 0.9 | 1.2 | 1.5 | 1.8 |
|---|---|---|---|---|---|---|
| Stretch in cm | 2.1 | 4.9 | 6.0 | 7.1 | 8.9 | 10.8 |

Spring

Mass

About how much stretch would a 1 kg mass produce?

**2.** The chart below shows temperature changes as a cold front approached.

| Time in hours from 1st reading | 0 | 1 | 2 | 3 | 4 |
|---|---|---|---|---|---|
| Temperature in °C | 21 | 17 | 14 | 12 | 7 |

Estimate the temperature 1.5 hours from the first reading.

```
10 DIM L[50]
20 PRINT "NUMBER OF POINTS ON GRAPH IS";
30 INPUT N
40 DATA .5,1.6,1,1.8,1.5,2,2,2.4,2.5,2.6,3,2.8
50 FOR I=1 TO N
60 READ X,Y
70 LET A=A+X
80 LET B=B+Y
90 LET C=C+X*X
100 LET D=D+X*Y
110 NEXT I
120 LET Q=N*C—A*A
130 LET R=INT(100*(N*D—A*B)/Q+.5)/100
140 LET S=INT(100*(B*C—A*D)/Q+.5)/100
145 PRINT
150 PRINT "EQUATION OF BEST FITTING LINE IS"
155 PRINT "Y=";R;"X";
160 IF S>=0 THEN 190
170 PRINT S
180 STOP
190 PRINT " ";"+";S
200 END

RUN
NUMBER OF POINTS ON GRAPH IS?6
EQUATION OF BEST FITTING LINE IS
Y= .5X + 1.32
END
```

yield of lima beans in kilograms

$y = 0.5x + 1.32$

3.3

water applied daily in centimeters

# 11-5 Graphing a System of Equations

**Objective** To solve systems of equations using graphs.

The graphs of two linear equations

$$x - y = -3 \quad \text{and} \quad x + y = -1$$

are shown here. Their point of intersection appears to have coordinates $(-2,1)$. If this point lies on the graph of each of the equations, its coordinates must be a solution that both equations have in common. To check whether or not this is true, let us see if the ordered pair $(-2,1)$ satisfies both of the given equations. Since

$$-2 - 1 = -3 \quad \text{and} \quad -2 + 1 = -1$$

are both true, $(-2,1)$ is a solution of the given **system of equations.** Such a system is usually written as

$$x - y = -3$$
$$x + y = -1$$

*Example* | Solve the system.

$$x + y = 6$$
$$x - y = 2$$

*Solution* | **Make tables of solutions and draw the graphs.**

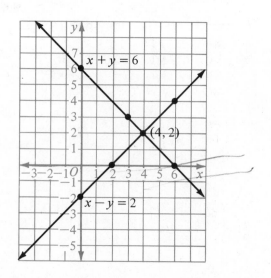

| $x + y = 6$ | | | $x - y = 2$ | |
|:---:|:---:|---|:---:|:---:|
| $x$ | $y$ | | $x$ | $y$ |
| 0 | 6 | | 0 | $-2$ |
| 6 | 0 | | 2 | 0 |
| 3 | 3 | | 6 | 4 |

Their intersection appears to be $(4,2)$. Check in both equations:

$$4 + 2 = 6 \quad \text{and} \quad 4 - 2 = 2.$$

Hence the solution is $(4,2)$.

The graphs of the equations in the system

$$x - y = -3$$
$$x - y = -1$$

are parallel lines. Since they do not intersect, this system of equations has no solution.

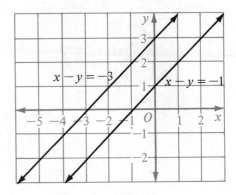

## Class Exercises

Is the given ordered pair of numbers a solution of the given system of equations?

1. $(4, -1)$, $x + y = 3$
   $x - y = 5$

2. $(5, -1)$, $x + y = 6$
   $x - y = 4$

3. $(3, 1)$, $x + 2y = 5$
   $x - y = 2$

4. $(-4, 4)$, $2x + y = 7$
   $x - y = 5$

## Exercises

Find the solution set of each system by graphing. Check your results. If no solution exists, so state.

**A**

1. $x + y = 4$
   $x - y = 2$

2. $x + y = 6$
   $x - y = -4$

3. $2x + y = 5$
   $x - y = 4$

4. $-2x + y = 5$
   $x + y = -1$

5. $3x + y = 6$
   $3x + y = 3$

6. $2x - y = 4$
   $2x - y = 6$

7. $x + 2y = 6$
   $x - y = 3$

8. $x - 2y = 0$
   $2x + y = 5$

9. $3x + 2y = 12$
   $2x + y = 7$

**B**

10. $2x + 3y = -10$
    $2x + y = -6$

11. $4x + 3y = 7$
    $x - 2y = -1$

12. $2x + y = 4$
    $x - 2y = -8$

13. $3x + 2y = 7$
    $2x - y = 0$

14. $4x + 3y = 4$
    $x - 3y = 1$

15. $x - 3y = -5$
    $x + 3y = 1$

16. $3x + 2y = -4$
    $2x + 3y = -6$

17. $2x + 3y = 4$
    $4x - 2y = 0$

18. $3x + 3y = 4$
    $x + 6y = 3$

# A Surgeon

Daniel Hale Williams (1856–1931) was one of the pioneers in open-heart surgery. He received his medical degree from Chicago Medical College in 1883. After completing his internship at Mercy Hospital in Chicago, he was appointed surgeon to the South Side Dispensary. In 1891, he founded Provident Hospital in Chicago. Not long after, he performed a landmark operation in heart surgery. The patient reportedly was the victim of a knife wound in an artery lying a few centimeters from the heart. Dr. Williams repaired the wound with an innovative and delicate surgical procedure. Newspaper reports of the operation brought him instant fame.

Among his many achievements, Dr. Williams was chief surgeon of Freedman's Hospital in Washington, D.C., and organized the National Medical Association in Atlanta, Georgia. For twenty-five years he made annual visits to Meharry Medical College in Nashville, Tennessee, serving without salary as a visiting professor of surgery.

In 1931, Dr. Williams was inducted into the American College of Surgeons. He published nine scientific papers and was awarded honorary degrees by Wilberforce University and Howard University.

**Research Activity** Find a picture of the human heart in a biology book or encyclopedia. What are the main parts of the heart? What are their functions? How is blood pressure measured?

**Career Activity** Find out what different kinds of jobs are to be found in a hospital and what kinds of training they require.

## Self-Test

Words to remember:
graph of the equation [p. 348]
linear equation in two variables [p. 348]
system of equations [p. 352]

State whether or not the given ordered pair is a solution of the equation.

**1.** $(3, -1)$, $2x - y = 7$    **2.** $(5, -3)$, $x - 2y = 11$    **[11-3]**

Give an equivalent equation for $y$ in terms of $x$.

**3.** $2x - 3y = 6$    **4.** $-5x + 4y = -40$

Find ordered pairs of the form $(x, 0)$ and $(0, y)$ that are solutions of the given equation.

**5.** $x + y = -7$    **6.** $-x + 2y = 11$    **[11-4]**

Graph each equation on a coordinate plane. Use a separate set of axes for each equation.

**7.** $3x - 4y = -12$    **8.** $y = -3$

Solve each system by graphing. If no solution exists, say so.

**9.** $x - y = -3$    **10.** $2x - 3y = 6$    **[11-5]**
  $2x + y = 0$       $y = -4$

**11.** $2x - y = -2$    **12.** $x + 2y = 4$
  $2x + y = 6$        $x + 2y = 6$

Self-Test answers and Extra Practice are at the back of the book.

# Chapter Review

Write the letter that labels the correct answer.

1. In a rectangular coordinate system, the axes intersect at the __?__.    [11-1]
   A. first component          B. ordinate
   C. origin                   D. ordered pair

2. Each point in the plane is located by a(n) __?__.
   A. pair of numbers          B. number
   C. axis                     D. ordered pair of numbers

3. The graphs of $(-3,0)$, $(4,0)$, $(4,2)$, and $(1,2)$ are the vertexes of
   a __?__.
   A. square                   B. trapezoid
   C. rectangle                D. parallelogram

4. The triangle whose vertexes have coordinates $(-1,-3)$, $(-2,5)$
   and $(6,5)$ has area equal to __?__.
   A. 32        B. 64          C. 8           D. 4

5. To move from the graph of $(-10,6)$ to the graph of $(-10,7)$
   we move __?__.
   A. up        B. down        C. left        D. right

6. If $(a,b)$ are the coordinates of a point in Quadrant I, then $(-a,-b)$    [11-2]
   are the coordinates of a point in __?__.
   A. Quadrant I               B. Quadrant II
   C. Quadrant III             D. Quadrant IV

7. A point with negative abscissa and positive ordinate must lie in
   Quadrant __?__.
   A. I         B. II          C. III         D. IV

8. If points $P$ and $Q$ have equal ordinates they must lie __?__.
   A. on the same horizontal line   B. on the same vertical line
   C. in the same quadrant          D. in different quadrants

9. The points for which the product of abscissa and ordinate is posi-
   tive lie in __?__.
   A. Quadrants I and II            B. Quadrants I and III
   C. Quadrants I and IV            D. Quadrant I only

10. A solution of the equation $2y = x + 1$ is __?__.    [11-3]
    A. $(-1,0)$                 B. $(0,1)$
    C. $(1,2)$                  D. $(2,1)$

11. If we solve for $y$ in terms of $x$ in the equation $x - 3y = 6$, we get __?__ .

    **A.** $x = 3y + 6$          **B.** $3y = x - 6$

    **C.** $y = \frac{1}{3}x - 6$          **D.** $y = \frac{1}{3}x - 2$

12. In the equation $2x - 7y = 4$, a solution with ordinate 6 is __?__ .

    **A.** $(6,23)$          **B.** $(23,6)$

    **C.** $\left(6,1\frac{1}{8}\right)$          **D.** $(-19,6)$

13. A solution of the equation $x - y = 3$ whose graph lies in Quadrant III is __?__ .

    **A.** $(7,4)$          **B.** $(-7,4)$

    **C.** $(-2,-5)$          **D.** $(-10,-7)$

14. The graph of $3x + 5y = 1$ does not pass through __?__ .     [11-4]

    **A.** Quadrant I          **B.** Quadrant II

    **C.** Quadrant III          **D.** Quadrant IV

15. The graph of $-3x + 8y = 12$ intersects the $y$-axis at the point whose coordinates are __?__ .

    **A.** $\left(0,1\frac{1}{2}\right)$          **B.** $(0,-4)$

    **C.** $(-4,0)$          **D.** $(0,12)$

16. The graph of $2x - y = 10$ intersects the $x$-axis at the point whose coordinates are __?__ .

    **A.** $(0,10)$     **B.** $(0,5)$     **C.** $(-10,0)$     **D.** $(5,0)$

17. The graph of $y = -2$ is __?__ .

    **A.** not a line          **B.** a vertical line

    **C.** a horizontal line          **D.** a line containing the origin

18. A solution of the system    $x + y = 1$   is __?__ .     [11-5]
                              $x - y = 1$

    **A.** $(0,1)$     **B.** $(3,-2)$     **C.** $(0,-1)$     **D.** $(1,0)$

19. If a system of linear equations has no solution, then the graphs of the two equations __?__ .

    **A.** intersect at the origin          **B.** lie in different quadrants

    **C.** are parallel          **D.** are the same

# Locating Points on Earth

Earth can be thought of as a sphere rotating about an *axis* that passes through two points at the ends of a diameter, the North Pole and the South Pole (N and S).

A **great circle** on a sphere is the intersection of the sphere with a plane passing through the center of the sphere. The great circle whose plane is perpendicular to the axis is called the **equator,** as shown in the figure at the right. The equator separates Earth into the Northern and Southern Hemispheres.

Any semicircle with endpoints at the poles is called a **meridian.** The meridian passing through the city of Greenwich, England, is the official **prime meridian.** Its intersection with the equator is labeled 0°.

Now we can set up a degree-coordinate system on Earth so that each point on the surface can be assigned an ordered pair of coordinates: (*longitude, latitude*).

The **longitude** is the number of degrees between 0° and 180° that any place is *east* or *west of the prime meridian.* The **latitude** is the number of degrees between 0° and 90° that the place is *north* or *south of the equator.* Thus, as indicated in the figure at the right, Vienna, Austria is about 20°E, 45°N.

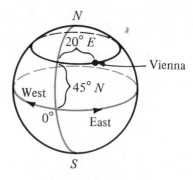

Globes or flat maps of Earth are often marked off in 10°-intervals of latitude (horizontal **parallels of latitude**) and longitude (vertical **meridians**).

A **Mercator Projection** is a flat map in which the meridians and parallels of latitude appear as lines crossing at right angles. Note in the Mercator Projection at the top of the next page that areas farther from the equator appear greater than they actually are.

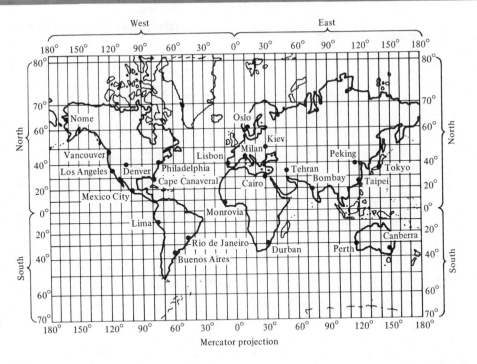

West East

Mercator projection

From the map of the world shown above, find the cities near the following locations.

**1.** 100°W, 20°N     **2.** 30°E, 30°S     **3.** 120°W, 35°N     **4.** 30°E, 30°N

**5.** 75°W, 10°S     **6.** 30°E, 50°N     **7.** 115°E, 30°S     **8.** 140°E, 35°N

**9.** 45°W, 25°S     **10.** 115°E, 40°N     **11.** 165°W, 65°N     **12.** 10°W, 5°N

From the map above, give the longitude and latitude of the following places to the nearest 5 degrees.

**13.** Oslo, Norway

**14.** Cape Canaveral, Florida

**15.** Peking, China

**16.** Vancouver, British Columbia

**17.** Buenos Aires, Argentina

**18.** Philadelphia, Pennsylvania

**19.** Bombay, India

**20.** Lisbon, Portugal

**21.** Denver, Colorado

**22.** Milan, Italy

**23.** Tehran, Iran

**24.** Canberra, Australia

# Chapter Test

1. Each ordered pair of numbers locates a __?__ in the plane. [11-1]

2. The negative direction on the vertical axis is __?__ .

3. The vertexes of a triangle have coordinates $(-5, 2)$, $(-1, 7)$, and $(-1, -1)$. The area of this triangle equals __?__ .

4. Every point in the plane is assigned a pair of __?__ . [11-2]

5. The $x$-coordinate of a point $P$ is called the __?__ of $P$.

6. If $x > 0$ and $y < 0$ then $(x,y)$ are the coordinates of a point in Quadrant __?__ .

7. If a point has ordinate 0, it lies on the __?__ .

8. Is $(4,3)$ a solution of the equation $y = x + 1$? [11-3]

9. A solution of the equation $3x - 5y = 14$ is $(-2, \underline{\phantom{?}})$.

10. Does Quadrant I contain any points whose coordinates are solutions of the equation $x + y = -1$?

11. A solution of the equation $4x - 3y = 12$ whose graph lies on the $y$-axis is __?__ .

12. The equation $2x + 17y - 11 = 0$ is an example of a(n) __?__ equation in two variables. [11-4]

13. The graph of an equation consists of all points whose coordinates are __?__ of the equation.

14. Does the graph of $y = 5$ cross the $x$-axis?

15. If the graph of $ax + by + c = 0$ passes through the origin, must $c = 0$?

16. Is $(2,3)$ a solution of the following system? [11-5]
$$x + y = 5$$
$$x - y = 1$$

17. If the graphs of two linear equations are parallel lines, the system of equations has __?__ solution(s).

18. A solution to a system of linear equations is found at the point of __?__ of the graphs of the equations.

# Skill Review

Convert the percent to a decimal.

**1.** 25%         **2.** 100%         **3.** 12.5%         **4.** 15%

**5.** 120%         **6.** 33%         **7.** 50%         **8.** 1550%

**9.** 200%         **10.** 11%         **11.** 47.32%         **12.** 22.2%

Convert the decimal to a percent.

**13.** 0.15         **14.** 1.25         **15.** 1.61         **16.** 0.76

**17.** 0.45         **18.** 0.782         **19.** 1.17         **20.** 0.21

**21.** 10.15         **22.** 0.133         **23.** 1.312         **24.** 5.5

Convert the percent to a fraction or mixed number in lowest terms.

**25.** 25%         **26.** 18%         **27.** 80%         **28.** 75%

**29.** 12.5%         **30.** 40%         **31.** 115%         **32.** 16%

**33.** 23%         **34.** 71%         **35.** 10%         **36.** 212%

Convert to a decimal; then to a percent.

**37.** $1\frac{1}{4}$         **38.** $\frac{1}{2}$         **39.** $\frac{4}{5}$         **40.** $\frac{7}{10}$

**41.** $2\frac{1}{8}$         **42.** $\frac{3}{4}$         **43.** $\frac{5}{2}$         **44.** $2\frac{3}{10}$

**45.** $\frac{15}{16}$         **46.** $\frac{7}{8}$         **47.** $1\frac{2}{5}$         **48.** $1\frac{1}{10}$

**49.** $\frac{16}{5}$         **50.** $11\frac{1}{4}$         **51.** $\frac{6}{5}$         **52.** $3\frac{5}{8}$

Convert to a fraction or mixed number in lowest terms.

**53.** 0.12         **54.** 1.60         **55.** 0.125         **56.** 0.8

**57.** 1.25         **58.** 3.05         **59.** 0.66         **60.** 0.45

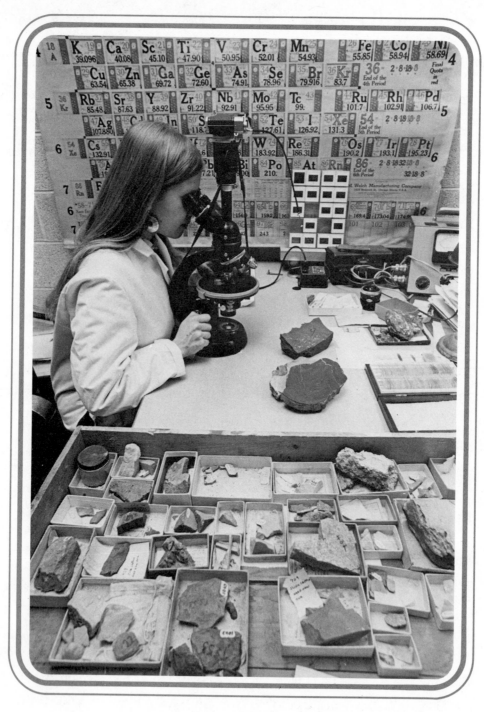

A geologist studying the structure of rock specimens.

# 12 Right Triangles

## 12-1 Square Roots

**Objective** To estimate the positive square root of a positive number by determining the two consecutive integers between which the square root lies.

Any nonnegative real number $n$ can be expressed as the product of two equal factors, $a \times a$. Each factor $a$ is called a **square root** of $n$. Thus, 2 is a square root of 4 because $2 \times 2 = 4$.

A positive number has two different square roots, which are opposites of each other. For example, the square roots of 4 are 2 and $-2$ because

$$2 \times 2 = 4 \quad \text{and also} \quad -2 \times -2 = 4.$$

The *positive* square root of a number $n$ is denoted by the symbol $\sqrt{n}$, and the *negative* square root by the symbol $-\sqrt{n}$. Thus

$$\sqrt{4} = 2 \quad \text{and} \quad -\sqrt{4} = -2.$$

If $n = 0$, then $a \times a = 0$. The only value $a$ can have is 0. Therefore,

$$\sqrt{0} = -\sqrt{0} = 0.$$

Suppose $n < 0$, say $n = -4$; then $a \times a = -4$. But there is no real number whose square is a negative number. Thus a negative number has no real-number square root.

In this chapter, we shall be concerned generally with the positive square roots of numbers.

If $\sqrt{n}$ is an integer, then $n$ is called a **perfect square.** For example, $\sqrt{4}$ is the integer 2, so 4 is a perfect square. The positive square root of a number is often not an integer. We can estimate such a square root by finding the next smaller and the next larger integer between which the square root lies.

*Example* | **Determine the two consecutive integers between which $\sqrt{52}$ lies.**

*Solution* | **Since $\sqrt{49} = 7$ and $\sqrt{64} = 8$,**

$$\sqrt{49} < \sqrt{52} < \sqrt{64}$$
$$7 < \sqrt{52} < 8$$

**Thus $\sqrt{52}$ lies between 7 and 8.**

## Class Exercises

Read each symbol.

1. $\sqrt{5}$       2. $\sqrt{76}$       3. $\sqrt{12}$       4. $-\sqrt{10}$       5. $-\sqrt{300}$

If the symbol names an integer, state the integer. If not, name the two consecutive integers between which the given number lies.

6. $\sqrt{9}$       7. $\sqrt{30}$       8. $\sqrt{36}$       9. $\sqrt{85}$       10. $\sqrt{11}$

11. $\sqrt{1}$      12. $\sqrt{81}$      13. $\sqrt{23}$      14. $-\sqrt{100}$      15. $-\sqrt{0}$

16. $\sqrt{55}$     17. $\sqrt{6}$      18. $\sqrt{74}$      19. $\sqrt{4}$       20. $\sqrt{47}$

## Exercises

If the symbol or expression names an integer, state the integer. If not, name the two consecutive integers between which the number lies.

A   1. $\sqrt{64}$       2. $\sqrt{121}$       3. $-\sqrt{400}$       4. $-\sqrt{144}$

5. $\sqrt{7^2}$       6. $\sqrt{0^2}$       7. $(\sqrt{3})^2$       8. $(\sqrt{14})^2$

9. $\sqrt{15}$       10. $\sqrt{37}$       11. $\sqrt{3}$       12. $\sqrt{92}$

13. $\sqrt{133}$      14. $\sqrt{850}$      15. $\sqrt{2600}$      16. $\sqrt{146}$

B   17. $\sqrt{25} - \sqrt{16}$       18. $\sqrt{100} + \sqrt{49}$       19. $\sqrt{144 + 25}$

20. $\sqrt{25 - 16}$       21. $\sqrt{45 + 45}$       22. $\sqrt{13 + 68}$

23. $\sqrt{200 - 164}$       24. $\sqrt{79 - 61}$       25. $\sqrt{49} + \sqrt{8}$

26. $\sqrt{64} + \sqrt{2}$       27. $\sqrt{121} - \sqrt{33}$       28. $\sqrt{100} - \sqrt{10}$

# 12-2 Approximating Square Roots

**Objective** To use the "divide and average" method to approximate square roots.

We can obtain a good approximation to the positive square root, $a$, of a number $n$ by using this fact:

If $\sqrt{n} = a$, then $n = a \times a$ and $\dfrac{n}{a} = a$.

That is, if we divide a number by its square root, the quotient is the same as the divisor. If we divide by an estimate for $a$ that is *greater* than $a$, then the quotient will be *less* than $a$. The average of the divisor and quotient can be used as a new estimate for $a$.

*Example* | Approximate $\sqrt{11}$ to the tenths' place.

*Solution* | **Step 1. Estimate $\sqrt{11}$.**
$\sqrt{9} = 3$ and $\sqrt{16} = 4$. Thus $3 < \sqrt{11} < 4$. Since 11 is closer to 9 than to 16, you might try a number closer to 3 than to 4, say 3.2, as a first estimate of $\sqrt{11}$.

**Step 2. Divide 11 by the estimate.**
At each stage, the approximation is correct to the number of matching decimal places in the divisor and quotient. Here, $\sqrt{11} \approx 3$.

**Step 3. Find the average of the divisor and the quotient.**

$\dfrac{3.2 + 3.43}{2} = \dfrac{6.63}{2} \approx 3.32$

$$
\begin{array}{r}
3.43 \\
3.2\overline{)11.0\,00} \\
9\,6 \\
\hline
1\,4\,0 \\
1\,2\,8 \\
\hline
1\,20 \\
96 \\
\hline
240
\end{array}
$$

Repeat Steps 1–2.
**Step 1.** $\sqrt{11} \approx 3.32$
**Step 2.** $11 \div 3.32 \approx 3.31$
Now the quotient and divisor agree to the tenths' place and $\sqrt{11} \approx 3.3$.

$$
\begin{array}{r}
3.31 \\
3.32\overline{)11.00\,00} \\
9\,96 \\
\hline
1\,04\,0 \\
99\,6 \\
\hline
4\,40 \\
3\,32 \\
\hline
1\,08
\end{array}
$$

## Class Exercises

State the first digit of the indicated square root.

1. $\sqrt{14}$      2. $\sqrt{40}$      3. $\sqrt{68}$      4. $\sqrt{22}$      5. $\sqrt{89}$

6. $\sqrt{3}$      7. $\sqrt{63}$      8. $\sqrt{300}$      9. $\sqrt{905}$      10. $\sqrt{721}$

State the next estimate for the square root of the dividend.

*Example*
$$\begin{array}{r} 2.8 \\ 2\overline{)5.6} \end{array}$$

*Solution*
The average of 2 and 2.8 is $\dfrac{2 + 2.8}{2} = 2.4$. Therefore, the next estimate is 2.4.

11. $\begin{array}{r} 4 \\ 3\overline{)12} \end{array}$    12. $\begin{array}{r} 6.6 \\ 6\overline{)39.7} \end{array}$    13. $\begin{array}{r} 4.18 \\ 4.3\overline{)18.0{,}00} \end{array}$    14. $\begin{array}{r} 8.4 \\ 8.5\overline{)71.4{,}0} \end{array}$

15. $\begin{array}{r} 16.0 \\ 14\overline{)225.0} \end{array}$    16. $\begin{array}{r} 12.8 \\ 13\overline{)167.0} \end{array}$    17. $\begin{array}{r} 20.3 \\ 20\overline{)406.0} \end{array}$    18. $\begin{array}{r} 9.5 \\ 10\overline{)95.0} \end{array}$

19. $\begin{array}{r} 5.38 \\ 5.2\overline{)28.00} \end{array}$    20. $\begin{array}{r} 7.12 \\ 7.3\overline{)52.00} \end{array}$    21. $\begin{array}{r} 0.50 \\ 0.6\overline{)0.30} \end{array}$    22. $\begin{array}{r} 0.92 \\ 0.9\overline{)0.83} \end{array}$

## Exercises

Find each square root to the tenths' place.

**A**    1. $\sqrt{8}$      2. $\sqrt{53}$      3. $\sqrt{33}$      4. $\sqrt{5}$

     5. $\sqrt{71}$      6. $\sqrt{13}$      7. $\sqrt{26}$      8. $\sqrt{84}$

     9. $\sqrt{42}$      10. $\sqrt{97}$      11. $\sqrt{63}$      12. $\sqrt{29}$

     13. $\sqrt{145}$      14. $\sqrt{190}$      15. $\sqrt{424}$      16. $\sqrt{254}$

**B**    17. $\sqrt{3.2}$      18. $\sqrt{15.9}$      19. $\sqrt{21.5}$      20. $\sqrt{72.8}$

     21. $\sqrt{387.1}$      22. $\sqrt{106.6}$      23. $\sqrt{790.4}$      24. $\sqrt{213.7}$

     25. $\sqrt{1058}$      26. $\sqrt{4723}$      27. $\sqrt{9999}$      28. $\sqrt{5476}$

     29. $\sqrt{0.8}$      30. $\sqrt{0.9}$      31. $\sqrt{0.05}$      32. $\sqrt{0.21}$

# 12-3 Using a Square-Root Table

**Objective** To use a table to approximate square roots.

We can use the table on page 394 to approximate the square roots of integers from 1 to 100. For example, to find $\sqrt{63}$ using the table, we locate 63 in the column headed "Number." We read off the value beside 63 in the "Square Root" column: 7.937.

$$\sqrt{63} \approx 7.937$$

To find an approximation for the square root of a number which lies between two entries in the table, we can use a process called **interpolation**. For example, to approximate $\sqrt{5.5}$, we assume that $\sqrt{5.5}$ is 0.5 of the way from $\sqrt{5}$ to $\sqrt{6}$.

$$\sqrt{5} \approx 2.236 \qquad \text{and} \qquad \sqrt{6} \approx 2.449$$

$$
\begin{aligned}
\sqrt{5.5} &\approx \sqrt{5} + 0.5(\sqrt{6} - \sqrt{5}) \\
&\approx 2.236 + 0.5(2.449 - 2.236) \\
&\approx 2.236 + 0.5(0.213) \\
&\approx 2.236 + 0.1065 \\
&\approx 2.34
\end{aligned}
$$

## Class Exercises

Use the table on page 394 to approximate each number.

1. $\sqrt{10}$

2. $\sqrt{13}$

3. $\sqrt{29}$

4. $\sqrt{36}$

5. $\sqrt{44}$

6. $\sqrt{58}$

7. $\sqrt{71}$

8. $\sqrt{95}$

9. $10\sqrt{2}$

10. $10\sqrt{83}$

11. $10\sqrt{64}$

12. $10\sqrt{17}$

13. $\frac{1}{10}\sqrt{55}$

14. $\frac{1}{10}\sqrt{34}$

15. $\frac{1}{10}\sqrt{79}$

16. $\frac{1}{10}\sqrt{49}$

State the two values between which the given square root lies.

17. $\sqrt{45.8}$

18. $\sqrt{7.1}$

19. $\sqrt{70.6}$

20. $\sqrt{19.5}$

21. $\sqrt{25.3}$

22. $\sqrt{68.2}$

# Exercises

Use the table on page 394 to approximate each number to the nearest hundredth.

*Example* | $6\sqrt{48}$

*Solution* | From the square-root table, $\sqrt{48} \approx 6.928$.
Thus $6\sqrt{48} \approx 6(6.928) = 41.568$.
To the nearest hundredth, $6\sqrt{48} = 41.57$.

**A**
1. $\sqrt{39}$
2. $\sqrt{43}$
3. $\sqrt{60}$
4. $\sqrt{18}$

5. $10\sqrt{63}$
6. $10\sqrt{77}$
7. $\frac{1}{10}\sqrt{82}$
8. $\frac{1}{10}\sqrt{90}$

9. $7\sqrt{6}$
10. $8\sqrt{88}$
11. $3\sqrt{12}$
12. $2\sqrt{31}$

**B**
13. $\sqrt{53} + \sqrt{21}$
14. $\sqrt{27} + \sqrt{81}$
15. $\sqrt{72} - \sqrt{25}$

16. $\sqrt{94} - \sqrt{48}$
17. $2\sqrt{54} - \sqrt{5}$
18. $\sqrt{66} - 4\sqrt{3}$

Use interpolation to approximate each number to the nearest hundredth.

19. $\sqrt{18.3}$
20. $\sqrt{97.5}$
21. $\sqrt{47.1}$
22. $\sqrt{61.8}$

23. $\sqrt{32.4}$
24. $\sqrt{8.7}$
25. $\sqrt{92.6}$
26. $\sqrt{50.9}$

27. $2\sqrt{59.2}$
28. $7\sqrt{23.4}$
29. $5\sqrt{74.8}$
30. $3\sqrt{86.1}$

**C**
31. $\sqrt{340}$ (Hint: $\sqrt{340} = \sqrt{100 \times 3.4} = 10\sqrt{3.4}$)
32. $\sqrt{1120}$

33. $\sqrt{0.77}$ $\left(\text{Hint: } \sqrt{0.77} = \sqrt{\frac{1}{100} \times 77} = \frac{1}{10}\sqrt{77}\right)$
34. $\sqrt{0.051}$

35. A square room has an area of 37.5 m². Find the length of a side of the room to the nearest 0.1 m.

36. The height of a triangle is the same as its base. If the area of the triangle is 45 cm², what is the length of the base to the nearest 0.1 cm?

37. The height of a parallelogram is half the length of its base. The parallelogram has an area of 35 cm². Find the height to the nearest 0.1 cm.

38. One base of a trapezoid is three times as long as the other base. The height of the trapezoid is the same as the shorter base. The trapezoid has an area of 72 cm². Find the height to the nearest 0.1 cm.

# *EXTRA!* More About Square Roots

Suppose we want to approximate $\sqrt{148}$. The table on page 394 does not list this square root. However, by using the following property we can approximate $\sqrt{148}$.

**property**

The positive square root of the product of two positive numbers is equal to the product of their positive square roots. That is, if $x > 0$ and $y > 0$, then
$$\sqrt{xy} = \sqrt{x} \times \sqrt{y}$$

Thus, since
$$148 = 4 \times 37$$

we can write
$$\begin{aligned} \sqrt{148} &= \sqrt{4 \times 37} \\ &= \sqrt{4} \times \sqrt{37} \\ &= 2\sqrt{37} \end{aligned}$$

From the table, $\sqrt{37} \approx 6.083$. Thus:
$$\sqrt{148} = 2\sqrt{37} \approx 2(6.083)$$
$$\sqrt{148} \approx 12.166$$

Use the table on page 394 to approximate each square root to the nearest hundredth.

**1.** $\sqrt{1025}$      **2.** $\sqrt{960}$      **3.** $\sqrt{252}$      **4.** $\sqrt{567}$

**5.** $\sqrt{1078}$      **6.** $\sqrt{468}$      **7.** $\sqrt{1216}$      **8.** $\sqrt{726}$

**9.** $\sqrt{2900}$      **10.** $\sqrt{270}$      **11.** $\sqrt{1184}$      **12.** $\sqrt{1836}$

**13.** $\sqrt{185}$      **14.** $\sqrt{341}$      **15.** $\sqrt{161}$      **16.** $\sqrt{249}$

**Calculator Activity** Many calculators have a "square-root key" which enables you to find the square root of a number directly. If such a calculator is available, use it to check your answers to Exercises 1–16, above.

# *EXTRA!* Square Root Symbol

When early mathematicians wrote about the square roots of numbers, they often used the term *radix,* which is the Latin word for root. The first widely used square root symbol, shown at the right, came from rx., an abbreviation of the word radix. The symbol $\sqrt{}$, which we use today, first appeared in print in 1525 in the book *Die Coss,* by Christoff Rudolff. The symbol may have come from a German form of the letter r. By the seventeenth century, $\sqrt{}$ became the standard symbol for square root.

## Self-Test

Symbols and words to remember:

$\sqrt{n}$ [p. 363]
square root [p. 363]
negative square root [p. 363]

$-\sqrt{n}$ [p. 363]
positive square root [p. 363]
interpolation [p. 367]

Name the two consecutive integers between which the square root lies.

**1.** $\sqrt{75}$  **2.** $\sqrt{3}$  [12-1]

**3.** $\sqrt{30}$  **4.** $\sqrt{59}$

State the next estimate for the square root of the dividend.

**5.** $4\overline{)14.0}$ with $3.5$  **6.** $7\overline{)55.0}$ with $7.8$  **7.** $9\overline{)74.0}$ with $8.2$  [12-2]

**8.** Find $\sqrt{68}$ to the tenths' place. (Do not use the square-root table.)

Use the table on page 394 to approximate each number to the nearest hundredth.

**9.** $\sqrt{84}$  **10.** $3\sqrt{7}$  [12-3]

**11.** $\sqrt{62} - \sqrt{60}$  **12.** $\sqrt{24.6}$

Self-Test answers and Extra Practice are at the back of the book.

# 12-4 The Pythagorean Property

**Objective** To apply the Pythagorean Property.

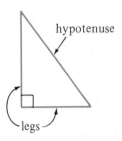

In a right triangle, the side opposite the right angle is called the **hypotenuse.** It is always the longest of the three sides. The other two sides are called the **legs.**

The following important property of right triangles was known to the Babylonians some 4000 years ago. However, it is believed that the first general proof of this property was given by the Greek mathematician, Pythagoras, about 2500 years ago. For this reason, it is usually named for him.

---

## property

**For any right triangle, the square of the length of the hypotenuse is equal to the sum of the squares of the lengths of the other two sides. (The Pythagorean Property)**

---

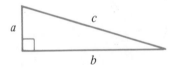

For the right triangle at the right, this property states that

$$c^2 = a^2 + b^2.$$

You can verify the Pythagorean Property for the right triangle in the diagram below by counting the small unit squares within each of the large squares. The total number of unit squares in the squares on the legs $(9 + 16)$ is equal to the number in the square on the hypotenuse (25).

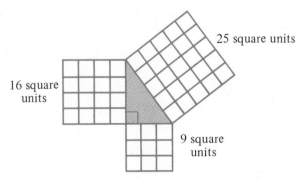

The following property is also true:

> ### property
>
> **If the square of the length of one side of a triangle is equal to the sum of the squares of the lengths of the other two sides, then the triangle is a right triangle.**

For the triangle at the right:
If $c^2 = a^2 + b^2$, then the triangle is a right triangle.

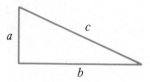

## Class Exercises

Verify the Pythagorean Property by counting the small squares in the diagrams.

**1.**

**2.**

State whether or not a triangle with sides of the given lengths is a right triangle.

*Example*  |  **2, 3, 4**

*Solution*  |  $2^2 = 4$, $3^2 = 9$, and $4^2 = 16$.
|  Since $4 + 9 \neq 16$, **2, 3, 4** cannot be the lengths of the sides of a right triangle.

**3.** 3, 4, 5          **4.** 4, 5, 6          **5.** 8, 15, 17          **6.** 8, 10, 12

**7.** 5, 12, 13          **8.** 6, 8, 10          **9.** $1\frac{1}{2}$, 2, $2\frac{1}{2}$          **10.** 4, 5.5, 7

## Exercises

State whether or not a triangle with sides of the given lengths is a right triangle.

**A**
1. 3 m, 5 m, 7 m
2. 10 m, 30 m, 32 m
3. 9 cm, 12 cm, 15 cm
4. 10 cm, 24 cm, 26 cm
5. 20 mm, 21 mm, 29 mm
6. 7 km, 11 km, 13 km
7. 10 cm, 14 cm, 16 cm
8. 11 mm, 20 mm, 21 mm

The lengths of the legs of a right triangle are given. Find the area of the square on the hypotenuse of the triangle.

| *Example 1* | **1 m, 3 m** |
|---|---|
| *Solution* | **Make a sketch. By the Pythagorean Property:** |

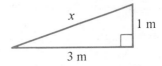

$$x^2 = 1^2 + 3^2 = 1 + 9 = 10$$

**Thus the area of the square on the hypotenuse is 10 m².**

9. 2 km, 2 km
10. 2 m, 5 m
11. 21 m, 30 m
12. 15 cm, 5 cm
13. 5.1 mm, 3.2 mm
14. 1.2 cm, 2.1 cm

A right triangle has sides of lengths $a$, $b$, and $c$, with $c$ the length of the hypotenuse. Find the length of the missing side of the triangle to the nearest hundredth.

| *Example 2* | **a. $a = 1$, $b = 5$** | **b. $a = 6$, $c = 8$** |
|---|---|---|
| *Solution* | **a.** $a^2 + b^2 = c^2$ | **b.** $a^2 + b^2 = c^2$ |

**a.**
$$a^2 + b^2 = c^2$$
$$1^2 + 5^2 = c^2$$
$$1 + 25 = c^2$$
$$26 = c^2$$
$$c = \sqrt{26} \approx 5.099$$
**To the nearest hundredth,**
$$c = 5.10$$

**b.**
$$a^2 + b^2 = c^2$$
$$6^2 + b^2 = 8^2$$
$$36 + b^2 = 64$$
$$b^2 = 64 - 36 = 28$$
$$b = \sqrt{28} \approx 5.292$$
**To the nearest hundredth,**
$$b = 5.29$$

**B**
15. $a = 2$, $b = 3$
16. $a = 4$, $b = 7$
17. $a = 5$, $c = 8$
18. $a = 3$, $c = 6$
19. $b = 2$, $c = 9$
20. $b = 4$, $c = 7$

**C**
21. $a = 0.8$, $b = 2.6$
22. $a = 5.3$, $b = 6.1$
23. $a = 3.4$, $c = 6.4$
24. $b = 2.9$, $c = 3$   (See Exercise 33, page 368)

## Problems

Solve. Give your answer to the nearest tenth.

B
1. A rectangle is 6 cm long and 4 cm wide. How long is a diagonal of the rectangle?

2. A square has sides that are 7 cm long. How long is a diagonal of the square?

3. Suzanne and Barry hiked 8 km east and then 5 km north. How far were they then from their starting point?

4. A right triangle has two sides of lengths 2 and 3. Find two possible lengths for the third side.

C
5. Find the height of an isosceles triangle with two sides of length 37 cm and the base of length 24 cm. (*Hint:* The height is the length of the line segment that bisects the base and is perpendicular to it.)

# *EXTRA!* Pythagorean Triples

The Pythagorean Property relates the lengths, *a* and *b*, of the two legs of a right triangle with the length *c* of the hypotenuse by the equation: $a^2 + b^2 = c^2$.

Any three *counting numbers* (*a*, *b*, *c*) that satisfy this equation are called a **Pythagorean Triple.** For example, 3, 4, and 5 form such a triple because $3^2 + 4^2 = 5^2$.

*Example* | Show that (6, 8, 10) is a Pythagorean Triple.

*Solution* | $6^2 + 8^2 = 36 + 64 = 100$
$10^2 = 100$
Since $6^2 + 8^2 = 10^2$, (6, 8, 10) is a Pythagorean Triple.

Notice that $6 = 3 \times 2$, $8 = 4 \times 2$, and $10 = 5 \times 2$. In general, if (*a*, *b*, *c*) is a Pythagorean Triple and *n* is a counting number, then (*an*, *bn*, *cn*) is also a Pythagorean Triple

Find the missing number in the Pythagorean Triple (*a*, *b*, *c*).

1. 5, 12, __?__
2. 20, 48, __?__
3. 15, __?__, 17
4. 30, __?__, 34
5. __?__, 84, 85
6. 20, 21, __?__
7. 60, 63, __?__
8. __?__, 24, 25
9. __?__, 48, 50
10. 9, 40, __?__
11. 45, 200, __?__
12. 11, __?__, 61

## 12-5 Special Right Triangles

**Objective** To find the lengths of the other two sides of an isosceles right triangle, and of a 30°–60° right triangle, given the length of one side.

In an **isosceles right** triangle, the two legs are equal in length. Also, the angles opposite the legs are equal in measure. Since

$$\angle A + \angle B + \angle C = 180°$$

and

$$\angle C = 90°,$$
$$\angle A + \angle B = 90°.$$

Since $\angle A = \angle B$, each has the measure 45°.

In the diagram, each leg is 1 unit long. From the Pythagorean Property:

$$c^2 = 1^2 + 1^2$$
$$c^2 = 2$$
$$c = \sqrt{2}$$

This suggests the following property:

**property**

If each leg of an isosceles right triangle has length $a$, then the hypotenuse has length $a \sqrt{2}$.

*Example 1* | A square has sides of length 5 cm. Find the length of a diagonal of the square.

*Solution* | The shaded right triangle shown has legs of length 5 cm. Thus, the hypotenuse $d$ has length $5\sqrt{2}$ cm.

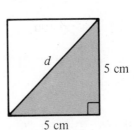

A **30°–60° right triangle,** such as $\triangle ABC$ at the right, can be thought of as half an equilateral triangle. Suppose $\overline{BC}$ is 1 unit long. Since $DB = AB$, $\overline{AB}$ is 2 units long. From the Pythagorean Property:

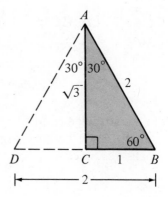

$$(AC)^2 + (BC)^2 = (AB)^2$$
$$(AC)^2 + 1^2 = 2^2$$
$$(AC)^2 = 3$$
$$AC = \sqrt{3} \approx 1.732$$

Notice that the larger the angle is, the longer its opposite side is. Thus in this 30°–60°–90° triangle, the sides have lengths 1, 1.7, and 2, respectively.

---

## property

**If the shorter leg of a 30°–60° right triangle has length $a$, then the other leg has length $a\sqrt{3}$, and the hypotenuse has length $2a$.**

---

*Example 2* | **Find the values of $x$ and $y$.**

*Solution* | **Since the hypotenuse is 8 cm long:**

$$x = \tfrac{1}{2} \times 8 \text{ cm} = 4 \text{ cm} \quad \text{and}$$

$$y = 4\sqrt{3} \text{ cm}$$

---

## Class Exercises

State the values of $x$ and $y$ in each triangle. Explain how you determined the values.

**1.**

**2.**

**3.**

**4.**

**5.**

**6.**

## Exercises

Use the table on page 394 to approximate the value of $x$ to the nearest hundredth.

**A**

**1.**

**2.**

**3.**

**4.**

**5.**

**6.**

**7.**

**8.**

**9.**

**10.**

**11.**

**12.**

Use the table on page 394 to approximate the values of $x$ and $y$ to the nearest tenth.

**B**  **13.**

**14.**

**15.**

**16.**

**17.**

**18.**

## Problems

Solve.

**A**  **1.** How long is the hypotenuse of an isosceles right triangle which has legs 25 mm long?

**2.** On a baseball field, the distance from home plate to first base is about 27 m. If the four bases are the vertexes of a square, what is the distance from second base to home plate?

**B**  **3.** A checkerboard has 8 squares on each side. If one side of each square is 5 cm long, how far is it from one corner of the board to the opposite corner?

**4.** Find the length of an altitude of an equilateral triangle with sides of length 12 cm.

**C**  **5.** The area of a square cake pan is 900 cm². What is the length of a diagonal of the pan?

**6.** A 10 m pole is supported in a vertical position by three 6 m guy wires. If one end of each wire is fastened to the ground at a 60° angle, how high on the pole is the other end fastened?

**7.** A rhombus has angles of 60° and 120°. Each side of the rhombus is 8 cm long. What are the lengths of the diagonals? (*Hint:* The diagonals bisect the angles of the rhombus.)

# 12-6 Trigonometric Ratios

**Objective** To calculate the sine, cosine, and tangent of an acute angle of a right triangle, given the lengths of two sides.

The left-hand diagram below shows three similar right triangles with an acute angle in common, $\angle A$. Since they are all $30°$–$60°$ right triangles, in each triangle the ratio of the length of the leg opposite $\angle A$ to the length of the hypotenuse is

$$\frac{a}{2a}, \quad \text{or} \quad \frac{1}{2}.$$

This ratio is called the **sine of** $\angle A$, usually abbreviated as **sin A.**

For each of the three similar right triangles in the right-hand diagram, where $\angle A = 60°$, you can see that

$$\sin A = \frac{a\sqrt{3}}{2a} = \frac{\sqrt{3}}{2}.$$

Thus you see that this **trigonometric ratio** depends on the measure of the angle $A$, but not on the size of the triangle. For a given length of hypotenuse, the greater the measure of $\angle A$, the greater the length of the leg opposite it. You can see from the diagram at the right that as the measure of $\angle A$ approaches $90°$, the leg opposite $\angle A$ approaches the same length as the hypotenuse. Thus, the sine ratio approaches $\frac{c}{c}$, or 1. As the measure of $\angle A$ approaches 0,

$\sin A$ approaches $\frac{0}{c}$, or 0.

Two other important trigonometric ratios that depend on the measure of an acute angle in a right triangle are the **cosine of ∠ A,** written **cos A,** and the **tangent of ∠ A,** written **tan A.**

Refer to the diagram at the right, in which the lengths of the opposite side, adjacent side, and hypotenuse are denoted by the abbreviations "opp.," "adj.," and hyp." Then:

$$\textbf{sin } A = \frac{\text{length of side opposite } \angle A}{\text{length of hypotenuse}} = \frac{\text{opp.}}{\text{hyp.}}$$

$$\textbf{cos } A = \frac{\text{length of side adjacent to } \angle A}{\text{length of hypotenuse}} = \frac{\text{adj.}}{\text{hyp.}}$$

$$\textbf{tan } A = \frac{\text{length of side opposite } \angle A}{\text{length of side adjacent to } \angle A} = \frac{\text{opp.}}{\text{adj.}}$$

*Example* | **In the triangle at the right, give the value of:**
**a. sin A   b. cos A   c. tan B**

*Solution* | **Find the value of x.**

$$4^2 + x^2 = 7^2$$
$$x^2 = 49 - 16 = 33$$
$$x = \sqrt{33}$$

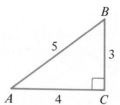

**a.** $\sin A = \dfrac{\text{opp.}}{\text{hyp.}} = \dfrac{\sqrt{33}}{7}$     **b.** $\cos A = \dfrac{\text{adj.}}{\text{hyp.}} = \dfrac{4}{7}$

**c.** $\tan B = \dfrac{\text{opp.}}{\text{adj.}} = \dfrac{4}{\sqrt{33}}$

## Class Exercises

Use the diagram at the right to state the value of each ratio.

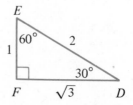

1. $\sin A$

2. $\cos A$

3. $\tan A$

4. $\sin B$

5. $\cos B$

6. $\tan B$

Use the 30°–60° right triangle shown to state the value of each ratio. Square-root signs are to be retained.

7. $\sin 60°$

8. $\cos 30°$

9. $\cos 60°$

10. $\sin 30°$

11. $\tan 30°$

12. $\tan 60°$

## Exercises

In each exercise, write the value of sin A, cos A, tan A, sin B, cos B, and tan B. Give each ratio in lowest terms. Square-root signs are to be retained.

**A** **1.**

**2.**

**3.**

**4.**

**5.**

**6.**

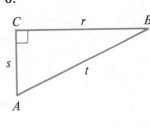

Find the value of x. Then find tan A.

**B** **7.**

**8.**

**9.**

Find the value of x. Then find sin A.

**10.**

**11.**

**12.**

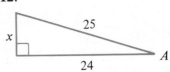

Find the value of x. Then find cos A.

**13.**

**14.**

**15.**

## 12-7 Using a Trigonometric Table

**Objective** To solve a right triangle by using a trigonometric table.

The table on page 395 gives the *approximate* values of the sine, cosine, and tangent of angles with measure $1°$, $2°$, $3°$, . . . , $90°$. For example, to find $\sin 30°$, look down the "$\angle A$" column to $30°$. To the right of it in the "$\sin A$" column, you see the value 0.5000. This agrees with the value $\frac{1}{2}$ that we determined for $\sin 30°$ on page 379. Do you see that

$$\tan 67° \approx 2.3559?$$

You can use the trigonometric table to **solve right triangles,** that is, to find approximations for the measures of the sides and angles.

**Example 1**

Solve $\triangle ABC$ by finding:
  a. the value of $x$   b. $\angle A$   c. $\angle B$

*Solution*

  a. $x^2 = 6^2 + 8^2 = 36 + 64 = 100$
   $x = \sqrt{100} = 10$

  b. $\tan A = \frac{8}{6} \approx 1.3333.$ **From the tangent column in the table, you find that the angle whose tangent is closest to 1.3333 has measure $53°$. Thus $\angle A \approx 53°$.**

  c. $\angle A + \angle B + \angle C = 180°$
   $53° + \angle B + 90° = 180°$
   $\angle B = 180° - 143° = 37°$
   Thus $\angle B \approx 37°$.

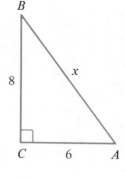

**Example 2**

Solve $\triangle ABC$ by finding:
  a. $\angle B$;   b. the value of $x$;
  c. the value of $y$.

*Solution*

  a. $\angle A + \angle B + \angle C = 180°$
   $50° + \angle B + 90° = 180°$
   $\angle B = 180° - 140° = 40°$

  b. Use one of the following equations:
   $\sin 50° = \frac{x}{8}$      $\cos 40° = \frac{x}{8}$
   $0.7660 \approx \frac{x}{8}$
   $x \approx 8 \times 0.7660 \approx 6.128$
   To the nearest whole number, $x = 6$.

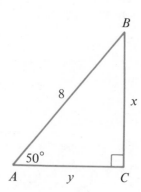

c. *Method 1*

$\sin 40° = \frac{y}{8}$

$0.6428 \approx \frac{y}{8}$

$y \approx 8 \times 0.6428$

$y \approx 5.1$

To the nearest whole number, $y = 5$.

*Method 2*

$6^2 + y^2 \approx 8^2$

$y^2 \approx 64 - 36$

$y^2 \approx 28$

$y \approx \sqrt{28} \approx 5.3$

## Class Exercises

Use the table on page 395 to state an approximation for each ratio.

**1.** $\sin 23°$      **2.** $\cos 81°$      **3.** $\tan 57°$      **4.** $\sin 35°$      **5.** $\cos 76°$

**6.** $\tan 19°$      **7.** $\sin 68°$      **8.** $\cos 4°$      **9.** $\tan 87°$      **10.** $\sin 42°$

Use the table on page 395 to find the measure of the angle to the nearest degree.

**11.** $\sin A = 0.9$      **12.** $\cos A = 0.5$      **13.** $\tan A = 1.3$      **14.** $\sin A = 0.36$

**15.** $\cos A = 0.84$      **16.** $\tan A = 1$      **17.** $\cos A = 0.22$      **18.** $\tan A = 0.6$

Find angle measures to the nearest degree and lengths to the nearest whole number.

**19.** $\angle A$      **20.** $x$      **21.** $\angle B$

**22.** $\angle B$      **23.** $x$      **24.** $y$

Exs. 19–21

Exs. 22–24

## Exercises

Use the table on page 395 to solve $\triangle ABC$ with $\angle C = 90°$. Find lengths to the nearest whole number and angle measures to the nearest degree.

 **B**

**1.** $x = 2$, $y = 5$      **2.** $x = 4$, $y = 6$

**3.** $x = 3$, $z = 6$      **4.** $y = 7$, $z = 9$

**5.** $\angle A = 47°$, $z = 5$      **6.** $\angle B = 62°$, $z = 8$

**7.** $\angle B = 15°$, $x = 20$      **8.** $\angle A = 70°$, $y = 30$

**9.** $\angle A = 28°$, $x = 10$      **10.** $\angle B = 39°$, $y = 9$

# A Sculptor

Is there a statue or piece of sculpture in your town hall or in your neighborhood park? Did you ever wonder who made it?

Edmonia Lewis was a famous sculptor of the nineteenth century. For the most part, she chose people as her subjects. One of her first works was a medallion of abolitionist John Brown, published in 1865. She also sculptured a bust of U.S. Civil War hero Colonel Robert Gould Shaw which she modeled from photographs, and busts of Abraham Lincoln and U.S. Senator Charles Sumner. At times, Edmonia Lewis would get ideas from abstract themes or from poetry. Henry Wadsworth Longfellow's poem *Hiawatha* was the inspiration for her sculpture of an American Indian group. Her most important early work was a composition of two emancipated slaves entitled *Forever Free*. In 1865, she went to Rome to study sculpture. She completed a sculpture of Longfellow in 1869, which she modeled mainly from observing him in the streets of Rome. The sculpture was later placed in the Harvard College Library.

Edmonia Lewis exhibited six of her works at the Philadelphia Centennial Exposition of 1876. Collections of her works have been placed on display at the Frederick Douglass Institute of Negro Arts and History, the Fogg Museum at Harvard University, the California Public Library at San José, and the Kennedy Gallery in New York.

**Research Activity** Find out about the different styles of sculpture. Can you find any examples of realistic or neo-classic sculpture? Try to find some photos in an art book of the works of Edmonia Lewis. Can you tell which style she used?

**Career Activity** Find out what types of materials and tools sculptors work with. Before they begin, do sculptors usually draw sketches of what they intend to make?

Henry Wadsworth Longfellow

## Self-Test

Symbols and words to remember:

$c^2 = a^2 + b^2$ [p. 371]
$\cos A$ [p. 380]
Pythagorean Property [p. 371]
30°–60° right triangle [p. 376]
sine [p. 379]
tangent [p. 380]

$\sin A$ [p. 379]
$\tan A$ [p. 380]
isosceles right triangle [p. 375]
trigonometric ratio [p. 379]
cosine [p. 380]
solving a right triangle [p. 382]

State whether or not a triangle with sides of the given lengths is a right triangle.

**1.** 7, 8, 10

**2.** 5, 12, 13

[12-4]

A right triangle has sides of lengths $a$, $b$, and $c$, with $c$ the length of the hypotenuse. Find the length of the third side.

**3.** $a = 5$, $b = 7$

**4.** $a = 9$, $c = 15$

Find an approximation to the nearest hundredth for $x$.

[12-5]

**5.**

**6.**

**7.**

**8.**

Use the diagram to name each ratio.

**9.** $\sin A$

**10.** $\sin B$

**11.** $\cos A$

**12.** $\tan B$

[12-6]

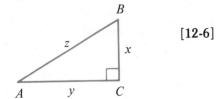

Refer to the diagram at the right.

**13.** Which equation is *incorrectly* written?

[12-7]

    **a.** $\cos E = \dfrac{8}{17}$  **b.** $\cos D = \dfrac{8}{17}$  **c.** $\sin D = \dfrac{8}{17}$

**14.** Find the value of $x$.

**15.** Find $\angle D$ to the nearest degree.

**16.** Find $\angle E$ to the nearest degree.

Self-Test answers and Extra Practice are at the back of the book.

# Chapter Review

Write the letter that labels the correct answer.

1. A positive number has exactly __?__ different square root(s).    [12-1]
   A. 1        B. 2        C. 3        D. 4

2. Which number lies between 8 and 9?
   A. $\sqrt{54}$    B. $\sqrt{85}$    C. $\sqrt{72}$    D. $\sqrt{61}$

3. If we divide a positive number $n$ by an estimate for $\sqrt{n}$, the __?__    [12-2]
   of the divisor and quotient can be used as a better estimate for
   $\sqrt{n}$.
   A. sum      B. product      C. average      D. greater

4. If 7.4 is used as an estimate for $\sqrt{55.5}$, the next estimate will be
   A. 7.5      B. 7.45      C. 7.42      D. 7.4

5. To find an approximation for the square root of a number which    [12-3]
   lies between two entries in a table, we use the process called
   __?__ .
   A. divide and average          B. estimation
   C. trigonometry                D. interpolation

6. To approximate $\sqrt{18.3}$ using a table, we assume that $\sqrt{18.3}$ is
   __?__ of the way from $\sqrt{18}$ to $\sqrt{19}$.
   A. 0.3      B. 0.5          C. one third    D. $\sqrt{0.3}$

7. A table gives $\sqrt{10} \approx 3.162$ and $\sqrt{11} \approx 3.316$, so a good approximation for $\sqrt{10.5}$ is __?__ .
   A. 3.239    B. 3.162        C. 3.316        D. 3.2

8. The side opposite the right angle of a right triangle is the __?__ .    [12-4]
   A. leg        B. hypotenuse    C. vertex        D. shortest side

9. For a right triangle with hypotenuse of length $c$ and legs of lengths
   $a$ and $b$, the Pythagorean Property states that __?__ .
   A. $c^2 = a^2 - b^2$              B. $c^2 + a^2 = b^2$
   C. $c^2 = a^2 + b^2$              D. $c^2 + b^2 = a^2$

10. A right triangle with legs of lengths 7 and 24 has hypotenuse of
    length __?__ .
    A. 625      B. 25          C. $\sqrt{527}$      D. $\sqrt{31}$

**11.** In an isosceles right triangle, each acute angle has measure __?__ .    [12-5]
    **A.** 30°    **B.** 45°        **C.** 60°        **D.** 90°

**12.** If each leg of an isosceles right triangle has length $a$, then the hypotenuse has length __?__ .

    **A.** $a\sqrt{2}$    **B.** $a\sqrt{3}$      **C.** $\dfrac{a}{2}$        **D.** $2a$

**13.** In a 30°–60°–90° triangle with hypotenuse of length 2, the side opposite the 60° angle has length __?__ .

    **A.** 1      **B.** $2\sqrt{2}$      **C.** $\sqrt{3}$      **D.** $\dfrac{\sqrt{3}}{2}$

**14.** Refer to the diagram. $\sin A =$ __?__    [12-6]

    **A.** $\dfrac{a}{b}$    **B.** $\dfrac{b}{c}$    **C.** $\dfrac{a}{c}$    **D.** $\dfrac{c}{a}$

**15.** $\cos A =$ __?__

    **A.** $\dfrac{a}{b}$    **B.** $\dfrac{b}{c}$    **C.** $\dfrac{a}{c}$    **D.** $\dfrac{c}{a}$

Exs. 14, 15

**16.** A right triangle has legs of lengths 3 and 4. The tangent of the angle opposite the leg of length 3 is __?__ .

    **A.** $\dfrac{3}{4}$    **B.** $\dfrac{3}{5}$      **C.** $\dfrac{4}{5}$      **D.** 5

**17.** The table on page 395 indicates that $\sin 57° \approx$ __?__ .    [12-7]
    **A.** 0.8387  **B.** 0.5446      **C.** 1.5399    **D.** 0.8290

**18.** If $\tan A \approx 0.5317$, the table on page 395 indicates that $\angle A$ = __?__ , to the nearest degree.
    **A.** 29°      **B.** 32°      **C.** 58°      **D.** 28°

**19.** Refer to the diagram. Use the table on page 395 to determine that $x =$ __?__ , to the nearest integer.
    **A.** 3      **B.** 4      **C.** 8      **D.** 5

# John Napier and Napier's Bones

The earliest known computing device was the ancient abacus, a plate of metal with grooves, and pebbles in the grooves. To perform a computation, the pebbles were moved and the answer was read from the final position of the pebbles.

An interesting second computing aid came centuries later when John Napier (1550–1617) made **Napier's rods,** or as they came to be known, **Napier's bones.** Workers in his father's business made frequent errors in arithmetic, so Napier, a Scottish mathematician, invented his computing rods to be used by the workers to multiply integers.

To make Napier's bones, start with ten long rectangular strips of paper or cardboard. Put a different digit at the top of each. The nine multiples of the digit are written in a column in nine squares below, with the tens' digit of each multiple in the top half of the square and the ones' digit in the bottom half.

**Example** | Use Napier's bones to multiply 7 × 38.

**Solution** | Place the three rod next to the eight rod as shown. The answer is then read from the seventh row.

Ones' place = 6

Tens' place = 5 + 1 = 6

Hundreds' place = 2

Answer: 266

388

The example below (6 × 239) shows how sometimes you must carry a digit from one place to the next.

Ones' place = 4
    8 + 5 = 13, Tens' place = 3

Hundreds'.place = 1 + 1 + 2 = 4
Thousands' place = 1
Answer: 1434

Inspecting the multiplication problem below suggests how you might use Napier's bones to carry out a multiplication when both factors have two digits or more.

$$\begin{array}{r} 62 \\ \times 21 \\ \hline 62 \\ 124 \phantom{0} \\ \hline 1302 \end{array}$$

62 ⟵ 1 × 62
124 ⟵ 2 × 62

In today's age of hand calculators, Napier's bones may seem cumbersome and impractical; but they remained popular for centuries following their invention.

Make a set of Napier's bones and use them to multiply the following numbers. (You may need to make duplicate rods for some digits.)

**1.** 6 × 27

**2.** 8 × 68

**3.** 5 × 623

**4.** 22 × 83

**5.** 47 × 79

**6.** 683 × 562

**Research Activity** Go to your library and find out more about John Napier. Find out what *logarithms* are.

# Chapter Test

1. $-\sqrt{49} = \underline{\quad?\quad}$    [12-1]

2. $\sqrt{29}$ lies between what two consecutive integers?

3. Using the divide and average method, $\sqrt{35} = \underline{\quad?\quad}$ to the tenths' place.    [12-2]

4. Using the divide and average method, $\sqrt{127.5} = \underline{\quad?\quad}$ to the nearest tenth.

5. Using the table on page 394, $3\sqrt{12} = \underline{\quad?\quad}$ to the nearest hundredth.    [12-3]

6. Using interpolation, $\sqrt{15.3} = \underline{\quad?\quad}$ to the nearest hundredth.

7. A triangle has sides of lengths 6, 12, and 13. Is it a right triangle?    [12-4]

8. A rectangle has sides of lengths 7 m and 24 m. How long is its diagonal?

9. How long is the hypotenuse of an isosceles right triangle which has legs 6 cm long?    [12-5]

10. Use the table on page 394 to approximate the value of $x$ to the nearest tenth.

11. $\sin A = \underline{\quad?\quad}$    [12-6]

12. $\tan 60° = \underline{\quad?\quad}$

13. Use the table on page 395 to find that $x = \underline{\quad?\quad}$ to the nearest whole number.    [12-7]

14. To the nearest degree, $\angle A = \underline{\quad?\quad}$

# Cumulative Review

1. A quarter, a nickel, and a dime are tossed. How many possible outcomes are there? What is the probability of each outcome? [Ch. 10]

Each of ten cards contains one of the letters from the word *strawberry*. A card is drawn at random. Find:
   a. the probability of each event
   b. the odds against each event

2. $p(a)$  3. $p(t \text{ or } b)$  4. $p(r)$  5. $p(a \text{ or } r)$

6. Of 120 students polled at Middlebury School, 54 owned skateboards. About how many of the 1800 students at the school own skateboards?

7. Graph and label the ordered pairs $(0, 5)$, $(3, 2)$, $(-1, 1)$ and $(3\frac{1}{2}, -4)$ on a coordinate plane. [Ch. 11]

8. Find the solutions of $6x - 5y = 2$ with abscissas $0$, $-2$, and $3$.

9. Graph $-2x + 3y = 5$.

10. Solve the system   $x - y = 2$
                      $2x + y = 4$

11. $\sqrt{57}$ is between what two consecutive integers? [Ch. 12]

12. Approximate $\sqrt{63}$ to the tenths' place.

13. A right triangle has hypotenuse of length 13 cm and one leg of length 12 cm. How long is the other leg?

14. In a 30°–60°–90° triangle, the shorter leg has length 5.5 m. How long is the other leg?

15. Find  a. $\sin A$
         b. $\tan B$

# Final Review

1. Draw a histogram for the data at the right.

2. Find the range, median, mean, and all the modes for the data at the right.

3. According to the graph below, the greatest temperature change was recorded between which two consecutive hours?

4. What is the range of recorded temperatures?

Quiz scores of
25 students

| 6 | 7 | 8 | 7 | 8 |
|---|---|---|---|---|
| 6 | 8 | 7 | 8 | 6 |
| 10 | 9 | 9 | 6 | 8 |
| 7 | 9 | 10 | 8 | 7 |
| 6 | 7 | 4 | 9 | 10 |

Exs. 1–2

Exs. 3–4

5. Write 20.903 in expanded form.

Compute.

6. $(6.3 - 8.7)(2.5 - 4.9)$    7. $(-3.1)(1.5)(-0.7)$    8. $1.7057 \div (-0.037)$

Express as a fraction in lowest terms.

9. $-4\frac{2}{3} \div \left(-3\frac{4}{15}\right)$    10. $1\frac{7}{9} + \left(\frac{5}{6} - \frac{8}{3}\right)$    11. $12\frac{5}{6} - 6\frac{3}{7} \div 1\frac{2}{7}$

Express each ratio as a fraction in lowest terms.

12. 3 min to 40 s    13. 130 cm to 2.6 m    14. 1.2 kg to 880 g

15. A distance of 2 cm on a map represents an actual distance of 75 km. What distance on this map would represent 525 km?

Complete.

16. 12% of 145 = __?__    17. 37 = __?__% of 40    18. 51 = 30% of __?__

19. A $40 clock is on sale for $32.80. Find the percent of discount.

**20.** A salesperson who is paid a 9% commission earned $270. What was the amount of sales?

Refer to the diagram at the right.

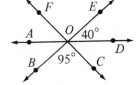

**21.** ∠ *EOC* = __?__ °    **22.** ∠ *FOE* = __?__ °

**23.** ∠ *FOB* = __?__ °

**24.** In the diagram at the right, $\overline{ST} \| \overline{RU}$. Find the values of *x* and *y*.

Which pairs of triangles must be congruent? Give your reason (SAS, ASA, or SSS).

**25.**            **26.**            **27.**

**28.** Solve: $\frac{5}{6}(2x + 1) = \frac{3}{2}x + 2.$    **29.** For which values of *t* is $-3t + 5 > 2$?

**30.** $800 is invested in an account which pays 5% compounded quarterly. What will be the value of the account in 6 months?

**31.** Find the area of a triangle with base 3 m and height 2.5 m.

**32.** Find the volume of a cone with height 9 cm and radius 2 cm. (Use $\pi \approx 3.14$.)

A coin is chosen at random from 3 pennies, 5 dimes, and 2 quarters.

**33.** What is the probability of choosing a quarter?

**34.** What are the odds against choosing a dime?

**35.** Graph (3,2), (−1,0), and (7,−5) on a coordinate plane.

Find the value of *x*. Then find sin *A*, cos *A*, and tan *A*.

**36.**            **37.**            **38.**

| Number | Square Root | Number | Square Root | Number | Square Root | Number | Square Root |
|---|---|---|---|---|---|---|---|
| 1 | 1.000 | 26 | 5.099 | 51 | 7.141 | 76 | 8.718 |
| 2 | 1.414 | 27 | 5.196 | 52 | 7.211 | 77 | 8.775 |
| 3 | 1.732 | 28 | 5.292 | 53 | 7.280 | 78 | 8.832 |
| 4 | 2.000 | 29 | 5.385 | 54 | 7.348 | 79 | 8.888 |
| 5 | 2.236 | 30 | 5.477 | 55 | 7.416 | 80 | 8.944 |
| 6 | 2.449 | 31 | 5.568 | 56 | 7.483 | 81 | 9.000 |
| 7 | 2.646 | 32 | 5.657 | 57 | 7.550 | 82 | 9.055 |
| 8 | 2.828 | 33 | 5.745 | 58 | 7.616 | 83 | 9.110 |
| 9 | 3.000 | 34 | 5.831 | 59 | 7.681 | 84 | 9.165 |
| 10 | 3.162 | 35 | 5.916 | 60 | 7.746 | 85 | 9.220 |
| 11 | 3.317 | 36 | 6.000 | 61 | 7.810 | 86 | 9.274 |
| 12 | 3.464 | 37 | 6.083 | 62 | 7.874 | 87 | 9.327 |
| 13 | 3.606 | 38 | 6.164 | 63 | 7.937 | 88 | 9.381 |
| 14 | 3.742 | 39 | 6.245 | 64 | 8.000 | 89 | 9.434 |
| 15 | 3.873 | 40 | 6.325 | 65 | 8.062 | 90 | 9.487 |
| 16 | 4.000 | 41 | 6.403 | 66 | 8.124 | 91 | 9.539 |
| 17 | 4.123 | 42 | 6.481 | 67 | 8.185 | 92 | 9.592 |
| 18 | 4.243 | 43 | 6.557 | 68 | 8.246 | 93 | 9.644 |
| 19 | 4.359 | 44 | 6.633 | 69 | 8.307 | 94 | 9.695 |
| 20 | 4.472 | 45 | 6.708 | 70 | 8.367 | 95 | 9.747 |
| 21 | 4.583 | 46 | 6.782 | 71 | 8.426 | 96 | 9.798 |
| 22 | 4.690 | 47 | 6.856 | 72 | 8.485 | 97 | 9.849 |
| 23 | 4.796 | 48 | 6.928 | 73 | 8.544 | 98 | 9.899 |
| 24 | 4.899 | 49 | 7.000 | 74 | 8.602 | 99 | 9.950 |
| 25 | 5.000 | 50 | 7.071 | 75 | 8.660 | 100 | 10.000 |

## SINES, COSINES, AND TANGENTS OF ANGLES
## FROM 1 TO 90 DEGREES

| Angle | Sine | Cosine | Tangent | Angle | Sine | Cosine | Tangent |
|-------|------|--------|---------|-------|------|--------|---------|
| 1° | .0175 | .9998 | .0175 | 46° | .7193 | .6947 | 1.0355 |
| 2° | .0349 | .9994 | .0349 | 47° | .7314 | .6820 | 1.0724 |
| 3° | .0523 | .9986 | .0524 | 48° | .7431 | .6691 | 1.1106 |
| 4° | .0698 | .9976 | .0699 | 49° | .7547 | .6561 | 1.1504 |
| 5° | .0872 | .9962 | .0875 | 50° | .7660 | .6428 | 1.1918 |
| 6° | .1045 | .9945 | .1051 | 51° | .7771 | .6293 | 1.2349 |
| 7° | .1219 | .9925 | .1228 | 52° | .7880 | .6157 | 1.2799 |
| 8° | .1392 | .9903 | .1405 | 53° | .7986 | .6018 | 1.3270 |
| 9° | .1564 | .9877 | .1584 | 54° | .8090 | .5878 | 1.3764 |
| 10° | .1736 | .9848 | .1763 | 55° | .8192 | .5736 | 1.4281 |
| 11° | .1908 | .9816 | .1944 | 56° | .8290 | .5592 | 1.4826 |
| 12° | .2079 | .9781 | .2126 | 57° | .8387 | .5446 | 1.5399 |
| 13° | .2250 | .9744 | .2309 | 58° | .8480 | .5299 | 1.6003 |
| 14° | .2419 | .9703 | .2493 | 59° | .8572 | .5150 | 1.6643 |
| 15° | .2588 | .9659 | .2679 | 60° | .8660 | .5000 | 1.7321 |
| 16° | .2756 | .9613 | .2867 | 61° | .8746 | .4848 | 1.8040 |
| 17° | .2924 | .9563 | .3057 | 62° | .8829 | .4695 | 1.8807 |
| 18° | .3090 | .9511 | .3249 | 63° | .8910 | .4540 | 1.9626 |
| 19° | .3256 | .9455 | .3443 | 64° | .8988 | .4384 | 2.0503 |
| 20° | .3420 | .9397 | .3640 | 65° | .9063 | .4226 | 2.1445 |
| 21° | .3584 | .9336 | .3839 | 66° | .9135 | .4067 | 2.2460 |
| 22° | .3746 | .9272 | .4040 | 67° | .9205 | .3907 | 2.3559 |
| 23° | .3907 | .9205 | .4245 | 68° | .9272 | .3746 | 2.4751 |
| 24° | .4067 | .9135 | .4452 | 69° | .9336 | .3584 | 2.6051 |
| 25° | .4226 | .9063 | .4663 | 70° | .9397 | .3420 | 2.7475 |
| 26° | .4384 | .8988 | .4877 | 71° | .9455 | .3256 | 2.9042 |
| 27° | .4540 | .8910 | .5095 | 72° | .9511 | .3090 | 3.0777 |
| 28° | .4695 | .8829 | .5317 | 73° | .9563 | .2924 | 3.2709 |
| 29° | .4848 | .8746 | .5543 | 74° | .9613 | .2756 | 3.4874 |
| 30° | .5000 | .8660 | .5774 | 75° | .9659 | .2588 | 3.7321 |
| 31° | .5150 | .8572 | .6009 | 76° | .9703 | .2419 | 4.0108 |
| 32° | .5299 | .8480 | .6249 | 77° | .9744 | .2250 | 4.3315 |
| 33° | .5446 | .8387 | .6494 | 78° | .9781 | .2079 | 4.7046 |
| 34° | .5592 | .8290 | .6745 | 79° | .9816 | .1908 | 5.1446 |
| 35° | .5736 | .8192 | .7002 | 80° | .9848 | .1736 | 5.6713 |
| 36° | .5878 | .8090 | .7265 | 81° | .9877 | .1564 | 6.3138 |
| 37° | .6018 | .7986 | .7536 | 82° | .9903 | .1392 | 7.1154 |
| 38° | .6157 | .7880 | .7813 | 83° | .9925 | .1219 | 8.1443 |
| 39° | .6293 | .7771 | .8098 | 84° | .9945 | .1045 | 9.5144 |
| 40° | .6428 | .7660 | .8391 | 85° | .9962 | .0872 | 11.4301 |
| 41° | .6561 | .7547 | .8693 | 86° | .9976 | .0698 | 14.3007 |
| 42° | .6691 | .7431 | .9004 | 87° | .9986 | .0523 | 19.0811 |
| 43° | .6820 | .7314 | .9325 | 88° | .9994 | .0349 | 28.6363 |
| 44° | .6947 | .7193 | .9657 | 89° | .9998 | .0175 | 57.2900 |
| 45° | .7071 | .7071 | 1.0000 | 90° | 1.0000 | .0000 | |

# Answers to Self-Tests

## CHAPTER 1

**Page 13** **1.** Crust  **2.** Inner Core  **3.** 3000–5000 km  **4.** Mantle  **5.** 110 kg  **6.** About 70 kg  **7.** About 45 kg  **8.** About 90 kg  **9.** About 6° to 22°  **10.** February and March  **11.** June  **12.** May

**Page 19** **1.**

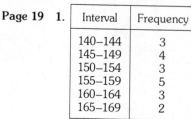

| Interval | Frequency |
|----------|-----------|
| 140–144  | 3 |
| 145–149  | 4 |
| 150–154  | 3 |
| 155–159  | 5 |
| 160–164  | 3 |
| 165–169  | 2 |

**2.**

Students' heights in cm

**3.** 155–159 cm  **4.** 5  **5.** 3  **6.** 9  **7.** 9  **8.** 10

## CHAPTER 2

**Page 39** **1.** $10^4$  **2.** $10^8$  **3.** $(4 \times 10^4) + (8 \times 10^2) + 7$  **4.** 8691  **5.** hundredths  **6.** $7 + (2 \times 0.1) + (4 \times 0.01) + (6 \times 0.001)$  **7.** 403.62  **8.** 65.009

**9.**   0.4  0.8  1.2  **10.** >  **11.** <  **12.** <, <  **13.** 8; 17; 31  **14.** 4; 40; 95

**15.** 36; 96; 480  **16.** 4; 10; 17

**Page 57** **1.** $n = 21 - 14$; $n = 7$  **2.** $n = 32 - 8$; $n = 24$  **3.** $n = 48 \div 6$; $n = 8$  **4.** $n = 24 \div 8$; $n = 3$  **5.** $x = 2$  **6.** $n = 0$  **7.** $t = 3$  **8.** $y = 8$  **9.** 49.646  **10.** 18.041  **11.** 8.494  **12.** 0.003  **13.** 15.504  **14.** 0.612  **15.** 0.01488  **16.** 13.2374  **17.** 4.1  **18.** 49.5625  **19.** 8.33  **20.** 0.27  **21.** 72 m  **22.** 5.5 km  **23.** 6.9 km  **24.** $2.25

## CHAPTER 3

**Page 81** **1.**   **2.**  **3.** 6  **4.** 1.2

**5.**  **6.**  **7.**

**8.**  **9.** ⁻5.4  **10.** 7.5  **11.** ⁻0.6  **12.** 1.99  **13.** ⁻3  **14.** 3.8  **15.** ⁻4

**16.** ⁻3.71

**Page 97** **1.** ⁻8  **2.** 4  **3.** $11 - 9 = 2$; $11 - 2 = 9$  **4.** $^-8 - 29 = {}^-37$; $^-8 - {}^-37 = 29$  **5.** $1.2 + (^-3.6)$  **6.** $8.72 + 13.51$  **7.** 4.7  **8.** 14.59  **9.** $-6.2$  **10.** 405  **11.** 0  **12.** 51  **13.** $-0.9$  **14.** 18.87  **15.** $-21.9648$  **16.** 70.097  **17.** $-4$  **18.** $-7.6$  **19.** 4.5  **20.** $-0.6$

## CHAPTER 4

**Page 120** **1.** $\frac{1}{9}$  **2.** 35  **3.** $\frac{4}{7}$  **4.** $7\frac{4}{5}$  **5.** $\frac{-2}{7}$; $\frac{2}{-7}$  **6.** $\frac{1}{-4}$; $-\frac{1}{4}$  **7.** $-37$  **8.** $-6\frac{2}{5}$  **9.** Answers will vary.  **10.** $\frac{25}{17}$  **11.** $-\frac{2}{9}$  **12.** $\frac{5}{9}$  **13.** $-\frac{3}{10}$  **14.** $\frac{3}{10}$  **15.** $-\frac{2}{7}$  **16.** 26

**Page 137** **1.** $\frac{36}{45}$; $\frac{10}{45}$  **2.** $-\frac{25}{30}$; $-\frac{2}{30}$  **3.** $\frac{70}{180}$; $\frac{75}{180}$; $\frac{12}{180}$  **4.** $\frac{63}{84}$; $\frac{48}{84}$; $-\frac{14}{84}$  **5.** $\frac{11}{24}$  **6.** $-\frac{17}{24}$  **7.** $1\frac{2}{15}$  **8.** $5\frac{8}{9}$  **9.** $1\frac{1}{2}$  **10.** $1\frac{1}{21}$  **11.** $-3\frac{1}{5}$  **12.** $-\frac{1}{4}$  **13.** $\frac{89}{50}$  **14.** $-\frac{13}{40}$  **15.** $0.958\overline{3}$  **16.** $-2.064$

## CHAPTER 5
**Page 152** **1.** $\frac{1}{4}$ **2.** $\frac{3}{5}$ **3.** $\frac{3}{50}$ **4.** $\frac{200}{1}$ **5.** Incorrect **6.** Correct **7.** $n = 4$ **8.** $n = 28$

**Page 165** **1.** 1.6 **2.** 18 **3.** 20% **4.** $26\frac{2}{3}$ **5.** 20% **6.** 12% **7.** 20 **8.** 5% **9.** $1928.40
**10.** $70.50 **11.** $1116 **12.** $24,220

## CHAPTER 6
**Page 189** **1.** one **2.** no **3.** 3500 **4.** 0.2 **5.** diameter **6.** 251.2 cm **7.** 132 **8.** 2.8 **9.** 45°
**10.** protractor **11.** 90° **12.** 50° **13.** parallel **14.** equal **15.** 138°, 42°, and 138° **16.** parallel
**Page 209** **1.** 90°, 60° **2.** Yes **3.** 60° **4.** Two **5.** T **6.** F **7.** F **8.** T **9.** F **10.** F **11.** 24 cm
**12.** 3.8 cm, 4 cm, 4 cm **13.** No **14.** $\triangle EFD$ **15.** $\angle C$ **16.** $CB$ **17.** Yes **18.** Yes **19.** No
**20.** No

## CHAPTER 7
**Page 230** **1.** $1 + x$ **2.** $12n$ **3.** The difference when $z$ is subtracted from thirteen
**4.** The sum when the product of five and $z$ is added to twelve **5.** $-12$ **6.** $-3$ **7.** 14 **8.** $\frac{1}{5}$ **9.** $\frac{y}{3} = -9$
**10.** $2(n + 4) = 14$
**11.** The product when three is multiplied by nine less than $y$ is less than or equal to negative eight.
**12.** The sum when the product of negative seven and $x$ is added to thirty-one is greater than four.
**13.** No **14.** No **15.** Yes **16.** Yes

**Page 239** **1.** 12 **2.** 8 **3.** $-54$ **4.** $-35$ **5.** $\{-3\}$ **6.** $\{22\}$ **7.** $\{8\}$ **8.** $\{-6\}$
**9.** $\{-1, 0, 1, 2, \ldots\}$ **10.** $\{-10, -11, -12, \ldots\}$ **11.** $\{-5, -4, -3, -2, \ldots\}$
**12.** $\{3, 2, 1, 0, \ldots\}$

## CHAPTER 8
**Page 254** Answers will vary. **1. a.** The sum of 20 and what number gives 39? **b.** There are 2 algebra classes and a total of 39 students. If there are 20 students in one class, how many students are in the other class?
**2. a.** What number multiplied by 12 gives 84? **b.** A small auditorium has 12 seats in each row. If the auditorium holds 84 seats, how many rows are there?
**3. a.** Seven less than what number is 23? **b.** Joanne needed 23 minutes to solve a difficult science problem. This was 7 minutes less than Sarah needed to solve the problem. How long did Sarah need to solve the problem?
**4. a.** One third of what number is 9? **b.** One third of the students in the glee club were chosen to be in the concert choir. If 9 students from the glee club were accepted in the concert choir, how many students are in the glee club? **5.** $18 + n = 51$ **6.** $n - 13 = 44$ **7.** $n + (n + 16) = 71$
**8.** $w + w + (w + 20) + (w + 20) = 120$ **9.** 19 **10.** 31 **11.** 19, 20 **12.** 12, 39
**Page 263** **1.** 1.625 km **2.** 6 cm by 7.5 cm **3.** $82.50 **4.** $5600 **5.** 359,970,000 km²
**6.** About $2,300,000

## CHAPTER 9
**Page 281** **1.** 36 cm² **2.** 1200 cm² **3.** 12 cm **4.** 32 cm **5.** 442 mm² **6.** 10.75 m² **7.** 12 cm²
**8.** 10 m **9.** $\frac{77}{8}$ square units **10.** 78.5 cm² **11.** $225\pi$ square units **12.** $12\pi$ m²
**Page 299** **1.** 471 cubic units **2.** 540 cubic units **3.** 3375 mm³ **4.** 1056 cm³ **5.** $26\frac{2}{3}$ cubic units
**6.** 140 cm³ **7.** 117.23 cubic units **8.** 2616.67 cubic units **9.** 135 square units
**10.** 48 square units; 72 square units **11.** 502.4 square units; 602.88 square units
**12.** 36 square units; 72 square units **13.** 5500 **14.** 0.4 **15.** 440 g **16.** 0.0899 g

**17.** $4\pi$ square units; $\frac{4}{3}\pi$ cubic units  **18.** 1256 square units  **19.** $14\frac{1}{7}$ cubic units
**20.** $\frac{32}{3}\pi$ cubic units

CHAPTER 10
**Page 317**  **1.** No  **2.** Yes  **3.** 5; $\frac{1}{5}$  **4.** 4; $\frac{1}{4}$  **5.** $\frac{4}{7}$  **6.** 0  **7.** $\frac{1}{7}$  **8.** 1  **9.** 1 to 2  **10.** 2 to 1  **11.** 1 to 5
**12.** 1 to 1

**Page 327**  **1.** $\frac{14}{15}$  **2.** $\frac{2}{5}$  **3.** $\frac{1}{2}$  **4.** $\frac{2}{3}$  **5.** $\frac{3}{400}$  **6.** $\frac{397}{400}$  **7.** 45 fuses  **8.** 397 to 3  **9.** 5.51  **10.** 12.6¢
**11.** 2.5  **12.** 5

CHAPTER 11
**Page 343**  **1. a.** $J$ **b.** $F$ **c.** $A$ **d.** $D$ **e.** $B$ **f.** $C$

**2. a.**

**3. a.**

**b.** $A = 2 \times 2 = 4$

**b.** $A = 3 \times 4 = 12$

**4. a.**

**b.** $A = \frac{1}{2} \times 5 \times 3 = 7.5$

**5. a.** $(-5, -4)$ **b.** $(-2, 3)$ **c.** $(-2, -3)$ **d.** $(3, 3)$ **e.** $(0, 4)$ **f.** $(2, -2)$  **6.** $A, K, M$
**7.** $A, C, D, E, F, H, K, M$  **8.** $D, O, J$

**Page 355** **1.** Yes **2.** Yes **3.** $y = \frac{2}{3}x - 2$ **4.** $y = \frac{5}{4}x - 10$ **5.** $(-7, 0)$, $(0, -7)$
**6.** $(-11, 0)$, $(0, 5\frac{1}{2})$

**7.**

**8.**

**9.**

**10.**

**11.**

**12.**

CHAPTER 12
**Page 370** **1.** 8 and 9 **2.** 1 and 2 **3.** 5 and 6 **4.** 7 and 8 **5.** 3.75 **6.** 7.4 **7.** 8.6 **8.** 8.2 **9.** 9.17
**10.** 7.94 **11.** 0.13 **12.** 4.96
**Page 385** **1.** No **2.** Yes **3.** $c = \sqrt{74}$ **4.** $b = 12$ **5.** $x = 14.14$ **6.** $x = 9$ **7.** $x = 12.12$
**8.** $x = 1.73$ **9.** $\frac{x}{z}$ **10.** $\frac{y}{z}$ **11.** $\frac{y}{z}$ **12.** $\frac{y}{x}$ **13.** b **14.** $x = 15$ **15.** $28°$ **16.** $62°$

# Extra Practice—Chapter 1

For use after page 13:

Use the table below for Exercises 1–6.

### Money Earned Annually by Student Organizations in Hopeville

| Year | Food Sales | Dances | Yard Care | Washing Cars | Craft Sales |
|------|-----------|--------|-----------|--------------|-------------|
| 1974 | $150 | $240 | $120 | $60 | $30 |
| 1975 | $163 | $260 | $130 | $65 | $33 |
| 1976 | $175 | $280 | $140 | $70 | $35 |
| 1977 | $188 | $300 | $150 | $75 | $38 |
| 1978 | $200 | $320 | $160 | $80 | $41 |

1. How much more did the student organizations earn in 1978 than in 1974?    [1-1]
2. Which activity earned the least amount from 1974 to 1978?
3. Which activity earned the greatest amount from 1974 to 1978?
4. Which activity earned twice as much as washing cars?
5. Which activities earned more than yard care?
6. How much more did the students earn with dances than with food sales from 1974 to 1978?

Use the bar graph at the right for Exercises 7–9.

7. What were the sales in produce?    [1-2]

8. What were the sales in all four departments?

9. What was the difference between meat sales and dairy sales?

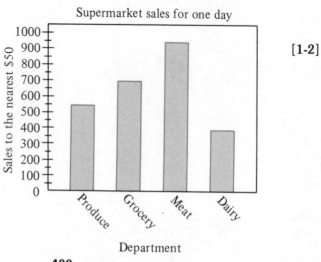

Supermarket sales for one day

**400**

Use the line graph at the right for Exercises 10–12. It shows the amount collected from a clothes washer each day of one week.

10. How much was collected on the busiest day?

11. How much was collected on the slowest day?

12. What is the range of the amounts collected?

Money collected from washer

[1-3]

---

For use after page 19:

For Exercises 1–8, use the data given at the right.

1. Make a frequency table.

2. Make a histogram.

3. Which mass has the greatest number of students?

4. How many students are at least 52 kg?

### Mass in Kilograms of 31 Students

| 50 | 52 | 52 | 51 | 53 | 52 | 50 |
|----|----|----|----|----|----|----|
| 52 | 54 | 50 | 52 | 50 | 53 |    |
| 51 | 52 | 54 | 51 | 52 | 53 |    |
| 53 | 50 | 54 | 53 | 54 | 52 |    |
| 52 | 54 | 54 | 50 | 54 | 51 |    |

[1-4]

5. Find the range.

7. Find the median.

6. Find the mean.

8. Find the mode.

[1-5]

For Exercises 9–12, use the data given at the right.

9. Find the range.

10. Find the mean.

11. Find the median.

12. Find the mode.

### DATA

| 75 | 75 | 85 | 95 | 80 |
|----|----|----|----|----|
| 70 | 70 | 75 | 90 | 75 |
| 65 | 85 | 45 | 80 | 70 |
| 50 | 80 | 55 | 75 | 55 |
| 75 | 75 | 60 | 70 | 60 |
| 70 | 80 | 60 | 65 | 65 |

# Extra Practice—Chapter 2

For use after page 39:

Write each numeral as a power of 10.

**1.** 100,000             **2.** 100,000,000             **[2-1]**

Express as a single power of 10.

**3.** $10^3 \times 10^1$             **4.** $10^2 \times 10^7$

Write in expanded form, using exponents.

**5.** 9164             **6.** 51,008

Write the decimal numeral for the following:

**7.** $(6 \times 1000) + (4 \times 100) + (1 \times 10) + 8$

**8.** $(5 \times 10{,}000) + (3 \times 1000) + (0 \times 100) + (5 \times 10) + 1$

Name the place value of the underlined digit.

**9.** 656.03<u>8</u>             **10.** <u>7</u>00.5608             **[2-2]**

**11.** 0.9<u>8</u>4             **12.** <u>1</u>0.00579

Write in expanded form.

**13.** 92.46             **14.** 3.0468

Write the decimal for the expanded form.

**15.** $(6 \times 100) + (4 \times 10) + 8 + (3 \times 0.1) + (5 \times 0.01)$

**16.** $(4 \times 100) + (3 \times 10) + 1 + (5 \times 0.1) + (9 \times 0.01)$

**17.** $(5 \times 10) + (4 \times 0.01) + (3 \times 0.0001)$

Write the decimal.

**18.** twenty-four and five hundredths

**19.** three hundred and sixteen thousandths

For each exercise, draw a number line and graph the given numbers.

**20.** 0.6, 0.2, 1, 1.8             **21.** 2.4, 0, 1.7, 2.6, 0.8             **[2-3]**

Replace each __?__ with < or > to make a true statement.

**22.** 1.011 __?__ 1.101             **23.** 9.202 __?__ 9.22

**24.** 0.75 __?__ 0.55 __?__ 0.35             **25.** 8 __?__ 8.17 __?__ 8.2

Evaluate the given expression for the given replacement set.

**26.** $7 + n$; $\{0, 3, 24\}$

**27.** $y - 19$; $\{23, 56, 101\}$

**28.** $13x$; $\{4, 9, 50\}$

**29.** $t \div 27$; $\{0, 81, 135\}$

**30.** $n + 9$; $\{16, 36, 96\}$

**31.** $15k$; $\{4, 40, 400\}$

**32.** $x \div 32$; $\{32, 256, 352\}$

**33.** $93 - z$; $\{55, 93, 0\}$

For use after page 57:

Write a related equation. Find the value of $n$.

**1.** $16 + n = 23$

**2.** $n - 9 = 35$                [2-5]

**3.** $7n = 56$

**4.** $n \div 6 = 6$

**5.** $n + 28 = 51$

**6.** $9n = 99$

Replace each variable to make a true equation.

**7.** $16 \times n = 0$

**8.** $9 \times (4 + 8) = (9 \times 4) + (9 \times l)$    [2-6]

**9.** $(8 + 9) + 6 = 8 + (p + 6)$

**10.** $z \times 8 = 8 \times 7$

Add or subtract.

**11.** $63.583 + 8.09$

**12.** $27.0564 + 281.4$           [2-7]

**13.** $2.4 + 3.183 + 9$

**14.** $4 + 0.463 + 43.4$

**15.** $83.407 - 29.49$

**16.** $85.604 - 85.2$

Multiply.

**17.** $9.1 \times 2.94$

**18.** $0.73 \times 0.18$           [2-8]

**19.** $8.74 \times 0.008$

**20.** $7.029 \times 3.3$

**21.** $0.364 \times 0.29$

**22.** $2.47 \times 24.7$

Divide. If the division is not exact, round the quotient to the nearest hundredth.

**23.** $130.24 \div 16.2$

**24.** $151.29 \div 12.3$          [2-9]

**25.** $2.0506 \div 0.24$

**26.** $328.865 \div 9.01$

**27.** $25.26 \div 1.06$

**28.** $2.8927 \div 2.8$

Solve.

**29.** A bicycle trail is 19.2 km long. Last week Frank rode the trail 6 times. How far    [2-10]
did he ride?

**30.** Joy commutes to work by bus at a cost of $1.50 and goes home by train at a cost
of $2.10. How much does it cost for her to commute each day?

**31.** During a flood, a river reached a high-water mark of 4.8 m. This was 1.9 m higher
than the record high. What was the record high before this flood?

**32.** Fran Johnson bought a camera for $17.65. She gave the clerk a $20 bill. How
much did she receive in change?

# Extra Practice—Chapter 3

For use after page 81:

Show the graph of the opposite of the given number on a number line.
1. 5
2. ⁻8
3. ⁻6
4. 1
5. 10
6. ⁻10

[3-1]

Write the missing number.
7. If $n = {}^-5$,
   then $-n = $ __?__
8. If $-n = 8$,
   then $n = $ __?__
9. If $-n = 4$,
   then $n = $ __?__
10. If $-n = {}^-7$,
    then $n = $ __?__
11. If $n = 0$,
    then $-n = $ __?__
12. If $-n = {}^-1$,
    then $n = $ __?__

Graph the numbers on a number line.
13. $1, {}^-1.5, 0, {}^-2$
14. $^-5, 5, {}^-4, 1$
15. $^-2, {}^-4, 2.5, {}^-3.5$
16. $3, 1.2, {}^-2.4, {}^-5$
17. $1, 1.5, {}^-2, 2.5$
18. $0, {}^-1, 2, {}^-3$

[3-2]

19. Draw an arrow starting at the graph of ⁻4 to represent the number 5.
20. Draw an arrow starting at the graph of 6 to represent the number ⁻8.
21. Draw an arrow with endpoint at the graph of ⁻5 to represent the number 6.
22. Draw an arrow with endpoint at the graph of 3 to represent the number ⁻6.

Complete.
23. $2.7 + 7.2 = $ __?__
24. $^-4.9 + {}^-7.6 = $ __?__
25. $^-3.8 + {}^-3.8 = $ __?__
26. $^-148 + {}^-256 = $ __?__
27. __?__ $+ {}^-2.3 = {}^-2.9$
28. $18.12 + $ __?__ $= 19.78$
29. $^-2.8 + {}^-3.9 = $ __?__
30. $1.9 + 19 = $ __?__
31. $^-3.7 + $ __?__ $= {}^-5$
32. __?__ $+ 19.14 = 19.45$

[3-3]

33. $^-8 + 6 = $ __?__
34. $6.1 + {}^-2.3 = $ __?__
35. $9 + {}^-12 = $ __?__
36. $^-5.2 + 2.9 = $ __?__
37. $4.1 + $ __?__ $= 0$
38. $^-14.75 + 9.94 = $ __?__
39. $^-2.25 + $ __?__ $= 0$
40. $4.038 + {}^-6 = $ __?__

[3-4]

For use after page 97:

Find the given difference.

**1.** $30 - 18$                     **2.** $16 - 24$                     [3-5]
**3.** $^-3 + {}^+8$                 **4.** $^-42 + {}^+31$
**5.** $43 + {}^+136$                **6.** $^-17 - 49$
**7.** $15 + {}^+3$                  **8.** $12 - 48$

Write two differences corresponding to each equation.

**9.** $12 + {}^-8 = 4$              **10.** $7 + 14 = 21$
**11.** $^-27 + 19 = {}^-8$          **12.** $^-33 + 49 = 16$
**13.** $^-30 + {}^-12 = {}^-42$     **14.** $^-57 + 49 = {}^-8$
**15.** $^-26 + 16 = {}^-10$         **16.** $^-46 + 19 = {}^-27$

Write the given difference as a sum.

**17.** $6.5 - {}^-1.3$              **18.** $^-3.1 - {}^-6.1$            [3-6]
**19.** $2.3 - 4.4$                  **20.** $^-31.2 - 4.3$
**21.** $44.4 - 57.6$                **22.** $28.9 - {}^-35.6$
**23.** $2.56 - {}^-9.83$            **24.** $30.01 - 18.87$

Find the given difference.

**25.** $33 - 19$                    **26.** $13 - 18$
**27.** $^-43 - 17$                  **28.** $25 - {}^-38$
**29.** $6.4 - {}^-2.9$              **30.** $^-2.6 - 4.9$
**31.** $^-8.7 - {}^-9.8$            **32.** $0.25 - 18.13$

Find the product.

**33.** $4(-26)$                     **34.** $-76(-6)$                   [3-7]
**35.** $-12(12)$                    **36.** $19(-8)$
**37.** $-10(-13 + 13)$              **38.** $-8(-6 - 8)$
**39.** $(-12 + 4)(7 - 8)$           **40.** $(8 - 10)(10 - 8)$

**41.** $2.4(-1.2)$                  **42.** $-1.4(3.4)$                 [3-8]
**43.** $-8.2(-6.1)$                 **44.** $-4.3(-3.4)$
**45.** $-2.15(1.15)$                **46.** $3.14(-8.1)$
**47.** $-4.25(-3.14)$               **48.** $1.11(-1.11)$

Simplify.

**49.** $-36 \div 9$                 **50.** $-65 \div (-5)$             [3-9]
**51.** $3.06 \div (-1.7)$           **52.** $-6.4 \div 0.8$
**53.** $(-43.16 \div 8.3) \div (-5.2)$   **54.** $(0.5)(-4.3) \div (-5)(-0.8)$
**55.** $(2.5)(-3.4) \div (-2.5)(1.7)$    **56.** $(-1.01)(-1.11) \div (1.25)(-0.1)$

# Extra Practice—Chapter 4

For use after page 120.

Complete.

**1.** $6 \times \underline{\phantom{?}?\phantom{?}} = 1$

**2.** $11 \div 12 = \underline{\phantom{?}?\phantom{?}}$

**3.** $3\frac{8}{9} = \frac{?}{9}$

**4.** $5\frac{7}{16} = \frac{?}{16}$

**5.** $\frac{19}{8} = \underline{\phantom{?}?\phantom{?}}$

**6.** $\frac{44}{7} = \underline{\phantom{?}?\phantom{?}}$

[4-1]

Write each fraction in two other ways.

**7.** $-\frac{4}{9}$

**8.** $-\frac{3}{7}$

**9.** $-\frac{5}{6}$

**10.** $-\frac{9}{10}$

[4-2]

Complete.

**11.** $-3\frac{3}{8} = \frac{?}{8}$

**12.** $-\frac{25}{4} = \underline{\phantom{?}?\phantom{?}}$

**13.** $-10\frac{7}{9} = \frac{?}{9}$

**14.** $-\frac{35}{6} = \underline{\phantom{?}?\phantom{?}}$

**15.** Give two fractions equal to $-\frac{11}{13}$.

**16.** Give two fractions equal to $-\frac{15}{16}$.

[4-3]

Reduce each fraction to lowest terms.

**17.** $\frac{32}{28}$

**18.** $-\frac{48}{54}$

**19.** $\frac{95}{145}$

**20.** $-\frac{63}{81}$

**21.** $\frac{180}{210}$

**22.** $-\frac{144}{96}$

Compute each product.

**23.** $-\frac{3}{4} \times \frac{4}{5}$

**24.** $\frac{21}{56} \times \frac{20}{25}$

**25.** $\frac{7}{8} \times \left(-\frac{4}{7}\right)$

**26.** $\frac{13}{27} \times \frac{81}{78}$

**27.** $-\frac{9}{14} \times \frac{18}{45}$

**28.** $-\frac{15}{16} \times \left(-\frac{56}{25}\right)$

**29.** $-\frac{21}{52} \times \left(-\frac{13}{15}\right)$

**30.** $6\frac{3}{4} \times \left(-1\frac{1}{3}\right)$

**31.** $-2\frac{5}{8} \times \left(-\frac{16}{19}\right)$

**32.** $-4\frac{2}{7} \times 2\frac{1}{4}$

[4-4]

For use after page 137.

Replace each set of fractions with equal fractions having the least common denominator (LCD).

1. $\frac{3}{4}, \frac{5}{6}$

2. $-\frac{8}{9}, \frac{7}{15}$ [4-5]

3. $-\frac{3}{7}, -\frac{2}{5}$

4. $\frac{5}{8}, -\frac{1}{6}$

5. $\frac{1}{4}, \frac{7}{12}, \frac{5}{18}$

6. $-\frac{1}{2}, \frac{3}{7}, \frac{5}{6}$

Express the sum or difference as a proper fraction in lowest terms or as a mixed number with fraction in lowest terms.

7. $\frac{5}{9} + \left(-\frac{1}{4}\right)$

8. $-\frac{9}{14} - \frac{5}{32}$ [4-6]

9. $3\frac{5}{7} - 2\frac{1}{3}$

10. $-4\frac{7}{12} + 2\frac{4}{5}$

11. $2\frac{7}{12} + \frac{1}{5} + 1\frac{1}{6}$

12. $3\frac{9}{14} - \left(-\frac{19}{21}\right)$

Divide. Express all results in lowest terms.

13. $\frac{4}{7} \div \frac{9}{20}$

14. $-\frac{11}{13} \div \left(-\frac{23}{52}\right)$ [4-7]

15. $-16 \div 2\frac{10}{11}$

16. $3\frac{5}{6} \div \left(-1\frac{5}{12}\right)$

17. $-\frac{5}{6} \div 4\frac{1}{2}$

18. $3\frac{5}{9} \div (-32)$

Express as a fraction or a mixed number in lowest terms.

19. 1.34

20. −1.75 [4-8]

21. 2.05

22. −3.025

23. 0.008

24. −0.048

Express as a terminating or repeating decimal.

25. $\frac{7}{4}$

26. $\frac{9}{2}$

27. $-\frac{21}{22}$

28. $\frac{7}{16}$

29. $-\frac{161}{189}$

30. $-\frac{287}{385}$

# Extra Practice—Chapter 5

For use after page 152.

Write each ratio as a fraction in lowest terms.

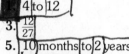

1. 4 to 12
2. 9 to 6       **[5-1]**
3. $\frac{12}{27}$
4. $\frac{175}{75}$
5. 10 months to 2 years
6. 3 kL to 90 L
7. 45 min to 2 h
8. 55 cm to 1 m

Tell whether or not the proportion is correct.

9. $\frac{2}{3} = \frac{6}{7}$
10. $\frac{4}{9} = \frac{24}{54}$
11. $\frac{10}{11} = \frac{20}{21}$
12. $\frac{8}{7} = \frac{9}{8}$       **[5-2]**
13. $\frac{11}{22} = \frac{44}{88}$
14. $\frac{21}{27} = \frac{7}{9}$

Solve the proportion.

15. $\frac{n}{4} = \frac{12}{9}$
16. $\frac{21}{n} = \frac{7}{12}$
17. $\frac{15}{2} = \frac{n}{5}$
18. $\frac{60}{48} = \frac{10}{n}$
19. $\frac{6}{5} = \frac{n}{35}$
20. $\frac{25}{31} = \frac{n}{100}$
21. $\frac{n}{90} = \frac{53}{100}$
22. $\frac{75}{3} = \frac{n}{2}$
23. $\frac{40}{n} = \frac{2}{3}$
24. $\frac{39}{2} = \frac{n}{3}$

For use after page 165.

Find the percent or number.

1. What is 5% of 60?
2. What is 15% of 84?
3. What is 8% of 24?
4. What is 40% of 75?
5. 12 is what percent of 14?
6. 11 is what percent of 11?
7. 16 is what percent of 20?
8. 20 is what percent of 15?
9. 30 is 25% of what number?
10. 8 is 45% of what number?
11. 36 is 200% of what number?
12. 29 is 87% of what number?

      **[5-3]**

Solve.

**13.** The Sport Shoppe sold 25 sets of golf clubs in May and 20% more than that in    **[5-4]**
June. How many did they sell in June?

**14.** Maggie planted 15 tomato plants. Six of the plants died. What percent of the
plants lived?

**15.** The band concert drew an audience of 275 persons on Thursday. On Friday,
50 more persons attended than on Thursday. What was the percent of increase?

**16.** Of 512 entrants in a walkathon, 32 did not finish. What was the percent of
decrease between the number of entrants and the number who finished the
walkathon?

**17.** The Flower Pot Place sold 115 lilac plants in May and 20% fewer than that in
June. How many did they sell in June?

**18.** An auctioneer receives a commission of 15% of sales. At one auction, the sales    **[5-5]**
were $13,750. What was the commission?

**19.** A potter pays an art store 25% commission to sell his pots. One set of pots sold
for $225. What commission did he pay the art store?

**20.** A real-estate agency pays its salespersons a commission of 6%. What would the
commission be on a house selling for $44,500?

**21.** A jewelry store pays its salespersons a commission of 14%. During one week the
total sales were $175,000. How much did the store pay in commissions?

**22.** A salesperson earns 8% commission on all furniture she sells. How much would
she earn for selling $2500 worth of furniture?

**23.** Tim Mayes earns a commission of 12% on what he sells. Last month his sales
totaled $14,500. How much did he earn?

**24.** A yacht salesperson worked for a commission rate of 7% of sales. Last year,
total sales were $350,000. Find the salesperson's commission for the year.

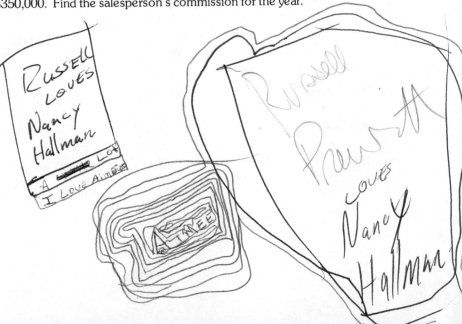

# Extra Practice—Chapter 6

For use after page 189.

Complete.

1. A segment has __?__ endpoint(s).                                                    [6-1]
2. 25 m = __?__ cm        3. 5300 m = __?__ km
4. 160 cm = __?__ mm      5. 400 mm = __?__ m

6. A chord of a circle is a __?__ joining two points of the circle.                    [6-2]
7. If the radius of a circle is 30 cm, then the circumference of the circle is __?__.
   (Use $\pi \approx 3.14$.)
8. If the radius of a circle is 3.5 cm, then the circumference of the circle is __?__.
   (Use $\pi \approx \frac{22}{7}$.)
9. If the diameter of a circle is 24, then the circumference of the circle is __?__.
   (Use $\pi \approx 3.14$.)
10. If the diameter of a circle is 14.7, then the circumference of the circle is __?__.
    (Use $\pi \approx \frac{22}{7}$.)
11. If the circumference of a circle is 26.4, then the radius of the circle is __?__.
    (Use $\pi \approx \frac{22}{7}$.)
12. If the circumference of a circle is 18.84, then the radius of the circle is __?__.
    (Use $\pi \approx 3.14$.)

13. The angles formed by bisecting an obtuse angle are both __?__.                     [6-3]
14. You can bisect an angle by using a __?__ or by using a __?__.
15. Angles with the same measure are called __?__ angles.
16. Two complementary equal angles each have measure __?__.
17. If one of two vertical angles has measure 65°, the other angle has measure __?__.
18. Perpendicular lines form __?__ angles.

19. Whenever two parallel lines are cut by a transversal, the alternate interior angles  [6-4]
    are __?__.
20. If two lines are cut by a transversal so that the corresponding angles are equal,
    then the two lines are __?__.
21. If two of the angles formed when two lines intersect have a sum of 95°, the
    sum of the measures of the other two angles is __?__.

For use after page 209.

1. If the measure of one angle of a right triangle is 60°, what are the measures of    [6-5]
   the other two angles?
2. What is true about the sides of an equilateral triangle?
3. What kind of triangle has sides 3 cm, 6 cm, and 5 cm?
4. How many acute angles does a right triangle have?

True or false? Write T or F.

5. Every rectangle is a parallelogram.    [6-6]
6. Every parallelogram is a quadrilateral.
7. Opposite sides of a trapezoid are parallel.
8. Opposite angles of a parallelogram are equal.

9. Octagons have fewer sides than hexagons.    [6-7]
10. Equilateral hexagons have seven equal sides.
11. What is the perimeter of a square with one side 65 mm?
12. If one side of a rectangle is 2.8 m long and the perimeter of the rectangle is
    17.2 m, how long are the other sides of the rectangle?
13. The perimeter of an equilateral pentagon is 131.5 cm. Find the length of each
    side.

14. If three angles of one triangle are equal to three angles of another triangle, must    [6-8]
    the triangles be congruent?
15. If two sides and the included angle of one triangle are equal to two sides and the
    included angle of another triangle, must the triangles be congruent?

Complete each statement for the
congruent triangles.

16. $\triangle DEF \cong$ __?__
17. $\angle C =$ __?__
18. $DE =$ __?__

19. Are all similar polygons also congruent polygons?    [6-9]
20. Are all triangles similar?
21. Are all equilateral triangles similar?
22. Are all quadrilaterals similar?
23. Are all isosceles trapezoids similar?
24. Are all equilateral octagons similar?

# Extra Practice—Chapter 7

For use after page 230.

Write a variable expression.

**1.** Nine less than $x$        **2.** $n$ divided by six       **[7-1]**

**3.** The difference when $z$ is subtracted from $t$

**4.** The quotient when eight is divided by $w$

Write a word phrase.

**5.** $x + 9$      **6.** $3y - 1$      **7.** $\frac{n}{4}$      **8.** $-2z - 3$

**9.** $\frac{3}{7}t$      **10.** $-x + 2$      **11.** $\frac{6}{z}$      **12.** $a - 1$

Evaluate the expressions if $z = -2$.

**13.** $-3 - z$      **14.** $\frac{1}{6}z$      **15.** $-2 + z$      **16.** $-\frac{2}{z}$      **[7-2]**

**17.** $2z - 2$      **18.** $-\frac{z}{4}$      **19.** $-3z + 3$      **20.** $2 + z$

Translate into a number sentence.

**21.** A number $x$ is the product of negative two and one half.       **[7-3]**

**22.** The quotient when $t$ is divided by negative one is twelve.

**23.** The sum of $y$ and four is less than seven.

Write a word sentence.

**24.** $2(x - 3) < 4$         **25.** $3(y - 1) \geq -4$

**26.** $5(1 - z) > -2$         **27.** $-4w - 3 \leq -5$

Tell whether or not the given number is a solution of the given open sentence.

**28.** $x - 10 > -2; 9$        **29.** $y + 1 \leq 0; -1$       **[7-4]**

**30.** $8 - 3x = -4; -4$       **31.** $-y - 1 = -1; 0$

**32.** $-2x \geq 12; -3$        **33.** $-3y \leq 0; 10$

**34.** $x < -6 - 2x; -1$       **35.** $x - 3 = 12 - 4x; 3$

Graph the solution set. The replacement set for $x$ is $\{-5, -4, -3, -2, -1, 0\}$.

**36.** $x + 2 < 0$         **37.** $x \leq 1$       **[7-5]**

**38.** $x = -4$           **39.** $x + 1 = -6$

**40.** $3 - x \leq 2$         **41.** $3x - 1 \geq 5$

**42.** $-x \geq -3$          **43.** $4x + 2 = -6$

**44.** $-x + 8 \leq 8$        **45.** $x - 4 \geq -6$

For use after page 239.

Use one of the properties of equality to form a true sentence.

1. If $x = 13$, then $x - 7 = $ ___?___
2. If $y = -3$, then $4y = $ ___?___  [7-6]
3. If $z = 5$, then $z + 3 = $ ___?___
4. If $t = 4$, then $-3t = $ ___?___
5. If $x = -11$, then $x + 4 = $ ___?___
6. If $y = 5$, then $3y = $ ___?___
7. If $z = -5$, then $-2z = $ ___?___
8. If $t = -4$, then $3 - t = $ ___?___

Solve each equation and check your solution.

9. $x + 3 = 5$
10. $y + 2 = 1$  [7-7]
11. $z - 3 = 6$
12. $t - 4 = 3$
13. $x - 5 = -7$
14. $y + 8 = -3$
15. $z + 7 = 9$
16. $t + \frac{1}{2} = \frac{1}{2}$
17. $6x = 36$
18. $-4x = 12$
19. $7z = -28$
20. $-9t = -45$
21. $\frac{2}{3}x = 4$
22. $-\frac{1}{2}x = 5$
23. $-\frac{3}{4}z = -9$
24. $\frac{5}{6}t = -15$
25. $-2 + 8 = x + 2$
26. $y + 6 = -3$
27. $z(5 - 3) = -20$
28. $t(3 - 5) = 10$
29. $x + 3x = 12$
30. $-y - 2y = -6$
31. $6z - 2z = 24$
32. $-t + (+3t) = -2$
33. $4x = 1 - 5$
34. $-3y = -2 + 13$
35. $\frac{1}{2}x = \frac{2}{3} + \frac{1}{6}$
36. $-\frac{1}{4}x = \frac{3}{4} - \frac{7}{8}$

Solve. The replacement set for $x$ is {the integers}.

37. $x - 2 > -4$
38. $x + 3 \le -4$  [7-8]
39. $x + 1 \ge -3$
40. $x - 4 < -2$
41. $x + 4 \le 4$
42. $x - 5 \ge 3$
43. $x + 5 > -1$
44. $x - 1 \le 0$
45. $x - 9 > 2$
46. $x + 6 \ge 7$
47. $20 < 4x$
48. $-25 > 5x$
49. $24 > -2x$
50. $-24 > -2x$
51. $-3x \ge 0$
52. $6x < -6$
53. $-7x \ge -70$
54. $-8x \le -80$
55. $-4 < -x$
56. $4 - 10 \le x$
57. $-x \le 1$
58. $9x > -18$
59. $-2x < -5$
60. $-3x > 7$

# Extra Practice—Chapter 8

For use after page 254.

Write two practical problems that are expressed by the given equation. For the first problem, use a simple direct question.

[8-1]

1. $x + 16 = 43$
2. $25 + x = 33$
3. $5x = 80$
4. $13x = 91$
5. $x - 9 = 36$
6. $17 - x = 11$
7. $\frac{1}{5}x = 7$
8. $\frac{2}{3}x = 12$

Write an equation that could be used to solve the problem.

[8-2]

9. The sum of 19 and some number is 41. Find the number.
10. When a certain number is subtracted from 32, the difference is 15. Find the number.
11. When 9 is subtracted from some number, the difference is 25. Find the number.
12. The sum of two numbers is 64, and one of the numbers is 14 greater than the other number. Find the numbers.
13. The sum of two numbers is 97, and one of the numbers is 56 greater than the other number. Find the numbers.
14. The perimeter of a square is 36 m. Find the length of each side.
15. The length of a rectangle is 35 cm greater than the width. The perimeter of the rectangle is 150 cm. Find the dimensions of the rectangle.

Write an equation and use it to solve the problem.

[8-3]

16. The sum of two numbers is 75, and one number is 17 greater than the other number. Find the lesser number.
17. The sum of two numbers is 53, and one number is 21 greater than the other number. Find the greater number.
18. The difference when 27 is subtracted from a number is 18. Find the number.
19. Find two consecutive integers whose sum is 43.
20. The sum of two numbers is 31, and one number is 17 greater than the other. One number is even and is 3 more than 3 times the other number, which is odd. Find the numbers.
21. Find two consecutive even integers whose sum is 46.

For use after page 263.

Solve.

1. The scale on a map of Vega City is 1 cm → 0.25 km. The distance on the map  **[8-4]**
   from the Largo Building to the Königsberg Bridge is 5.5 cm. What actual distance does this represent?

2. The scale on a map of Lasco Desert is 1 cm → 0.25 km. The distance on the
   map from Point Peso to the Verdi Oasis is 12.6 cm. What actual distance does
   this represent?

3. On a scale drawing of a rectangular-shaped table top the scale is 1 cm → 0.5 m.
   The table top measures 4 m by 3 m. What size is the drawing?

4. A map of Dallas, Texas, has the scale of 1 cm → 0.5 km. What map distance
   corresponds to an actual distance of 11 km?

5. Lee Chung deposited $800 at 6.5% interest for 2 years. What was the simple  **[8-5]**
   interest earned?

6. Gerda Cohen deposited $900 at 5.5% interest for 3 years. What was the simple
   interest earned?

7. Bob Esposito invested $2000 at 6% annual interest. How much must he invest
   at 7% annual interest for his annual income from both investments to total $470?

8. Althea Washington invested $2000 at 7% annual interest. How much must she
   invest at 6% annual interest for her annual income from both investments to
   total $410?

9. What is the annual cost of operating a 300 W color television if it is used an  **[8-6]**
   average of 4 h per day and the electric rate is 6.5¢ per kW · h?

10. A helium balloon, Double Eagle II, made the first successful balloon crossing of
    the Atlantic Ocean in August, 1978. It traveled approximately 5200 km in 137 h.
    What was its average rate of speed in kilometers per hour?

11. A pipeline system is about 1500 km long and about 0.75 m in diameter. The
    pipeline cost $3.1 billion to complete. What is the cost per kilometer?

# Extra Practice—Chapter 9

For use after page 281.

1. A square has side 8 cm. What is its area?    [9-1]
2. A rectangle has base 15 cm and height 7 cm. What is its area?
3. A parallelogram has base 7 m and height 8 m. What is its area?
4. A rectangle has area 96 cm² and base 16 cm. What is its height?
5. A square has area 64 cm². What is its perimeter?
6. A square has perimeter 32 cm. What is its area?
7. A parallelogram has area 48 cm² and height 6 cm. What is its base?
8. A rhombus has perimeter 36 m. What is its base?

9. The base of a triangle is 28 mm long and its height is 36 mm. What is its area?    [9-2]
10. The base of a triangle is 31 cm long and its height is 22 cm. What is its area?
11. A trapezoid has bases 4 m and 5 m, and height 4.6 m. What is its area?
12. A trapezoid has bases 12 cm and 19 cm, and height 14 cm. What is its area?
13. The legs of a right triangle are 6 m and 8 m. What is its area?
14. The legs of a right triangle are 21 mm and 28 mm. What is its area?
15. The area of a triangle is 18 m². The base is 6 m. What is the height?
16. The area of a triangle is 35 cm². The base is 20 cm. What is the height?

Find the area of the circle described.
17. radius = $1\frac{1}{2}$ units (Use $\pi \approx \frac{22}{7}$.)    [9-3]
18. diameter = 12 cm (Use $\pi \approx 3.14$.)
19. circumference = $20\,\pi$ (Leave answer in terms of $\pi$.)
20. Find the area of the shaded part of the figure. (Use $\pi \approx 3.14$.)

3 m

5 m

For use after page 299.

Find the volume. In Exercises 1 and 2, leave answers in terms of $\pi$.
1. A cylinder with base diameter 12 and height 8.    [9-4]
2. A cylinder with base radius 4 and height 14.
3. A prism whose base is a triangle with area 32 and whose height is 9.
4. A prism whose base is a square with area 35 and whose height is 10.
5. A cube with edge 12 cm.
6. A rectangular prism which measures 14 m by 11 m by 6 m.

7. A hexagonal pyramid with base 40 cm² and height 8 cm. [9-5]
8. A pentagonal pyramid with base 48 cm² and height 9 cm.
9. A cone whose base has radius 5 and which has height 11. (Leave answer in terms of $\pi$.)
10. A cone whose base has diameter 18 mm and whose height is 21 mm. (Leave answer in terms of $\pi$.)

11. The base of a prism is a triangle with sides 4, 6, and 7. The height of the prism [9-6]

Find the lateral area and the total surface area of each solid below.
Leave your answer to Exercise 14 in terms of $\pi$.

12.
13.
14.

Complete.
15. 4.6 L = __?__ cm³
16. 600 g = __?__ kg [9-7]
17. 850 mL = __?__ L
18. 800 cm³ = __?__ L

19. If the mass of 1 cm³ of gold is 19.3 g and of 1 cm³ of aluminum is 2.7 g, what is the difference in mass of 25 cm³ of each?

20. If the mass of 1 cm³ of milk is 1.03 g, what is the mass of 1 L of milk?
21. If the mass of 1 cm³ of gasoline is 0.66 g, what is the mass of 1 L of gasoline?
22. Find the area and volume (in terms of $\pi$) of a sphere with radius 2. [9-8]
23. What is the area of a sphere with radius 20 cm? (Use $\pi \approx 3.14$.)
24. What is the volume of a sphere with radius $\frac{3}{4}$? (Leave answer in terms of $\pi$.)
25. If the area of a sphere is $16\pi$, what is its volume in terms of $\pi$?

# Extra Practice—Chapter 10

For use after page 317.

Is the experiment random?

1. You choose a frozen yogurt from 6 flavors available at a shop.

**[10-1]**

2. You spin a spinner with 8 possible outcomes.
3. You choose a one-dollar bill, a five-dollar bill, a ten-dollar bill, and a twenty-dollar bill from a container.
4. You choose 1 card from a standard deck of 52 cards.

Write the number of possible outcomes and the probability of each outcome.

5. A letter is randomly chosen from $a$, $b$, $c$, $d$, $e$, and $f$.
6. A marble is drawn at random from a hat containing a red, a green, a white, and a yellow marble.
7. A tag is drawn at random from a bag containing a white, a blue, an orange, a black, a red, and a green tag.
8. One card is drawn at random from a standard deck of 52 cards.
9. One marble is chosen at random from a bag with 8 differently colored marbles.
10. One team is selected from 14 teams.
11. The pointer on a spinner stops at one of the numbers 1, 2, 3, or 4.
12. The pointer on a spinner stops at one of the letters $a$, $b$, $c$, or $d$.
13. A penny and a nickel are tossed.
14. A penny, a nickel, and a dime are tossed.

The letters of the word *mathematics* are written on 11 cards. If a card is drawn at random, what is the probability of drawing:

| | | |
|---|---|---|
| 15. an $m$? | 16. an $a$? | **[10-2]** |
| 17. an $i$? | 18. a $t$? | |
| 19. an $e$? | 20. a $d$? | |
| 21. an $a$ or an $e$? | 22. an $m$ or a $t$? | |
| 23. an $a$, an $s$, or an $m$? | 24. an $a$, an $m$, or a $t$? | |

Jesse has 8 tape cassettes in her car. One cassette stars the Rockers, 2 star Clarence Klow, 3 star Sue and the Stompers, and 2 star Queen Quigley. Jesse selects a cassette at random. What are the odds:

25. in favor of selecting a cassette by Clarence?

**[10-3]**

26. against selecting a cassette by Sue and the Stompers?

For use after page 327.

Answer the question asked. Base your answer on the evidence given in the problem.

1. Ray has 15 hits out of 27 times at bat. What is the probability that he will make a hit the next time at bat?                                                                          **[10-4]**

2. A train arrived on time 4 out of the past 7 days. What is the probability that it will not be on time tomorrow?

3. A wrestler has won 7 of his last 8 matches. What is the probability that he will win his next match?

4. A meteorologist has predicted the weather correctly 865 times out of 1000. What is the probability she will be correct the next time?

An inspector on an assembly line chose 200 condensers at random out of 4000 condensers. He found that 6 of the 200 condensers were defective.

5. What is the probability that a consumer will get a defective condenser?                    **[10-5]**

6. What is the probability that a consumer will not get a defective condenser?

7. About how many defective condensers would you expect to find in the 4000 condensers?

8. If you randomly choose a condenser, what are the odds against your getting a defective condenser?

9. If you randomly choose a condenser, what are the odds for your getting a condenser that is not defective?

# Extra Practice—Chapter 11

For use after page 343.

**1.** Name the graph of each ordered pair:

| | |
|---|---|
| **a.** (1,6) | **b.** (5,0) |
| **c.** (6,1) | **d.** (−3,4) |
| **e.** (−3,−5) | **f.** (4,−5) |
| **g.** (0,0) | **h.** (−5,−4) |
| **i.** (−6,3) | **j.** **(6,6)** |
| **k.** **(2,−3)** | **l.** (2,2) |
| **m.** (−6,0) | **n.** (0,−6) |
| **o.** (6,−2) | **p.** (−2,−2) |
| **q.** (0,4) | **r.** (4,5) |
| **s.** (4,−1) | **t.** (−4,6) |

[11-1]

On a coordinate plane, **a.** sketch the polygon whose vertexes are given and **b.** find the area of the polygon.

**2.** (3,3), (−3,−3), (3,−3), (−3,3)

**3.** (3,4), (−2,4), (−2,−2), (3,−2)

**4.** (0,5), (3,−3), (−3,−3)

**5.** (−3,−1), (−3,2), (6,2), (6,−1)

**6.** (0,5), (5,5), (5,−2)

**7.** (1,1), (4,4), (1,4), (4,1)

**8.** (2,−1), (6,−1), (6,−5), (2,−5)

Exercises 9–14 refer to the figure at the right.

**9.** Write the coordinates of the given points:

[11-2]

| | | |
|---|---|---|
| **a.** M | **b.** A | **c.** S |
| **d.** C | **e.** P | **f.** R |
| **g.** B | **h.** Q | **i.** E |
| **j.** H | **k.** D | **l.** G |

**10.** Name all points shown whose ordinates are negative.

**11.** Name all points shown whose abscissas are 0.

**12.** Name all points shown in Quadrant IV.

**13.** Name all points shown on the x-axis.

**14.** Name all points shown whose ordinates are 0.

For use after page 355.

State whether or not the given ordered pair is a solution of the equation.

**1.** $(3,1)$, $2x + y = 5$        **2.** $(-1,4)$, $x - 2y = -9$

**3.** $(-2,-2)$, $y - 3x = 4$        **4.** $(-2,-2)$, $y - 3x = -4$

**5.** $(0,-3)$, $3x - 2y = -6$        **6.** $(-3,0)$, $2x - 3y = -6$

**7.** $(5,-2)$, $x - y = 3$        **8.** $(-4,-3)$, $3x + 2y = 18$

Give an equivalent equation for y in terms of x.

**9.** $3x + 2y = 6$        **10.** $2y - 3x = -6$

**11.** $2x - 4y = 2$        **12.** $3y - 5x = 10$

**13.** $4x + 5y = 0$        **14.** $y - 6x = 12$

**15.** $3y = 4x - 12$        **16.** $3x + 9 = 6y$

Find ordered pairs of the form $(x,0)$ and $(0,y)$ that are solutions of the given equation.

**17.** $x + y = 2$        **18.** $x + y = -3$

**19.** $x - y = -1$        **20.** $x + 2y = 4$

**21.** $2x - y = 4$        **22.** $3x + 2y = 6$

**23.** $-3x + 4y = 12$        **24.** $4y - 5x = -10$

Graph each equation on a coordinate plane. Use a separate set of axes for each equation.

**25.** $x - 2y = 3$        **26.** $x = -2$

**27.** $2x + 3y = 6$        **28.** $y = 1$

**29.** $3x - y = 3$        **30.** $y = x - 3$

**31.** $2x = y - 2$        **32.** $4x - 2y = 3$

Solve each system by graphing. If no solution exists, say so.

**33.** $2x - y = 0$
    $x + y = -3$        **34.** $2x - 4y = 6$
                      $x = 5$

**35.** $y - 2x = -3$
    $y - 2x = 3$        **36.** $2x + 3y = 5$
                      $x - y = 0$

**37.** $2x + y = 4$
    $x - 2y = -8$        **38.** $3x + 3y = 4$
                      $x + 6y = 3$

**39.** $3x + y = 2$
    $3x + y = 3$        **40.** $-2x + y = 5$
                      $x + y = -1$

**41.** $2x + 3y = -10$
    $2x + y = -6$        **42.** $x - 2y = 0$
                      $2x + y = 5$

# Extra Practice—Chapter 12

For use after page 370.

Name the two consecutive integers between which the square root lies.

1. $\sqrt{8}$      2. $\sqrt{2}$      3. $\sqrt{7}$      [12-1]

4. $\sqrt{12}$      5. $\sqrt{19}$      6. $\sqrt{22}$

7. $\sqrt{27}$      8. $\sqrt{33}$      9. $\sqrt{39}$

10. $\sqrt{60}$      11. $\sqrt{43}$      12. $\sqrt{73}$

13. $\sqrt{58}$      14. $\sqrt{80}$      15. $\sqrt{78}$

State the next estimate for the square root of the dividend.

16. $5\overline{)28.0}$   (5.6)    17. $8\overline{)57.0}$   (7.1)    18. $6\overline{)37.0}$   (6.1)    [12-2]

19. $4\overline{)15.0}$   (3.7)    20. $9\overline{)70.0}$   (7.7)    21. $7\overline{)59.0}$   (8.4)

22. $8\overline{)71.0}$   (8.8)    23. $6\overline{)40.0}$   (6.6)    24. $5\overline{)33.0}$   (6.6)

25. $9\overline{)83.0}$   (9.2)    26. $7\overline{)62.0}$   (8.8)    27. $6\overline{)44.0}$   (7.3)

Find each square root to the tenths' place. (Do not use the square-root table.)

28. $\sqrt{10}$      29. $\sqrt{17}$      30. $\sqrt{24}$

31. $\sqrt{29}$      32. $\sqrt{31}$      33. $\sqrt{82}$

34. $\sqrt{90}$      35. $\sqrt{37}$      36. $\sqrt{48}$

37. $\sqrt{87}$      38. $\sqrt{75}$      39. $\sqrt{94}$

Use the table on page 394 to approximate each number to the nearest hundredth.

40. $\sqrt{14}$      41. $\sqrt{28}$      42. $\sqrt{35}$      [12-3]

43. $\sqrt{43}$      44. $\sqrt{53}$      45. $\sqrt{83}$

46. $2\sqrt{6}$      47. $3\sqrt{5}$      48. $4\sqrt{3}$

49. $8\sqrt{19}$      50. $6\sqrt{41}$      51. $10\sqrt{8}$

52. $2\sqrt{76}$      53. $10\sqrt{3}$      54. $10\sqrt{24}$

55. $\sqrt{21} - \sqrt{19}$      56. $\sqrt{37} - \sqrt{27}$      57. $\sqrt{8} - \sqrt{3}$

58. $\sqrt{10} + \sqrt{10}$      59. $\sqrt{13} + \sqrt{8}$      60. $\sqrt{27} + \sqrt{2}$

For use after page 385.

State whether or not a triangle with sides of the given lengths is a right triangle.

**1.** 3, 4, 5                          **2.** 30, 40, 50          [12-4]

**3.** 8, 15, 17                        **4.** 8, 10, 12

**5.** 6, 8, 10                         **6.** 10, 20, 24

A right triangle has sides of lengths $a$, $b$, and $c$, with $c$ the length of the hypotenuse.
Find the length of the missing side to the nearest hundredth.

**7.** $a = 3$, $b = 4$               **8.** $a = 10$, $b = 20$

**9.** $a = 5$, $b = 5$               **10.** $a = 3$, $b = 6$

**11.** $a = 6$, $b = 8$              **12.** $a = 7$, $b = 9$

Find an approximation to the nearest hundredth for $x$.

**13.**      **14.**      **15.**      [12-5]

**16.**      **17.**      **18.**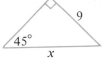

Use the diagram to name each ratio.

**19.** $\tan A$                        **20.** $\sin A$          [12-6]

**21.** $\cos A$                        **22.** $\tan B$

**23.** $\cos B$                        **24.** $\sin B$

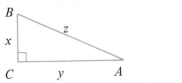

Refer to the diagram at the right.

**25.** Which equation is incorrectly written?          [12-7]

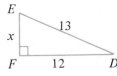

   **a.** $\cos D = \frac{12}{13}$        **b.** $\sin E = \frac{12}{13}$

   **c.** $\cos E = \frac{13}{12}$        **d.** $\tan E = \frac{12}{x}$

   **e.** $\sin D = \frac{x}{13}$

**26.** Find the value of $x$.

**27.** Find $\angle D$ to the nearest degree.

**28.** Find $\angle E$ to the nearest degree.

# Glossary

**Abscissa** (p. 340) The first number in an ordered pair of numbers which are coordinates assigned to a point in the plane. Also called the *x*-coordinate.

**Absolute value of a number** (p. 80) The absolute value of a number *a*, denoted by $|a|$, equals *a* if *a* is positive or zero and equals the opposite of *a* if *a* is negative.

**Acute angle** (p. 180) An angle between 0° and 90°.

**Acute triangle** (p. 190) A triangle with three acute angles.

**Alternate interior angles** (p. 185) One of two pairs of angles formed when two lines are cut by a transversal. In the diagram, $\angle 3$ and $\angle 6$ are one such pair, and $\angle 4$ and $\angle 5$ the other.

**Angle** (p. 180) A figure formed by two rays with a common endpoint.

**Arc of a circle** (p. 177) A portion of a circle which joins two points on the circle.

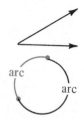

**Area** (p. 271) Amount of interior surface of a geometric figure.

**Associative property** (p. 42) Changing the grouping of addends in a sum, or of factors in a product, does not change the sum or product. For any numbers *a, b,* and *c,*
$a + (b + c) = (a + b) + c$ and $a \times (b \times c) = (a \times b) \times c.$

**Bar graph** (p. 5) A graph in which the length of each bar is proportional to the number it represents.

**Base, numerical** (p. 27) A number which is raised to some power. In $10^4$, 10 is the base.

**Base of a geometric figure** See names of specific figures.

**Beaufort scale** (p. 12) A scale which assigns the numbers 0 through 12 to various ranges of wind speeds.

**Binary system** (p. 60) The place value numeration system in which a number is expressed as a sum of powers of two.

**Bisector of an angle** (p. 181) A ray which divides an angle into two equal angles.

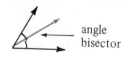

**Chord** (p. 177) A line segment joining two points of a circle.

**Circle** (p. 177) A plane figure whose points are all the same distance from a given point in the plane, called the *center* of the circle.

**Circumference** (p. 177) The distance around a circle.

**Common denominator** (p. 121) A common multiple of the denominators of two or more fractions.

**Commutative property** (p. 42) Changing the order of addends in a sum, or of factors in a product, does not change the sum or product. For any numbers *a* and *b,*
$a + b = b + a$ and $a \times b = b \times a.$

**Complementary angles** (p. 180) Two angles whose sum is 90°.

**Cone** (p. 286) If a point which is not in the plane of a circle is joined by line segments to each point of the circle, the solid formed is a cone.

424

**Congruent polygons** (p. 201) Polygons which have the same size and same shape.

**Coordinate** (p. 34) The number paired with a point on the number line.

**Coordinates of a point** (p. 340) An ordered pair of numbers assigned to a given point in the plane.

**Corresponding angles** (p. 185) One of four pairs of angles formed when two lines are cut by a transversal. The corresponding angles shown are $\angle 1$ and $\angle 5$, $\angle 2$ and $\angle 6$, $\angle 3$ and $\angle 7$, and $\angle 4$ and $\angle 8$.

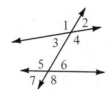

**Corresponding parts** (p. 201) Parts of two polygons which are paired in a one-to-one correspondence.

**Cosine of an angle** (p. 380) If $\angle A$ is one of the acute angles in a right triangle, the cosine of $\angle A$ ($\cos A$) is the ratio of the length of the side adjacent to $\angle A$ to the length of the hypotenuse.

$$\cos A = \frac{b}{c}$$

**Cylinder** (p. 282) A solid with two parallel bases that are congruent circles and one curved lateral face.

base

**Decibel** (p. 23) A unit for measuring the level of sound.

**Decimal system** (p. 28) The number system which is based on powers of ten.

**Diameter of a circle** (p. 177) A chord which contains the center of a circle. Also, the length of such a chord.

diameter

**Distributive property** (p. 43) For any numbers $a, b, c, a(b + c) = ab + ac$.

**Endpoint** (p. 173) A boundary point of a line segment or ray.

endpoint

**Equation** (p. 222) A number sentence in which two number phrases are connected by the symbol "$=$."

**Equator** (p. 358) The great circle on Earth whose plane is perpendicular to the axis. It separates Earth into the Northern and Southern Hemispheres.

**Equilateral polygon** (p. 197) A polygon with all sides equal.

**Equilateral triangle** (p. 190) A triangle with all sides equal.

**Equivalent equations** (p. 234) Equations which have the same solutions.

**Equivalent inequalities** (p. 237) Inequalities which have the same solutions.

**Evaluate an expression** (p. 37) To replace a variable in an expression with one of its values and then complete the indicated arithmetic.

**Expected value of a random variable** (p. 324) To find the expected value of a random variable, multiply each possible value by its probability and add the results.

**Experimental probability of an event** (p. 318) The number of times an event occurs divided by the number of times the experiment is performed.

**Event** (p. 310) A collection of possible outcomes of an experiment.

**Exponent** (p. 27) A number which indicates the power to which the base is to be raised.

**Factor** (p. 27) Any of two or more numbers which are multiplied to form a product.

**Frequency polygon** (p. 16) A broken-line graph connecting the midpoints of the tops of the bars of a histogram.

**Graph of an equation** (p. 348) The line consisting of all points whose coordinates satisfy the equation.

**Graph of a number** (p. 34) The point on the number line paired with the number.

**Great circle** (p. 358) The intersection of a sphere with a plane passing through the center of the sphere.

**Histogram** (p. 14) A bar graph that displays numerical data which have been organized into equal intervals.

**Hypotenuse** (p. 371) The side of a right triangle which is opposite the right angle.

**Improper fraction** (p. 105) A fraction in which the numerator is greater than or equal to the denominator.

**Inequality** (p. 222) A number sentence in which the two phrases are connected by an inequality symbol.

**Integers** (p. 66) The set of whole numbers and their opposites: $\{\ldots, -2, -1, 0, 1, 2, \ldots\}$

**Inverse operations** (p. 40) Adding a number and subtracting the same number are inverse operations. Similarly, multiplying by a number and dividing by the same number are inverse operations.

**Isosceles right triangle** (p. 375) A right triangle in which the two legs are equal.

**Isosceles trapezoid** (p. 194) A trapezoid in which the non-parallel sides are equal.

**Isosceles triangle** (p. 190) A triangle having at least two sides equal.

**Lateral area of a prism or cylinder** (pp. 290, 291) The surface area not including the bases.

**Lateral edge of a pyramid** (p. 285) An edge of a pyramid which does not belong to the base.

**Lateral face of a pyramid or prism** (pp. 285, 290) A face which is not a base.

**Latitude** (p. 358) The number of degrees between 0° and 90° that a place is north or south of the equator.

**Least common denominator (LCD)** (p. 121) The least common multiple of the denominators of two or more fractions.

**Least common multiple (LCM)** (p. 121) The least positive number that is a multiple of two or more given numbers.

**Line** (p. 173) A line segment extended without end in both directions.

**Line segment** (p. 173) A part of a line consisting of two endpoints and all the points between them.

**Longitude** (p. 358) The number of degrees between 0° and 180° that any place is east or west of the prime meridian.

**Lowest terms** (for fractions) (p. 113) A fraction whose numerator and denominator have no common factor except 1 is said to be in lowest terms.

**Mass** (p. 293) Quantity of matter.

**Mean** (p. 17) The sum of a set of numbers divided by the number of numbers in the set.

**Median** (p. 17) In a set of numbers arranged in increasing order, the median is the middle number if there is an odd number of numbers. If the number of numbers is even, the median is the mean of the two middle numbers.

**Metric system** (p. 54) A system of measurement based on powers of ten.

**Mixed number** (p. 105) A whole number and a fraction.

**Mode** (p. 17) The number which occurs most frequently in a set of data.

**Multiple** (p. 121) The product of a given number and a whole number.

**Napier's rods** (p. 388) A computing device invented by John Napier (1550–1617) in order to calculate products.

**Negative numbers** (p. 66) Numbers graphed to the left of the zero reference point on a horizontal number line.

**Nonrepeating decimal** (p. 140) A decimal in which the digits do not exhibit a repeating pattern.

**Obtuse angle** (p. 180) An angle between 90° and 180°.

**Obtuse triangle** (p. 190) A triangle which contains an obtuse angle.

**Odds** (p. 313) The ratio of the probability of an event occurring to the probability of the event not occurring is called the odds in favor of the event.

**Open sentence** (p. 222) A sentence that contains a variable, such as $2p - 1 > 5$.

**Opposite numbers** (p. 66) Two numbers whose sum is zero are opposites.

**Ordered pair of numbers** (p. 335) A pair of numbers in which one is designated as the first component and the other as the second component.

**Ordinate** (p. 340) The second number in an ordered pair of numbers which are coordinates assigned to a point in the plane. Also called the $y$- coordinate.

**Origin** (p. 34) The point on the number line whose coordinate is zero. The zero reference point.

**Parallel lines** (p. 185) Lines in the same plane which do not intersect.

**Parallelogram** (p. 194) A quadrilateral with opposite sides parallel. Any side of a parallelogram can be considered as the *base*.

**Perfect square** (p. 364) An integer whose square root is also an integer.

**Perimeter of a polygon** (p. 197) The sum of the lengths of the sides of the polygon.

**Perpendicular lines** (p. 180) Lines that intersect to form $90°$ angles.

**Pictograph** (p. 22) A graph which uses visual symbols to represent data.

**Point** (p. 173) A mathematical figure which can be pictured by a dot.

**Polygon** (p. 197) A closed plane figure formed by connecting line segments at their endpoints.

**Positive numbers** (p. 66) Numbers graphed to the right of the zero reference point on a horizontal number line.

**Power** (p. 27) A product of equal factors.

**Prime factorization** (p. 122) The representation of a whole number greater than zero as the product of primes.

**Prime number** (p. 122) A whole number greater than 0 having only two factors, itself and one.

**Prism** (p. 282) If two congruent polygons are placed in parallel planes so that their corresponding sides are parallel and their corresponding vertexes are joined by line segments, the solid formed is called a prism.

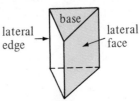

**Probability** (p. 307) A number between, and including, 0 and 1 which measures how likely it is that an event will occur.

**Proper fraction** (p. 105) A fraction in which the numerator is smaller than the denominator.

**Property of one in multiplication** (p. 43) The product of one and any given number $a$ is the given number. That is, $1 \times a = a$.

**Property of zero in addition** (p. 42) Zero added to any number $a$ gives the sum $a$; that is, $0 + a = a$.

**Property of zero in multiplication** (p. 42) The product of any number and zero is zero. That is, $0 \times a = 0$.

**Protractor** (p. 180) An angle-measuring device.

**Pythagorean property** (p. 371) For any right triangle, the square of the length of the hypotenuse is equal to the sum of the squares of the lengths of the other two sides.

**Pythagorean triples** (p. 374) Any three counting numbers $a, b, c$ which satisfy the equation $a^2 + b^2 = c^2$.

**Quadrant** (p. 340) One of the four regions into which the axes of rectangular coordinate system separate the plane.

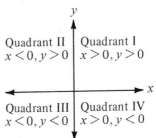

**Quadrilateral** (p. 194) A four-sided polygon.

**Radius** (p. 177) A segment joining any point of a circle to the center of the circle. Also, the length of such a segment.

radius

**Random experiment** (p. 307) An experiment in which the outcome is a matter of chance.

**Random sample** (p. 320) A sample in which each member of the population is equally likely to appear.

**Random variable** (p. 323) A variable whose value is determined by the outcome of a random experiment.

**Range of a set of data** (p. 17) The difference between the greatest number and the least number in the set.

**Rational number** (p. 110) Any number which can be represented as the quotient $\frac{a}{b}$ of two integers $a$ and $b$, $b$ not zero.

**Ray** (p. 173) A line segment extended without end in one direction only.

**Reciprocal** (p. 130) For all rational numbers $a$ and $b$, if $ab = 1$, then $a$ is the reciprocal of $b$ and $b$ is the reciprocal of $a$.

**Rectangle** (p. 194) A parallelogram which contains a right angle.

**Rectangular coordinate system** (p. 335) A system which consists of two number lines perpendicular to each other and intersecting at the origin of each. It is used to assign coordinates to points in the plane.

**Repeating decimal** (p. 133) A decimal in which a pattern of digits repeats without end.

**Repetend** (p. 133) The repeating part of a repeating decimal.

**Replacement set for a variable** (p. 37) The set of numbers which may be used to replace the variable.

**Rhombus** (p. 194) A quadrilateral with all sides equal.

**Right angle** (p. 180) A 90° angle.

**Right triangle** (p. 190) A triangle which contains a right angle.

**Scalene triangle** (p. 190) A triangle in which no two sides are equal.

**Scientific notation** (p. 100) The system of representing any positive number as the product of a power of ten and a number between 1 and 10.

**Semicircle** (p. 177) An arc which joins the endpoints of a diameter.

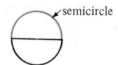
semicircle

**Side of an angle** (p. 180) One of the rays of an angle.

**Similar polygons** (p. 206) Polygons which have the same shape.

**Sine of $\angle A$** (p. 379) For an acute angle $A$ of a right triangle, the sine of $\angle A$ (sin $A$) is the ratio of the length of the side opposite $\angle A$ to the length of the hypotenuse.

**Solution of an open sentence** (p. 225) A value of a variable which yields a true statement.

**Solution set of an open sentence** (p. 227) The set of all values in the replacement set which are solutions.

**Solving a right triangle** (p. 382) The process of finding the measures of the sides and angles of a right triangle.

**Sphere** (p. 296) The set of all points in space which are a given distance from a fixed point.

**Square** (p. 194) A parallelogram with all sides equal and four right angles.

**Square root** (pp. 128, 363) If $a^2 = n$, then $a$ is a square root of $n$.

**Supplementary angles** (p. 180) Two angles whose sum is 180°.

**System of equations** (p. 352) A set of two or more equations in the same variables.

**Tangent of $\angle A$** (p. 380) For an acute angle $A$ of a right triangle, the tangent of $A$ (tan $A$) is the ratio of the length of the side opposite angle $A$ to the length of the side adjacent to angle $A$.

**30°–60° right triangle** (p. 376) A right triangle in which the two acute angles are 30° and 60°.

**Transversal** (p. 185) A line which intersects two other lines.

**Trapezoid** (p. 194) A quadrilateral with exactly two sides parallel. The parallel sides are the *bases* of the trapezoid.

**Trigonometric ratio** (p. 379) Any of the sine, cosine, or tangent ratios.

**Unit fraction** (p. 106) A fraction whose numerator is one.

**Value of a variable** (p. 37) Any member of the replacement set of a variable.

**Variable** (p. 37) A letter which is used to stand for any member of a given set of numbers.

**Vertex of an angle** (p. 180) The common endpoint of the sides of an angle.

**Vertex of a polygon** (p. 197) A common endpoint of two sides.

**Vertical angles**
(p. 181) Two angles whose sides form two pairs of opposite rays. In the diagram, ∠ 1 and ∠ 2 are vertical angles as are ∠ 3 and ∠ 4.

**Volume** (p. 282) The amount of space occupied by a solid.

**x-axis** (p. 335) The horizontal axis of a rectangular coordinate system.

**y-axis** (p. 335) The vertical axis of a rectangular coordinate system.

**Zero meridian** (p. 358) The semicircle on Earth which has end points at the poles and passes through Greenwich, England.

**Zero reference point** (p. 65) The point on the number line whose coordinate is zero.

# Index

# Credits

Creative art: Terry Presnall
Mechanical art: ANCO

Page viii, Lew Merrim, Monkmeyer Press
Photo Service
Page 19, Erich Hartmann, Magnum Photos,
Inc.
Page 26, Robert Ginn
Page 47, Historical Pictures Service
Page 64, Robert Ginn
Page 87, National Library of Medicine,
Bethesda, Md.
Page 104, Peter Vandermark, Stock, Boston
Page 131, Colorguild of Wellesley College
Page 144, Daniel S. Brody, Stock, Boston
Page 164, U.S. Government Patent Office
Page 168, (top left) The Bettmann Archive
(top right) Editorial Photocolor Archives/
Scala (bottom) Sidney Janis Gallery, N.Y.
Page 172, Paul Fusco, Magnum Photos, Inc.

Page 216, Bohdan Hrynewych, Stock,
Boston
Page 224, (both) NASA
Page 246, Bob S. Smith, Rapho/Photo
Researchers, Inc.
Page 257, University of California
Page 270, Julie O'Neil, Stock, Boston
Page 298, Culver Pictures
Page 306, Julie O'Neil
Page 334, Owen Franken, Stock, Boston
Page 354, (top) Brown Brothers (bottom)
Massachusetts General Hospital
Page 362, Frederik D. Bodin
Page 384, (top) Schomburg Center for
Research on Black Culture, The New
York Public Library, Astor, Lenox and
Tilden Foundations (bottom) Harvard
University Portrait Collection, Meta and
Paul J. Sachs Collection